INTERNATIONAL SERIES OF MONOGRAPHS IN

PURE AND APPLIED MATHEMATICS

GENERAL EDITORS: I. N. SNEDDON AND M. STARK

EXECUTIVE EDITORS: J. P. KAHANE, A. P. ROBERTSON AND S. ULAM

VOLUME I

AN INTRODUCTION TO
ALGEBRAIC TOPOLOGY

An Introduction to

ALGEBRAIC TOPOLOGY

by

ANDREW H. WALLACE

University of Pennsylvania

THE QUEEN'S AWARD
TO INDUSTRY 1966

PERGAMON PRESS

OXFORD · LONDON · EDINBURGH · NEW YORK
TORONTO · SYDNEY · PARIS · BRAUNSCHWEIG

Pergamon Press Ltd., Headington Hill Hall, Oxford
4 & 5 Fitzroy Square, London W.1
Pergamon Press (Scotland) Ltd., 2 & 3 Teviot Place, Edinburgh 1
Pergamon Press Inc., 44-01 21st Street, Long Island City, New York 11101
Pergamon of Canada, Ltd., 6 Adelaide Street East, Toronto, Ontario
Pergamon Press (Aust.) Pty. Ltd., Rushcutters Bay, Sydney, N.S.W.
Pergamon Press S.A.R.L., 24 rue des Écoles, Paris 5ᵉ
Vieweg & Sohn GmbH, Burgplatz 1, Braunschweig

First edition 1957
Second impression 1961
Third impression 1963
Fourth impression 1967

Library of Congress Catalog Card No. 67-29178

PRINTED IN GREAT BRITAIN BY COMPTON PRINTING LTD., AYLESBURY, BUCKS.
08 000118 1

CONTENTS

v

PREFACE

THIS book is based on courses I gave at the University College of North Staffordshire and judging from that experience I should estimate that the material could be covered by a three-term course of two hours per week along with a weekly tutorial or problem hour.

Apart from the stated prerequisites, it is assumed that the student has some knowledge of the real numbers and real analysis. I do not assume the prerequisite, apparently fashionable now, of some mathematical maturity, because I think that topology is an ideal field for the development of this quality, displaying as it does the transition from geometrical intuition to rigorous algebraic formulation.

Although the book is called *Algebraic Topology*, the algebra does not make its appearance until Chapter IV. The first three chapters are inserted to make the treatment self-contained, and to cater for the student approaching the subject with no previous knowledge of it. Thus a reader who has already learned some point-set topology can proceed straight to Chapter IV. But, whatever parts of the book the reader may choose to omit, I should like to ask him to regard the exercises as an integral part of the text. For they include theorems which are every bit as important as some of those whose proofs are given in full.

Finally, let me take here the opportunity of thanking Dr. A. H. STONE and Mr. T. W. PARNABY, who assisted in the task of proofreading, and all those students who unwittingly acted as my guinea-pigs in the first stages of the preparation of this book.

ANDREW H. WALLACE

University College of North Staffordshire
April 1957

PREREQUISITES

THE topics of the following three sections are treated only in the barest outline. For further details the reader should consult textbooks on algebra and set-theory. Suitable references are:

N. BOURBAKI; *Théorie des Ensembles* (Hermann, Paris).

G. BIRKHOFF AND S. MACLANE; *Survey of Modern Algebra* (Macmillan, New York).

W. LEDERMANN; *Theory of Finite Groups* (Oliver and Boyd, Edinburgh).

H. ZASSENHAUS; *The Theory of Groups* (English translation, Chelsea, New York).

1. Set theory

The precise notions of abstract set theory will not be discussed here; a set will be thought of from the purely intuitive point of view of a collection of objects which are either enumerated or are defined by the possession of some common property.

The notation $x \in E$ will mean that x is a member of the set E.

A subset F of a given set E is a set each of whose elements is a member of E. The notation for this is $F \subset E$ or $E \supset F$. The statement $F \subset E$ is to include the possibility of the equality of E and F. The two statements $E \subset F$ and $F \subset E$ together imply that $E = F$. In particular, the set containing no members is called the empty set, and denoted by $\emptyset$. $\emptyset$ is regarded as a subset of every set.

If E and F are two sets, their union is the set consisting of all the elements of E and all the elements of F taken together. This union is denoted by $E \cup F$. More generally, if any collection of sets E_i is given, $\bigcup_i E_i$ denotes the set consisting of all the elements of all the E_i taken together. $\bigcup_i E_i$ is called the union of the E_i.

The intersection of two sets E and F is the set of all elements which belong both to E and to F; this set is written as $E \cap F$. More generally, for any family of sets E_i, $\bigcap_i E_i$ denotes the set of all elements belonging to every one of the E_i, and is called the intersection of the E_i.

1

If subsets of a fixed set E are being discussed, the complement of a subset A with respect to E consists of all the elements of E not in A. If there is no danger of confusion the phrase "with respect to E" will be omitted. The complement of A is denoted by $\complement A$.

The following rules of calculation with $\cup$, $\cap$, and $\complement$ are not hard to check:

$$E \cup (F \cap G) = (E \cup F) \cap (E \cup G),$$

$$E \cap (F \cup G) = (E \cap F) \cup (E \cap G);$$

and more generally:

$$E \cup \bigcap_i F_i = \bigcap_i (E \cup F_i),$$

$$E \cap \bigcup_i F_i = \bigcup_i (E \cap F_i),$$

$$\complement (\bigcup_i E_i) = \bigcap_i (\complement E_i),$$

$$\complement (\bigcap_i E_i) = \bigcup_i (\complement E_i).$$

The operation of taking a relative complement is sometimes useful; if A and B are subsets of a given set E the relative complement of B with respect to A is the set of elements of A which are not in B. This set is denoted by $A - B$. Clearly $A - B = A \cap \complement B$ (where $\complement$ denotes the complement with respect to E).

Let E and F be any two sets. A mapping f of E into F is a law which assigns to each element x of E a uniquely defined element $f(x)$ of F. A shorthand notation for the statement that f is a mapping of E into F is $f{:}E \to F$.

A mapping $f{:}E \to F$ is called onto if every element of F can be written as $f(x)$ for some $x \in E$. f is called 1-1 or, in words, one-one, if $f(x) = f(y)$ implies $x = y$.

The image of a mapping $f{:}E \to F$ is the set of all y in F such that $y = f(x)$ for some x in E; the image of f is written as $f(E)$. More generally if $A \subset E$, $f(A)$ is the set of all y in F such that $y = f(x)$ for some x in A. $f(A)$ is called the image of A under f.

If $f{:}E \to F$ is a given mapping and $B \subset F$, $\overset{-1}{f}(B)$ is the subset of E consisting of all the elements $x \in E$ such that $f(x) \in B$; $\overset{-1}{f}(B)$ is called the inverse image of B under f. Note that $\overset{-1}{f}$ is not in general a mapping, since $\overset{-1}{f}(y)$, for a single element $y \in F$, may consist of more than one element of E. $\overset{-1}{f}$ is a mapping of F into E if and only if f is one-one and onto.

Two special cases of mappings occur so often that they require names. The first is the identity mapping of a set E onto itself. This mapping i is defined by $i(x) = x$ for all $x \in E$. The second is the inclusion mapping of a subset F of E into E. This mapping j is defined by $j(x) = x$ for all $x \in F$. Note that the inclusion reduces to the identity when $F = E$.

Let E, F, G be three sets and $f:E \to F$, $g:F \to G$ two mappings. For each x in E, $g(f(x))$ is a uniquely defined element of G and so the correspondence $x \to g(f(x))$ is a mapping of E into G. It is called the composition mapping of f and g and is denoted by $g \circ f$.

The question of cardinal numbers will not be discussed here; but the following particular terms will be required. A set is called finite if it can be mapped by a one-one mapping onto a set $1, 2, \ldots, n$ of the natural numbers for some n. A set is called denumerable if it can be mapped by a one-one mapping onto the set of *all* the natural numbers. A set satisfying neither of these conditions is called non-denumerable. For example the set of rational numbers is denumerable, but not the set of all real numbers.

2. Algebra

Some results from group theory are required in Chapters IV to IX; these results will now be sketched. It will be recalled that a group is a set of elements G closed under an operation . (usually called multiplication) satisfying the following axioms:

(1) $x \cdot (y \cdot z) = (x \cdot y) \cdot z$ for all x, y, z in G;

(2) there is a unique element $e \in G$ called the identity such that $x \cdot e = e \cdot x = x$ for all $x \in G$;

(3) given $x \in G$, there is a unique element x^{-1} of G called the inverse of x such that $x \cdot x^{-1} = x^{-1} \cdot x = e$.

A subset H of G is called a subgroup if H is a group (using the same operation as is given in G). It can be shown that a set H of elements of a group G is a subgroup if and only if $ab^{-1} \in H$ for all a and b in H.

A mapping $f:G \to H$ of one group into another is called a homomorphism if $f(x \cdot y) = f(x) \cdot f(y)$ for all x, y in G; here the same symbol, namely . , is used for the operation in both groups.

It can be shown that if $f:G \to H$ is a homomorphism then $f(G)$ is a subgroup of H, and if e' is the identity element of H then $f(e')^{-1}$ is a subgroup of G. $f(G)$ is called the image of f; and $f(e')^{-1}$ is called the kernel of f.

Two groups G and H are called isomorphic if there is a one-one mapping f of G onto H such that $f(x . y) = f(x) . f(y)$ for all x and y in G. The mapping f is called an isomorphism; it is clearly a special case of a homomorphism. The statement that G and H are isomorphic is written as $G \cong H$.

It can be shown that the necessary and sufficient condition that a homomorphism $f:G \to H$ should be an isomorphism is that f should be onto and its kernel should consist of the identity element of G only.

If G is a group and S a set (finite or infinite) of elements of G such that every element of G can be expressed as a product of elements of S and their inverses, then G is said to be generated by S, and the elements of the set S are called generators of G.

It will in general be possible to find products of generators and their inverses (not including factors of the type $x . x^{-1}$, which can always be cancelled out) which turn out to be equal to the identity of G. Such a product is called a relation. The group G is fully defined by giving a set of generators and relations. If there are no relations the group G is called a free group.

It is not hard to see that, if G is a group given by generators and relations, a homomorphism $f:G \to H$ is fully defined by the values of f on the generators of G. In addition it can be shown that, if f is given any values on the generators of G such that $f(R)$ is the identity of H for each relation R of G, then f can be extended to a homomorphism of G into H.

In particular, if G is a free group and H any other group and f is given arbitrary values in H on the generators of G, f can be extended to a homomorphism of G into H.

Apart from the groups appearing in Chapter IV, most of the groups occurring in topology satisfy, in addition to the axioms (1), (2), (3) stated above, the commutative law; namely $x . y = y . x$ for all x and y in G. Such groups are called abelian. It is usual in this case to write the group operation as $+$ instead of $.$, and to call it addition. Also the identity element of such a group is written as 0 and the inverse of x as $-x$. Written in this notation a group satisfying the commutative law is called an additive abelian group.

If an additive abelian group G is specified by generators and relations, since $x + y = y + x$, the expression $x + y - x - y$ is zero and so will appear among the relations for all x and y in the group. If the only relations are of this form or are linear combinations of relations of this form, G is called a free abelian group. The remarks above on the definition of homomorphisms by defining their values on the generators hold in the abelian case, provided that the group H into which G is mapped is also abelian.

If an additive abelian group can be specified by a finite number of generators it is said to be finitely generated. It is a fundamental theorem that for such groups a set of generators $a_1, a_2, \ldots, a_m$, $b_1, b_2, \ldots, b_n$ can be chosen in such a way that the a_i do not appear in any relation and the b_j satisfy equations of the form $r_j b_j = 0$, where the r_j are positive integers such that r_j is a factor of r_{j+1}.

In particular if a group has just one generator it is called a cyclic group. It is clear that, in the theorem just stated, a_i generates an infinite cyclic subgroup G_i of G and b_j generates a finite cyclic subgroup H_j, for each i and j, and the special form of the relations of G implies that each element of G can be expressed in exactly one way as a sum of elements, one taken from each of the subgroups $G_1, G_2, \ldots, G_m, H_1, H_2, \ldots, H_n$. This result is usually stated by saying that G is the direct sum of the G_i and H_j.

More generally, if G is any additive abelian group and the G_i are subgroups, finite or infinite in number, such that every element of G can be expressed in exactly one way as a sum of elements, one from each G_i, and only a finite number non-zero, then G is called the direct sum of the G_i. This is written $G = \overset{.}{\sum} G_i$.

If G is any additive abelian group and H a subgroup, G can be split up into a family of subsets called cosets of H, two elements x and y of G belonging to the same coset if and only if $x - y \in H$. Two cosets a and b can be added by taking an element from each of them, say x from a and y from b, and defining $a + b$ to be the coset to which $x + y$ belongs; it can be shown that this definition does not depend on the particular representatives x and y picked from the given cosets a and b. The cosets of H, with this operation of addition, form a group, called the quotient group of G with respect to H and written G/H.

If G is a finitely generated abelian group so is any subgroup H, and so is the corresponding quotient group G/H.

If f is a homomorphism of G *onto* G', where these are additive abelian groups, and if H is the kernel of f, then G' is isomorphic to G/H. In fact the inverse image under f of each element of G' is a coset of H in G, that is to say an element of G/H, and this correspondence gives the required isomorphism.

3. Euclidean spaces

Euclidean spaces and certain of their subsets will be used frequently in this book. Euclidean space of n dimensions, or Euclidean n-space, is the set of all n-tuples $(x_1, x_2, \ldots, x_n)$ of real numbers, each such n-tuple being a point of the space. In particular 1-space is the set of real numbers. The distance d between the points $(x_1, x_2, x_3, \ldots, x_n)$ and $(y_1, y_2, \ldots, y_n)$ is given by the formula $d^2 = \sum\limits_{i=1}^{n}(x_i - y_i)^2$.

An open solid n-sphere or open n-cell is the set of points $(x_1, x_2, \ldots, x_n)$ in Euclidean n-space satisfying an inequality of the form $\sum\limits_{i=1}^{n}(x_i - a_i)^2 < r^2$. The point $(a_1, a_2, \ldots, a_n)$ is called the centre of the sphere and r its radius. A closed solid n-sphere or closed n-cell is defined in the same way but with the inequality $<$ replaced by $\leqslant$.

Note that a 2-cell is a circular disc and a 1-cell is a line segment.

An n-dimensional sphere or n-sphere is the set of points in Euclidean $(n + 1)$-space satisfying an equation of the form $\sum\limits_{i=1}^{n}(x_i - a_i)^2 = r^2$. $(a_1, a_2, \ldots, a_n)$ is its centre and r its radius.

Note that a 1-sphere is the circumference of a circle, and a 0-sphere is a pair of points.

An open n-dimensional rectangular block is a set of points in Euclidean n-space satisfying inequalities of the type $a_i < x_i < b_i$, $i = 1, 2, \ldots, n$. A closed rectangular block is the same thing with each $<$ replaced by $\leqslant$.

CHAPTER I

INTRODUCTION

1. Continuity and neighbourhoods

In analysis one's first introduction to the idea of continuity is usually based on the idea that a continuous function f of the real variable x should be such that small changes in x result in small changes in $f(x)$; the requirement being in fact that the graph $y = f(x)$ should not have any breaks in it, but should be, in the intuitive sense, a continuous curve. The next step in analysis is to make this notion precise by introducing the ε-terminology.

For the present purpose, however, it is more convenient to preserve a geometrical outlook, by noting first that the function f may be thought of as a mapping of the x-axis into the y-axis, each value of x being mapped on a uniquely determined value $f(x)$ of y. The continuity of f at x' can then be expressed by saying that points sufficiently near to x' on the x-axis are mapped by f into points arbitrarily near $f(x')$ on the y-axis.

In analysis the phrases "sufficiently near" and "arbitrarily near" would be expressed explicitly by means of inequalities. But the advantage of the geometrical language is that the same words can be used to define continuity in a more general situation. Namely, let E_m and E_n be any two Euclidean spaces, of dimensions m and n respectively, and let f denote a mapping of some sub-set A of E_m into E_n. That is to say, f is a law which assigns to each point of A a uniquely defined point of E_n. Then, as in the case of the function of one variable, f will be said to be continuous at the point p in A if all points of A sufficiently near to p are mapped into points arbitrarily near $f(p)$ in E_n. It should be noted at this point that if $n = 1$ the notion just defined coincides with the analytical concept of a real valued function of m variables continuous in these variables. It should also be verified as an exercise that the mapping f of a subset of E_m into E_n is continuous at a point with coordinates $(x'_1, x'_2, \ldots, x'_m)$ if and only if the coordinates $(y_1, y_2, \ldots, y_n)$ of the image under f of a variable point $(x_1, x_2, \ldots, x_m)$ of E_m are continuous functions of $x_1, x_2, \ldots, x_m$ at $(x'_1, x'_2, \ldots, x'_m)$.

7

The concept of continuity of a mapping of one Euclidean space into another extends the notion of a continuous function of one variable, and has been phrased in such a way that the same words describe both situations. That it is desirable to try to extend this idea still further to mappings between sets other than subsets of Euclidean spaces may be seen by considering the following simple example. In analysis one often wants to work with a family of functions f_t depending continuously on a parameter t. What one usually does is to think of the symbol $f_t(x)$ as if it were a function of two variables $f(t, x)$ continuous or uniformly continuous in the first. But, logically, this means a shift of view-point, since each f_t is a function defined on some set of real numbers, while f, defined so that $f(t, x) = f_t(x)$, is an operator defined on some set in the (t, x)-plane. It would be more satisfactory if one could describe what one meant by a continuous family of functions without this change of terminology.

A convenient and natural way of reformulating the notion of a continuous family of functions is to think first of dependence on a parameter t as being given by a mapping $t \rightarrow f_t$ of the real numbers into the set of all real valued functions of a real variable. Then to say that the f_t depend continuously on t one would like to say that this mapping is continuous. In order that one may be able to do this it is necessary to know what one means by saying that two functions f_t and $f_{t'}$ are near to one another; if this idea is defined then the same wording can be used to define the continuity of the mapping $t \rightarrow f_t$ as has been used already to define the continuity of a mapping between Euclidean spaces.

The remark made in the last sentence, although concerned with a special example, is much more general in implication. Namely, if A and B are any sets of objects of any kind among which a concept of nearness is defined, then the idea of a continuous mapping of A into B can be formulated. The example of a continuous family of functions shows that such a general notion of continuity has applications: many more examples could be given, and indeed will be in later sections, to show that the idea is worth following up.

2. The abstract concept of neighbourhood

The idea introduced at the end of the last section, namely of a set A along with a definition of nearness of two elements of A, is essentially the starting point of the subject of point-set topology. The idea is not quite in its most satisfactory form, since nearness in its only familiar form so far, that is in Euclidean space, is measured by a distance formula; and it is not always convenient, or even possible, to give such a numerical measure in more general cases. That this defect can be remedied will now be seen from a further analysis of the idea of continuity of a mapping f of a set in a Euclidean space into another Euclidean space.

If one adopts the rather natural course of calling points of a Euclidean space near a point p a neighbourhood of p, then to say that a mapping f of a subset A of E_m into E_n is continuous at p means that, if U is a preassigned arbitrarily small neighbourhood of $f(p)$, then all the points of a sufficiently small neighbourhood V of p are mapped into U. This is simply a restatement of the definition of continuity already given in §1. The first thing to notice about this restatement is that one can actually omit the word "small," and simply say that f is continuous at p if, for a preassigned neighbourhood U of $f(p)$, there exists a neighbourhood V of p all of whose points are mapped into U by f. Naturally the preassigned neighbourhoods of $f(p)$ will include arbitrarily small ones, and common sense shows that the corresponding V must be sufficiently small; but there is no need to say so.

The omission of the word "small" may seem a trivial matter, but it is a logical step forward. For the restated definition of continuity at p does not contain any explicit mention of the idea of distance, but is formulated in terms of neighbourhoods of p and $f(p)$. That is to say, continuity at p is defined in terms of certain families of point-sets assigned to the points p and $f(p)$, and called neighbourhoods of p and $f(p)$ respectively. Of course, in defining these neighbourhoods the idea of distance has to be used. But a separation of the continuity into two stages has been effected, as stated in the following definitions:

DEFINITION **A**. *A neighbourhood of a point p* in a Euclidean space is the set of all points within a distance r of p for some r.

DEFINITION **B**. If f is a mapping of a set A in a Euclidean space into another Euclidean space, then *f is continuous at a point p* if, given any neighbourhood U of $f(p)$, there is a neighbourhood V of p such that $f(V \cap A) \subset U$.

The significance of this separation of ideas is that it may be possible to assign to each member p of an abstract set A (not necessarily now a subset of a Euclidean space) a family of subsets of A to be called neighbourhoods of p, a similar assignment being made to the elements of a second abstract set B. This having been done, one can define a mapping of A into B to be continuous at p if, for any preassigned neighbourhood U of $f(p)$, there exists a neighbourhood V of p such that all members of V are mapped into U by f. Of course this assignment of neighbourhoods to the members of an abstract set cannot be made in an arbitrary way. For example, one obviously wants a set which is to be called a neighbourhood of p actually to contain p. To see what further conditions must be imposed on a family of subsets of an abstract set A before they can reasonably be called neighbourhoods of some member of A, a closer inspection will be made of the situation in a Euclidean space.

As already pointed out, the concept of continuity can be adequately defined if one takes as neighbourhoods of a point p in Euclidean space the family of all spheres with centre p. But as this definition of neighbourhoods is rather too closely tied up with the notion of distance, the following question will be considered first: what is the most general meaning one can give to the word "neighbourhood" without changing the meaning of continuity? To make this question more explicit, consider real-valued functions defined on a Euclidean space. And suppose that, according to some law or other, each point p of this space has assigned to it a family of subsets called $N(p)$. Then the following property of a real-valued function f will be called the property C:

The function f will be said to have the property C at a point p if, for any preassigned positive number ε, there exists a set U belonging to $N(p)$ such that $|f(p') - f(p)| < \varepsilon$ for all p' in U. In any case $p \in U$ for all U in $N(p)$ will be assumed.

Then the question being asked is: what is the most general definition which can be made for the families $N(p)$ such that, for every function f, f has the property C at a point p if and only if it is continuous (in the ordinary sense) at p?

To answer this question, let V be one of the sets belonging to the family $N(p)$, and define a real-valued function f by setting $f(q) = 0$ whenever $q \in V$, and $f(q) = 1$ whenever $q \notin V$. Then this function f has the property C at p. For, given any ε, there is a set of $N(p)$, namely V itself, such that $|f(p') - f(p)| < \varepsilon$ (in fact $|f(p') - f(p)| = 0$) for $p' \in V$. If, now, the family $N(p)$ is chosen so that the property C at p is equivalent to continuity at p, there must be a sphere U with centre p such that $|f(p') - f(p)| < \varepsilon$ for all p' in U, ε being preassigned. Taking $\varepsilon < 1$, and remembering the definition of the function f, it follows that $U \subset V$.

It has thus been shown that, if the property C is to be equivalent to continuity at each point, the families $N(p)$ must satisfy the necessary condition that each member V of $N(p)$ contains a sphere U with centre p. An exactly similar argument, starting off from the definition of a function g which is zero on a given sphere W of centre p and equal to 1 elsewhere, shows that a further necessary condition is that every sphere of centre p must contain some member of the family $N(p)$.

These two necessary conditions for the equivalence of the property C to continuity are also sufficient. For suppose that they are both satisfied, and let f be a real valued function continuous at p. Then, given a positive number ε, there is a sphere U of centre p such that $|f(p') - f(p)| < \varepsilon$ for $p' \in U$. But by one of the conditions being assumed, there is a member V of $N(p)$ contained in U, and so the inequality $|f(p') - f(p)| < \varepsilon$ holds for all p' in V; that is, the function f has the property C at p. Similarly it can be shown that, under the two assumed conditions, a function f which has the property C at p is also continuous at p.

Summing up, the above discussion shows that, so far as real-valued functions on a Euclidean space E_m are concerned, the meaning of continuity is not changed if spherical neighbourhoods of each point p are replaced by a family of sets $N(p)$ such that every member of $N(p)$ contains a spherical neighbourhood of p and every spherical neighbourhood of p contains a member of $N(p)$.

Something more general than this has, in fact, been achieved. For let E_m and E_n be two Euclidean spaces of dimensions m and n respectively, and in each of these spaces let a family of sets $N(p)$ be assigned to each point with the properties that, in each of the given spaces, any member of a family $N(p)$ contains a sphere of centre p, and any sphere of centre p contains a set of the corresponding family $N(p)$. Then let a mapping f of E_m into E_n be said to have the property C' if, for any given member U of $N(f(p))$ in E_n there is a member V of $N(p)$ in E_m such that all points of V are mapped into U by f. It will now be shown that the property C' at p is equivalent to continuity at p. For let f have the property C' at p. Let W be a given sphere with centre $f(p)$. Then, by hypothesis, there is a set U belonging to $N(f(p))$ in E_n such that $U \subset W$. The property C' at p implies that there is a set V belonging to $N(p)$ in E_m all of whose points are mapped into U by f, and again by hypothesis, there is a sphere Z of centre p contained in V. Thus all the points of Z are mapped into W by f, and so f is continuous at p. Similarly it can be shown that if f is continuous at p it has the property C' at p.

It follows from what has just been shown that the meaning of continuity, defined in terms of neighbourhoods as described earlier in this section, is unaltered if one replaces the family of spherical neighbourhoods of each point p in each space by a family of neighbourhoods $N(p)$ having the properties assumed in the last paragraph. Now the most general family of this type which can be attached to a point p (that is, the family containing the most sets) is the collection of all sets each of which contains some sphere with centre p. If this collection is called $N(p)$, then each member of $N(p)$ contains, by definition, a sphere of centre p, and each sphere of centre p contains a member of $N(p)$, namely itself. This family $N(p)$ will from now onwards be called the family of neighbourhoods of the point p in the Euclidean space under consideration. This has the virtue of being the most general definition of neighbourhood in a Euclidean space which, when used along with Definition **B**, instead of Definition **A** above, preserves the usual notion of continuity.

Having now achieved maximum generality in the concept of neighbourhood in a Euclidean space, the next step is to see what properties of neighbourhoods one will want to incorporate in an abstract definition of the neighbourhoods of elements of some abstract set. The choice will be governed by the principle that there are some properties of continuity and nearness which one will want to hold even in the most abstract situations.

For example, if f and g are two continuous real valued functions, it is desirable that, as in the elementary case of functions of a real variable, $f + g$ should also be continuous. Suppose, now that f and g are real-valued functions defined on a Euclidean space, and let ε be a preassigned positive number. For any point p of the Euclidean space E_m, f and g are to be continuous at p, and so there are neighbourhoods U and V of p such that $|f(p') - f(p)| < \varepsilon/2$ for all p' in U, and $|g(p'') - g(p)| < \varepsilon/2$ for all p'' in V. From these inequalities it follows at once that $|(f(p') + g(p')) - (f(p) + g(p))| < \varepsilon$ for all p' in $U \cap V$. The continuity of $f + g$ will follow if $U \cap V$ is a neighbourhood of p. But, since U and V are both neighbourhoods of p each of these sets contains a sphere of centre p. $U \cap V$ therefore contains the smaller of these spheres, and so is a neighbourhood of p.

The proof just given of the continuity of $f + g$ for continuous functions f and g clearly rests on the fact that the intersection of two neighbourhoods of p is also a neighbourhood of p. This, then, is one of the properties which it is desirable to retain in an abstract theory.

Again, it will be noticed that, since a neighbourhood U of a point p in a Euclidean space contains a sphere U' of centre p, of radius r, say, and since a sphere of sufficiently small radius entirely contained in U' can be drawn about any point p' at distance less than r from p, it follows that U is also a neighbourhood of any such point p'. Now the set U'' of points at distance less than r from p is a neighbourhood of p, for it contains any sphere of centre p and radius less than r. It has thus been shown that a neighbourhood U of a point p in a Euclidean space is also a neighbourhood of every point p' in a certain neighbourhood U'' of p. It can be seen that this is a very natural intuitive property of the concept of nearness if one expresses it as follows: points near p are also near to all other points which are sufficiently near to p. The naturalness of this attribute of nearness suggests that it should certainly be carried over into an abstract theory.

Finally, as already noted, a neighbourhood of a point p in a Euclidean space contains p itself, and it is desirable that this should also be true of neighbourhoods in an abstract set. Also, by the very mode of definition of a neighbourhood in a Euclidean space, any set containing a neighbourhood of p is itself a neighbourhood of p, and it is a matter of formal convenience to extend this to more abstract situations.

CHAPTER II

TOPOLOGICAL SPACES

1. Definition of a topological space

As suggested in the last section, the concept of neighbourhood can be defined in an abstract set, the conditions which were found above to be natural requirements for a concept of neighbourhood being taken as axioms. A set furnished in this way with neighbourhoods will be called a topological space. The formal definition is as follows:

DEFINITION 1. A *topological space* consists of an abstract set E along with an assignment of a non-empty family of subsets of E to each element of E. The elements of E will be called *points*, and the subsets assigned to a point p of E will be called *neighbourhoods* of p. The assignment of neighbourhoods to each point of E must be made subject to the following conditions:

(1) If U is a neighbourhood of p then $p \in U$;

(2) Any subset of E containing a neighbourhood of p is itself a neighbourhood of p;

(3) If U and V are neighbourhoods of p, so is $U \cap V$;

(4) If U is a neighbourhood of p, there is a neighbourhood V of p such that U is a neighbourhood of every point of V.

The process of assigning neighbourhoods to each element of a set E, so making E into a topological space, is sometimes called giving E a topology or defining a topology on E.

Examples. (1) If E is a Euclidean space of any dimension, and a neighbourhood of a point p of E is any set U containing a sphere of centre p (as in Chapter I, §2) then the above conditions are satisfied, and so E is a topological space.

When in future Euclidean spaces are mentioned it will always be assumed (unless something is said to the contrary) that they are topological spaces with the topology defined in this way. In particular, if "sphere of centre p" is replaced by "interval of midpoint p" this is the topology always to be assumed on the real numbers unless something is said to the contrary.

(2) If E is any set a rather trivial topology may be defined on E by taking as neighbourhoods of a point p any subset of E which contains p. This topology is called the discrete topology on E.

(3) Let E be the set of integers (positive, negative and zero) and let q be a fixed prime number. A set U of integers will be called a neighbourhood of the integer n if U contains all the integers $n + mq^r$ for some r and all $m = 0, \pm1, \pm2, \pm3, \ldots$ (That is to say, for a given neighbourhood r is fixed but m varies). Conditions (1) and (2) on the neighbourhoods in the definition of a topological space are easily seen to be satisfied here. To check (3), let U and V be two neighbourhoods of the integer n. There will be, by the definition of the neighbourhoods in this example, two integers r and s such that U contains all the integers $n + mq^r$ $(m = 0, \pm1, \pm2, \ldots)$ and V contains all the integers $n + mq^s$ $(m = 0, \pm1, \pm2, \ldots)$. Now if $s \leqslant r$, every integer of the form $n + mq^r$ is also of the form $n + m'q^s$, with $m' = mq^{r-s}$. Thus if $s \leqslant r$, $U \cap V$ will contain all the integers $n + mq^r$ $(m = 0, \pm1, \pm2, \ldots)$ and so $U \cap V$ is a neighbourhood of n. A similar argument can be used if $r < s$. And so condition (3) is verified. To check (4) let U be a neighbourhood of n and suppose U contains the set V of integers $n + mq^r$ $(m = 0, \pm1, \pm2, \ldots)$. Then V is itself a neighbourhood of n. If $n_0 = n + m_0q^r$, for some m_0, is any integer in V, then it is not hard to see that the collection of integers $n_0 + mq^r$ $(m = 0, \pm1, \pm2, \ldots)$ coincides with V. It follows at once that U is a neighbourhood of n_0. This holds for any n_0 in V, and so condition (4) in the definition of a topological space is verified.

This example is introduced here to show that a topology can sometimes be defined in a situation which appears, at first sight, purely algebraic in contrast to the more or less pictorial notion of neighbourhood in Euclidean spaces. The fact that notions of continuity and neighbourhood can be introduced into apparently non-geometrical subjects has advantages of two kinds. In the first place, purely algebraic results can often be stated more simply and elegantly in the language provided by topology, and on the other hand the algebra and the topology often combine to give powerful results which could not otherwise be obtained.

(4) As a last example in this section, let E be the set of all real-valued functions of the real variable x defined on the interval $a \leqslant x \leqslant b$ and integrable over that interval. If f is an element of E, define an ε-neighbourhood of f to be the set of all functions g of E

such that $\int_a^b |f - g|\, dx < \varepsilon$, ε being a positive number. And let a set in E be called a neighbourhood of f if it contains an ε-neighbourhood of f for some ε. It is not hard to check that conditions (1) to (4) of Definition 1 hold, and so E becomes a topological space. Note that here, as in Euclidean space, the neighbourhoods are defined by a distance function, $\int_a^b |f - g|\, dx$ being regarded as the distance between f and g. The ε-neighbourhoods as defined here correspond to spheres in Euclidean space.

Exercises

1. Let E be a set and suppose that to each pair of elements x and y of E there is assigned a real number $d(x, y)$ to be called the distance between x and y and satisfying the following conditions:

    (i) $d(x, y) \geqslant 0$ and $d(x, y) = 0$ if and only if $x = y$;

    (ii) $d(x, y) = d(y, x)$ for all x and y of E;

    (iii) $d(x, z) \leqslant d(x, y) + d(y, z)$ for any three elements x, y, z of E.

Define an ε-neighbourhood of $x \in E$ as the set of all $y \in E$ such that $d(x, y) < \varepsilon$. Define a neighbourhood of $x \in E$ to be any set in E containing an ε-neighbourhood of x. Prove that with these definitions E becomes a topological space. A space defined in this way will be called a *metric space*.

2. Prove that a Euclidean space is a metric space.

3. Let E be the set of continuous functions of the real variable x on the interval $a \leqslant x \leqslant b$. Prove that E becomes a metric space if $d(f, g)$ is taken as $\int_a^b |f - g|\, dx$. If E is allowed to contain all integrable functions on $a \leqslant x \leqslant b$, does this definition of $d(f, g)$ make E into a metric space?

4. If A and B are any sets, the set of all pairs (a, b) with $a \in A$ and $b \in B$ will be denoted by $A \times B$ and called the product set of A and B.

Let E and F be two topological spaces. Call a set $W \subset E \times F$ a neighbourhood of $(x, y) \in E \times F$ $(x \in E, y \in F)$ if there is a neighbourhood U of x in E and a neighbourhood V of y in F such that $U \times V \subset W$. Prove that $E \times F$ becomes in this way a topological space. $E \times F$, given a topology in this way, will be called the topological product of E and F.

5. Prove that the Euclidean plane is the product $R \times R$, where R is the space of real numbers.

More generally, prove that $E_{m+n} = E_m \times E_n$, where the E's denote Euclidean spaces of dimensions shown by the suffixes.

2. Open sets

By means of neighbourhoods in a topological space as defined in the last section it is possible to give precise meanings to a number of terms which have a fairly clear intuitive meaning when one draws

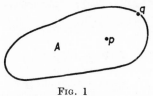

FIG. 1

diagrams on paper. For example, when one speaks of a set in the plane one usually represents it diagrammatically as in Fig. 1 by a region surrounded by a curve. When one speaks of an interior point of such a set one thinks of a point such as p, while it is natural to speak of a point such as q as a frontier point. The distinction one is making here may be expressed intuitively by saying that a point of a set A is an interior point if it is entirely surrounded by points of A, and otherwise it is a frontier point.

The statement that an interior point of A is surrounded by points of A could be made precise by saying that such a point has a neighbourhood entirely contained in A; this will now be taken as the definition of an interior point of a set in any topological space. (The notion of the frontier of a set will receive attention in §8 of this Chapter).

DEFINITION 2. Let A be a set of points in a topological space E. A point p of A will be said to be an *interior point* of A if there is a neighbourhood U of p such that $U \subset A$. The collection of all interior points of A will be called the *interior* of A and will be denoted by $\mathring{A}$.

Examples. (1) In the (x, y)-plane let A be the set of points such that $x^2 + y^2 \leqslant 1$. The interior of this set consists of the points such that $x^2 + y^2 < 1$.

(2) The set of points in the (x, y)-plane such that $x^2 + y^2 < 1$ consists entirely of interior points, and so is its own interior.

(3) If A is the set of points in the (x, y)-plane such that $x = 0$ then A contains no interior points.

Example (2) shows the existence of sets consisting entirely of interior points. Such a set will be called open. In detail the definition is as follows:

DEFINITION 3. A set A in a topological space will be called an *open set* if, for each point $p \in A$, there is a neighbourhood U of p such that $U \subset A$.

Examples. (4) The open intervals of analysis, that is sets of real numbers satisfying an inequality $a < x < b$ for some a and b, are open sets on the real line.

(5) The set of points in Euclidean n-space such that $\sum_{1}^{n} x_i^2 < 1$ is an open set. More generally, any solid open n-sphere in Euclidean n-space is an open set.

(6) The set of points in Euclidean n-space satisfying inequalities of the form $a_i < x_i < b_i$ $(i = 1, 2, \ldots, n)$, where the a_i and the b_i are fixed, that is, an open n-dimensional rectangular block, is an open set.

(7) Let E be the topological space formed by the integers with the topology of Example (3) of §1. Then for any fixed n and r, the set of integers $n + mq^r$ $(m = 0, \pm 1, \pm 2, \ldots)$ is an open set. For it was shown in the course of discussing this example that this set is a neighbourhood of every integer belonging to it; and so each integer in this set has a neighbourhood contained in the set, namely the set itself.

The following theorem seems to be very easy to prove, and does not appear on the surface to be a very strong result. It is all the more remarkable, then, that the result proved can be taken as a set of axioms to give an alternative definition of a topological space, as will be shown in §3.

THEOREM 1. *Let E be a topological space. Then* (1) *the union of an arbitrary collection of open sets in E is an open set;* (2) *the intersection of a finite collection of open sets in E is an open set;* (3) *the whole space E is an open set;* (4) *the empty set is an open set.*

PROOF. (1) Let W be the union of some family of open sets (this family may be finite or infinite), and let p be a point of W. Then p

is in at least one of the open sets belonging to the given family; suppose $p \in U$ where U is one of the sets of this family. Then, since U is an open set, there is a neighbourhood V of p such that $V \subset U$. But $U \subset W$, and so it has been shown that each point p of W has a neighbourhood V contained in W. Hence W is open.

(2) Let V and W be two open sets in E, and let p be a point of $V \cap W$. Since V is open and $p \in V$ there is a neighbourhood U of p such that $U \subset V$. Similarly, there is a neighbourhood U' of p such that $U' \subset W$. But by condition (3) on the assignment of neighbourhoods in a topological space, $U \cap U'$ is also a neighbourhood of p and is clearly contained in $V \cap W$. Thus to each $p \in V \cap W$ there is a neighbourhood of p contained in $V \cap W$, which is therefore an open set. To prove that the intersection of any finite collection of open sets is open one can now proceed by induction. It is important to emphasize here that the word "finite" cannot be left out. For example, let E be the real line, a neighbourhood of a point being any set containing an interval of which the given point is mid-point, and let U_n be the open interval $|x| < \frac{1}{n}$. $U_1, U_2, \ldots$ is an infinite family of open sets on the line, but the intersection of this family is not open, for the only point in this intersection is the point $x = 0$.

(3) This part of the theorem is rather trivial, for every point of E has at least one neighbourhood and E certainly contains it.

(4) To say that the empty set $\emptyset$ is open means that there is a neighbourhood of p contained in $\emptyset$ for each point p belonging to $\emptyset$, and since there are, in fact, no points belonging to $\emptyset$, this statement is true.

The following theorem gives a new characterization of the interior of a set in a topological space.

THEOREM 2. *If A is any set in a topological space then $\mathring{A}$ is an open set and is the largest open set contained in A.*

The term "largest open set contained in A" requires some explanation. It is intended to mean an open set contained in A and containing every other open set contained in A; but it is not clear without some justification that such a set exists. The necessity for justifying the use of the term "largest" as applied to sets of some specified type (in this case open sets contained in A) is easily seen if one replaces the word "open" by "finite" for example. For if A contains an infinite number of points there is no such thing as the largest finite subset of A; that is, there is no finite subset containing all other finite subsets.

The proof of Theorem 2 will now be carried out.

PROOF. Let p be a point of $\mathring{A}$. Then, by the definition of interior, there is a neighbourhood U of p such that $U \subset A$. On the other hand, by condition (4) on the neighbourhoods in Definition 1, there is a neighbourhood V of p such that U is a neighbourhood of every point of V. It follows at once from this that every point of V is in $\mathring{A}$. Thus to each point p of $\mathring{A}$ there is a neighbourhood V of p such that $V \subset \mathring{A}$, which shows that $\mathring{A}$ is open. To complete the proof, let W be an open set such that $W \subset A$. If p is any point of W then, since W is open, there is a neighbourhood Z of p such that $Z \subset W$. But Z is contained also in A, and so p is an interior point of A. This holds for any point of W and so $W \subset \mathring{A}$. That is to say, any open set contained in A is actually contained in $\mathring{A}$, as was to be shown.

The following theorems describe two further important properties of open sets.

THEOREM 3. *U is a neighbourhood of p in a topological space E if and only if U contains an open set W containing p.*

PROOF. In the first place, let U contain an open set W containing p; since W is open there is a neighbourhood V of p such that $V \subset W$. But then U contains the neighbourhood V of p, and so, by condition (2) in Definition 1, U is a neighbourhood of p.

To prove the converse, let U be a neighbourhood of p. p is an interior point of U, for there certainly is a neighbourhood of p contained in U, namely U itself. Thus p is contained in the subset $\mathring{U}$ of U, and by the last theorem $\mathring{U}$ is open. And so, as required, p is contained in an open set contained in U.

THEOREM 4. *A set U in a topological space is open if and only if it is a neighbourhood of every one of its points.*

PROOF. If U is open and p is in U, then, by the definition of an open set, there is a neighbourhood V of p such that $V \subset U$. Then U, being a set containing a neighbourhood of p is itself a neighbourhood of p. And this is true for every point of U.

Conversely, if U is a neighbourhood of each of its points, all its points must be interior points; for each point of U has a neighbourhood, namely U itself, contained in U. It then follows from the definition of an open set that U is open.

Exercises

1. Let $f(x_1, x_2, \ldots, x_n)$ be a continuous function of $x_1, x_2, \ldots, x_n$ (in the ordinary sense of analysis). Prove that the following sets of points are open in the Euclidean space in which the x_i are coordinates:

(a) the set of points at which $f \neq 0$;

(b) the set of points at which $f < c$ for some constant c;

(c) the set of points at which $c_1 < f < c_2$ for some constants c_1 and c_2.

2. Let M_n denote the set of square n-rowed matrices with real elements. If the elements are taken as coordinates in n^2-dimensional Euclidean space M_n becomes a topological space. Prove that the set of matrices of rank greater than or equal to r for any $r \leqslant n$ is an open set in this space.

3. What are the open sets in the Example (3) of §1?

4. Let E be the space of real numbers and let A be the set of rational numbers. Prove that A has no interior points. Prove also that $\complement A$ has no interior points.

5. Let E be any topological space and let A and B be two sets in E. Prove the following properties of the operation of forming the interior of a set:

(a) $\mathring{\mathring{A}} = \mathring{A}$;

(b) if $C = A \cup B$, $\mathring{C} \supset \mathring{A} \cup \mathring{B}$;

(c) if $C = A \cap B$, $\mathring{C} = \mathring{A} \cap \mathring{B}$.

In the case of (b) give an example of two sets A and B in the space of real numbers such that $\mathring{C} \neq \mathring{A} \cup \mathring{B}$.

6. Let E be the space of functions of Example (4) of §1. Let A be the subset of E consisting of functions continuous over the interval (a, b). Prove that A has no interior points.

[Hint: Construct a discontinuous function of arbitrarily small integral.]

3. Another definition of a topological space

It was hinted before Theorem 1 that the properties of open sets established in that theorem could be used to set up the notion of a topological space in a different way. This alternative method of definition will now be described, the procedure being based on the following theorem.

THEOREM 5. *Let E be an abstract set and let $\mathbf{O}$ be a family of subsets of E satisfying the following conditions*:

(1) *The union of any collection of sets belonging to $\mathbf{O}$ is a set belonging to $\mathbf{O}$*;

(2) *The intersection of a finite collection of sets belonging to* O *is a set belonging to* O;

(3) *The whole set E belongs to* O;

(4) *The empty set $\emptyset$ belongs to* O.

Then there is one and only one way of making E into a topological space (i.e. of assigning neighbourhoods to the elements of E) so that O *is the family of open sets of E, namely by saying that a set U is a neighbourhood of $p \in E$ if and only if there is a set W belonging to* O *such that $p \in W \subset U$.*

PROOF. Define neighbourhoods of each $p \in E$ as stated at the end of the theorem; that is, U is to be a neighbourhood of p if and only if there is a set W belonging to O such that $p \in W \subset U$. In order to justify the name "neighbourhood" it must be shown that this assignment satisfies the four conditions in the definition of a topological space.

(1) If U is a neighbourhood of p as just defined, p is contained in a set of O contained in U, and so, in particular, $p \in U$.

(2) Let U be a neighbourhood of p and let V be a set in E such that $U \subset V$. Then, by the definition of neighbourhoods in the present situation, there is a set W of O such that $p \in W \subset U$. Hence $p \in W \subset V$, and so V is a neighbourhood of p in the present sense.

(3) Let U and V be two neighbourhoods of p. Then there are two sets of the family O, say W and W', such that $p \in W \subset U$ and $p \in W' \subset V$. By condition (2) imposed on the family O in the present theorem, $W \cap W'$ belongs to O. But $p \in W \cap W' \subset U \cap V$, and so, by the definition of neighbourhood being adopted here, $U \cap V$ is a neighbourhood of p.

(4) Let U be a neighbourhood of p in the sense of this theorem. Then there is a set W of the family O such that $p \in W \subset U$. W is itself a neighbourhood of p, since W contains a set of the family O, namely W itself, which contains p. And in addition, if q is any point of W, the inclusion relations $q \in W \subset U$ imply that U is a neighbourhood of q. Thus the given neighbourhood U of p contains a neighbourhood W of p such that U is a neighbourhood of every point q in W.

The above four steps show that the neighbourhoods defined in this theorem in terms of the given family of sets O satisfy the conditions imposed on the neighbourhoods in the definition of a topological space. And so E is made in this way into a topological space.

The next thing is to show that, when E is made as above into a topological space, the open sets are precisely those sets which belong to the given family $\mathbf{O}$. First let U be a set belonging to the family $\mathbf{O}$, and let p be any point of U. Then U contains a set of $\mathbf{O}$ containing p, namely U itself. And so, by the definition of neighbourhood adopted in this theorem, U is a neighbourhood of p. That is to say, U is a neighbourhood of every one of its points, and so, by Theorem 4, U is open. It has thus been shown that every set of $\mathbf{O}$ is an open set. Conversely let U be an open set, that is a set such that, for every point $p \in U$, there is a neighbourhood W of p satisfying $p \in W \subset U$; then it has to be shown that U belongs to the family $\mathbf{O}$. To do this let $p \in U$ and let W be a neighbourhood of p such that $p \in W \subset U$. Since W is a neighbourhood of p, there is a set $V(p)$ of the family $\mathbf{O}$ such that $p \in V(p) \subset W$. A set $V(p)$ of the family $\mathbf{O}$ can be obtained in this way corresponding to each point p of U, and since $p \in V(p) \subset U$ for each $p \in U$, it is clear that $U = \bigcup V(p)$, the union being taken over all $p \in U$. But by condition (1) imposed on the family $\mathbf{O}$ in the statement of this theorem, $\bigcup V(p)$ belongs to $\mathbf{O}$ since each $V(p)$ belongs to $\mathbf{O}$. It has therefore been shown that every open set U belongs to the family $\mathbf{O}$. Combining this with the converse already proved, it follows that the family of opens sets coincides with the family $\mathbf{O}$.

Finally, it has to be verified that the method adopted here of making E into a topological space is the only one in which the sets of the given family $\mathbf{O}$ coincide with the open sets. That is to say, if E is to be made into a topological space in such a way that the sets of $\mathbf{O}$ are the open sets, it has to be checked that the neighbourhoods must be defined as in the statement of this theorem. This follows at once from Theorem 3. For if the sets of $\mathbf{O}$ are to be the open sets of the space, that theorem says that a set U can be a neighbourhood of p if and only if there is an open set V, that is a set of $\mathbf{O}$, such that $p \in V \subset U$, and this is exactly the definition adopted for neighbourhoods in this theorem. The proof of Theorem 5 is thus completed.

The essential significance of this theorem is that a topological space can be defined by giving the open sets instead of assigning neighbourhoods to each point. That is to say, in order to define a topological space E, one can pick a family $\mathbf{O}$ of sets in E satisfying the conditions (1), (2), (3), (4) of the last theorem, and one can define them to be the open sets of E. The last theorem shows that the topological space E is fully defined in this way, for there is only one way of defining the neighbourhoods of points so that the selected family of sets are the open sets. The initial definition of a topological space in terms of neighbourhoods is probably the most convenient from the intuitive point of view, depending as it does on a common-sense notion of nearness. But from a logical point of view the definition in terms of open sets has certain advantages. In the first place it seems logically simpler to name a single family of open sets in E rather than to name a family of sets attached to each point of E. But more important than this is the fact that many definitions can be made and theorems proved much more simply and elegantly in terms of open sets than in terms of neighbourhoods. Several examples of this will appear later.

Some examples will now be given of topological spaces defined by the naming of the family of open sets.

Examples. (1) Let E be the set of real numbers, and assume that the word "interval" means a set of numbers satisfying an inequality of the form $a < x < b$. Define a set of numbers to be an open set if and only if it is a union of intervals. It is not hard to see that the four conditions of Theorem 5 are satisfied by the family of open sets so defined. Then by Theorem 5, E is a topological space, and a neighbourhood of a number x is any set of numbers containing an open set, that is union of intervals, containing x. This is however the same as saying that a neighbourhood of x is a set containing an interval containing x, and it is easy to see that this defines the same topology on E as has already been used for illustrative purposes.

(2) Similarly, the ordinary topology on a Euclidean space of any dimension can be defined by taking the open sets to be arbitrary unions of open solid spheres.

(3) It should not be thought that a given set E has necessarily any natural topology attached to it, although often one particular topology happens to be specially familiar. For example the topology defined on the real numbers in Example (1) above is the familiar one which, as has already been pointed out, is the one used in defining ordinary continuous functions. For some purposes, however, one may want to define a different topology on the real numbers. The following is an example of such an alternative topology. The set E is to be the set of real numbers and a subset of E will be called open if and only if it is the whole line E or the null set $\emptyset$, or the set of numbers satisfying an inequality of the form $x > a$ for some real number a.

It is easy to see that the conditions of Theorem 5 on unions and intersections are satisfied, and so a topology is thus defined on the set of real numbers. In this topology a neighbourhood of a number a is a set of numbers including all the numbers satisfying an inequality of the form $a - \varepsilon < x$. Thus, in particular, any number greater than a is thought of as being near a in this sense.

(4) As a further example of this type, a rather unfamiliar topology on the (x, y)-plane may be set up by saying that an open set is any union of horizontal line-intervals without end points. In this sense two points vertically above one another, however close together they might appear in a diagram, would not be regarded as near to one another. Points could only be near together if they were, in the first place, in the same horizontal line.

(5) The topology on the integers given in Example (3), §1, can be redefined in terms of open sets as follows. Let E be the set of integers. Denote by $U(n, r)$ the set of integers of the form $n + mq^r$, where n and r are fixed for the set considered while m takes the values $0, \pm 1, \pm 2, \ldots$. A set in E will be called open if and only if it is a union of sets (not necessarily finite in number) of the type $U(n, r)$ for various values of n and r. It is not hard to verify that this definition for open sets satisfies the conditions of Theorem 5, and that the topology so defined is in fact the same as that defined by means of neighbourhoods in §1.

Exercises

1. Let E be the set of real numbers and let a set be called open if and only if it is empty or is the complement of a finite set of numbers. Prove that E is made into a topological space in this way. (Note that although the same underlying set is used here as in the space of real numbers this is a different space because the open sets, and consequently neighbourhoods of points, are not the same as in the space of real numbers.)

2. Let E be the set of points of the (x, y)-plane for real x and y. Let a set in E be called open if and only if it is empty or is the complement of a set which is either finite or is an algebraic curve or is the union of a finite set and an algebraic curve. (An algebraic curve is the set of points defined by a polynomial equation $f(x, y) = 0$). Prove that E is thus made into a topological space.

3. What are the possible topologies on a space consisting of three points? That is to say, what families of subsets satisfy the conditions of Theorem 5?

4. Subspaces of a given space

In many applications of topology one is concerned with sets contained in a Euclidean space, and it is natural to think of such a set as a topological space by regarding points in it as being near together if they are near together in the surrounding Euclidean space. To express this more precisely, let E denote the Euclidean space, and F a subset of E. If p is a point of F, then it is natural to define a neighbourhood of p in F to be the intersection of F with a neighbourhood of p in E. In this way, for example, a neighbourhood of a point p on a sphere would be a set of points on the sphere containing all the points within a distance of ε from p, where ε is some positive number and the distances are to be measured in the surrounding Euclidean space.

It is clear, however, that the definition of neighbourhoods in a subset F of a topological space E as intersections of F with neighbourhoods in E can be applied equally well to sets in any space E, and not only to Euclidean spaces. This motivates the next definition.

DEFINITION 4. Let E be a topological space and F a subset of E. If p is a point of F, a subset U of F will be said to be a *neighbourhood of p in F* if and only if $U = F \cap V$ for some neighbourhood V of p in E.

Before one can be sure that this definition of neighbourhoods in a subset F of E sets up a topology in F, the conditions (1) to (4) in the definition of a topological space must be verified.

(1) It is obvious that, if U is a neighbourhood of p in F, then $p \in U$; for $U = V \cap F$ where V is a neighbourhood of p in E, and $p \in V$.

(2) Let U be a neighbourhood of p in F, and let $U = V \cap F$ where V is a neighbourhood of p in E. Also let W be a subset of F such that $W \supset U$. Then $W \cup V$ contains V and so is a neighbourhood of p in E, by the definition of a topological space. And so, by the definition of neighbourhoods in F, $(W \cup V) \cap F = W$ is a neighbourhood of p in F.

(3) Let U and U' be two neighbourhoods of p in F, and let $U = V \cap F$, $U' = V' \cap F$, where V and V' are neighbourhoods of p in E. By condition (3) in the definition of a topological space $V \cap V'$ is a neighbourhood of p in E, and so $V \cap V' \cap F = U \cap U'$ is a neighbourhood of p in F.

(4) Finally let U be a neighbourhood of p in F, $U = V \cap F$, where V is a neighbourhood of p in E. Then by condition (4) in the

definition of a topological space, there is a neighbourhood W of p in E such that V is a neighbourhood of every point of W. Then, by definition, $W \cap F$ is a neighbourhood of p in F, V is a neighbourhood in E of every point of $W \cap F$, and so U is a neighbourhood in F of every point of $W \cap F$.

It has thus been shown that the four conditions in the definition of a topological space are satisfied by the neighbourhoods in F as defined above. This justifies the use of the term "neighbourhoods" here and also the following definition:

DEFINITION 5. Let E be a topological space and F a sub-set. Then the neighbourhoods in F of the points of F define a topology on F. This will be called the *topology induced* on F by E, and F with this topology will be called a *subspace* of E.

It has already appeared in this definition and the discussion leading up to it that one must be careful, when speaking of a space and a subspace, to distinguish between neighbourhoods in the space and neighbourhoods in the subspace. Since open sets are defined in terms of neighbourhoods it follows that there will have to be a corresponding distinction between sets which are open in the space and those which are open in the subspace. The following examples illustrate this point.

Examples. (1) Let E be the (x, y)-plane, and let F be the x-axis. As usual, a neighbourhood of a point p in E, is any set containing a circular disc with centre p; while a neighbourhood of a point p in F is any set in F containing an interval with mid-point p. Then if U is an open interval in F, that is, an interval without its end-points, U is open in F but not open in E, since U certainly contains no circular disc. The fact that the usual topologies on E and F make F a subspace of E can be seen by noting that, if $p \in F$, the intersection of F with a disc of centre p is an interval with mid-point p.

(2) Let E be the (x, y)-plane in its usual topology, and let F be the square defined by the inequalities $0 \leq x \leq 1, 0 \leq y \leq 1$. Let p be a point on a side of this square. A circular disc with centre p is a neighbourhood of p in E, and so the intersection of such a disc with F is a neighbourhood of p in F. Thus a set U can be a neighbourhood of a point p in F, although it appears, when one draws a diagram, that p is on the edge of U. Thus p, although interior to U in the topology of F does not look like an interior point, and indeed is not an interior point of U in E. The notion of interior is thus, like that of neighbourhood and open set, relative to the space being considered.

To complete this example, it is clear that if V is the intersection of F with a circular disc not including the points of the circumference, then V is open in F; but if V contains points on the sides of the square F it will not be open in E. This is a special case of the next theorem to be proved.

THEOREM 6. *Let E be a space and F a subspace. Then a subset U of F is open in F if and only if there is an open set V in E such that $U = V \cap F$.*

PROOF. First suppose that $U = V \cap F$ where V is an open set in E. Let p be any point of U. Then since $p \in V$ and V is open in E, there is a neighbourhood W of p in E such that $W \subset V$. By the definition of the topology induced on F, $W \cap F$ is a neighbourhood of p in F, and is certainly contained in $V \cap F = U$. That is to say, for each $p \in U$ there is a neighbourhood of p in F contained in U, and so U is open in F.

Conversely, let U be given as open in F. If p is any point of U, there is, by the definition of an open set, a neighbourhood $V(p)$ of p in F such that $V(p) \subset U$. By the definition of neighbourhoods in a subspace there is a neighbourhood $W(p)$ of p in E such that $V(p) = W(p) \cap F$. On the other hand Theorem 3 says that the neighbourhood $W(p)$ of p in E contains an open set $W'(p)$ (open in E, that is to say) containing p. Let V denote the union of all the $W'(p)$ so obtained for all $p \in U$. Since the $W'(p)$ are all open in E, part (1) of Theorem 1 shows that V is open. For each $p \in U$ the inclusion relation $p \in W'(p) \cap F$ holds, and so it follows at once that the union of the p's, namely U itself, is contained in the union of the $W'(p)$, and in F. That is to say, $U \subset V \cap F$, where V is open in E. On the other hand, $W'(p) \cap F \subset W(p) \cap F = V(p) \subset U$ for each $p \in U$; and so $V \cap F \subset U$. Combining the two inclusion relations just proved it follows that $U = V \cap F$, and the theorem is established.

Exercises

1. Let E_m and E_n be Euclidean spaces of dimensions m and n ($m < n$) such that $E_m \subset E_n$. If E_m and E_n have their usual topologies prove that E_m is a subspace of E_n in the topology induced by that of E_n.

2. By Theorem 5 it should be possible to define a subspace by naming open sets. Let E be a topological space and F a subset of E. Define $U \subset F$ to be open in F if and only if $U = V \cap F$ for some set V open in E. Show that the family of sets so defined as being open in F satisfies the conditions of Theorem 5, and so defines a topology on F. Prove that this coincides with the induced topology as defined in Definition 5.

3. Let A and F be subsets of a topological space E. As usual $\mathring{A}$ denotes the interior of A in the space E. Prove that $\mathring{A} \cap F$ is contained in the interior of $A \cap F$ regarded as a subset of the subspace F.

By taking E as the real numbers and A, F as suitable subsets show that $\mathring{A} \cap F$ may be different from the interior of $A \cap F$ in the space F.

5. Limits

The simplest notion which can be expressed in terms of the idea of neighbourhoods in a topological space is that of the limit of a sequence of points. The definition is very similar to that given in analysis.

DEFINITION 6. A sequence of points p_1, p_2, ... in a topological space E is said to have a *limit* p, or *to converge to* p, if, for any preassigned neighbourhood U of p, there is an integer N such that $p_n \in U$ for all $n \geqslant N$.

Clearly if E is the space of real numbers, and if the sequence $\{p_n\}$ is taken to be a sequence of real numbers $\{x_n\}$ and the point p a real number x, then the preassigned neighbourhood U can be taken as an interval $(x - \varepsilon, x + \varepsilon)$, and the definition just given becomes the definition of a limit as usually stated in analysis. Another elementary case is that in which E is a Euclidean space. In this case the preassigned neighbourhood U can be taken to be a sphere with centre p and radius ε, where ε is a preassigned positive number. The sequence p_1, p_2, . . . converges to p if the distance of p_n from p is less than ε for all sufficiently large values of n.

There are two warnings to be given in connection with the definition of limits in an arbitrary topological space. In the first place the Cauchy criterion for the convergence of a sequence of real numbers has in general no analogue in a topological space. For this criterion says that a sequence x_1, x_2, . . . converges to some limit if and only if $|x_i - x_j| < \varepsilon$ for preassigned ε whenever i and j are sufficiently large. And the possibility of stating such a criterion depends on the possibility of saying that two points are near to each other according to some given standard of nearness (in this case saying that $|x_i - x_j| < \varepsilon$). But the standard of nearness required for this must be a uniform standard which one can apply to a *variable pair* of points. And this is just what one does not have in a topological space. All one can do in general is to say that *one variable point* is near a fixed point, nearness being expressed by using the family of neighbourhoods of the fixed point.

The second warning associated with the notion of limit is that, in a topological space as defined so far, there is no guarantee that the limit of a sequence of points, if it exists, is unique. For example, let E be the set of points of the (x, y)-plane; but instead of using the ordinary topology of the Euclidean plane, define a set U to be a neighbourhood of a point (x_0, y_0) if and only if U contains all points (x, y) satisfying an inequality of the form $|x - x_0| < \varepsilon$ where ε is some positive number, y being unrestricted. That is to say, a neighbourhood of (x_0, y_0) is a set containing a strip parallel to the y-axis, the point (x_0, y_0) being on the central line of this strip. Now let (x_1, y_1), (x_2, y_2), ... be a sequence of points in E such that $x_1, x_2, \ldots$ converges in the sense of ordinary real number convergence to a limit x. Then the point (x, y), for any y, is a limit of (x_n, y_n) in the sense of the topology just defined on E.

To explain the situation illustrated here, consider the proof in ordinary analysis of the uniqueness of the limit of a sequence of real numbers. Suppose that x and x' are both limits of the sequence $x_1, x_2, \ldots$ and that $x \neq x'$. Take $\varepsilon > 0$ such that the intervals $(x - \varepsilon, x + \varepsilon)$ and $(x' - \varepsilon, x' + \varepsilon)$ do not overlap; that is, take ε less than half the difference between x and x'. This leads to a contradiction, since the definition of limit requires that, for sufficiently large n, x_n should lie in both of the intervals $(x - \varepsilon, x + \varepsilon)$ and $(x' - \varepsilon, x' + \varepsilon)$. The proof clearly depends on the choice of ε so that these two intervals do not overlap, that is, on the choice of a neighbourhood U of x and a neighbourhood U' of x' such that $U \cap U' = \emptyset$. It is the possibility of such a choice which breaks down in the example given above.

It is often desirable to restrict attention to topological spaces satisfying a condition which will enable the proof of the uniqueness of the limit of a sequence of points to be proved. The required condition is given by the following definition.

DEFINITION 7. A topological space is called a *Hausdorff space*, or is said to satisfy the *Hausdorff separation axiom*, if, for every pair p, q of points of E with $p \neq q$, there is a neighbourhood U of p and a neighbourhood V of q such that $U \cap V = \emptyset$.

THEOREM 7. *Let E be a Hausdorff space and suppose that a sequence $\{p_n\}$ has a limit p. Then this limit is unique.*

PROOF. Suppose that the sequence also has another limit $q \neq p$. Let U and V be non-intersecting neighbourhoods of p and q, respectively. Then $p_n \in U$ for sufficiently large n and also $p_n \in V$ for sufficiently large n, which contradicts $U \cap V = \emptyset$. Hence the sequence cannot have more than one limit.

Examples. (1) The real line is a Hausdorff space. In general, a Euclidean space of any dimension in its usual topology is a Hausdorff space, since any two distinct points can be surrounded by non-overlapping spheres of sufficiently small radius.

(2) Let E be the topological space introduced in the Example (3) of §1, consisting of the set of integers with neighbourhoods defined as in the quoted example. This is a Hausdorff space. For let n and n' be two distinct integers, and choose the positive integer r so large that q^r is larger than the numerical value of $n - n'$. This choice ensures that q^r is not a factor of $n - n'$. Let U be the set of integers $n + mq^r$ $(m = 0, \pm 1, \pm 2, \ldots)$ and let U' be the set $n' + hq^r$ $(h = 0, \pm 1, \pm 2, \ldots)$. Then by the definition of neighbourhoods in this topology, U is a neighbourhood of n and U' is a neighbourhood of n'. And $U \cap U' = \emptyset$; for if these neighbourhoods had an element in common the equation $n + mq^r = n' + hq^r$ would hold for suitably chosen m and h; and this equation can be written as $n - n' = (h - m)q^r$, implying that $n - n'$ is divisible by q^r, which is known to be impossible. The Hausdorff separation condition thus holds in E as was asserted.

As this example is not based on any familiar geometrical picture, it is of interest to ask what sort of sequences are convergent in this space E. If the sequence $n_1, n_2, \ldots$ converges in E to the limit n, then, given any neighbourhood of n, n_r must be contained in this neighbourhood for all sufficiently large values of r. Taking as a preassigned neighbourhood of n the set of integers $n + mq^s$ $(m = 0, \pm 1, \pm 2 \ldots)$, it follows that if $n_1, n_2, \ldots$ has n as limit, the difference $n - n_r$ must be divisible by an arbitrarily high power of q for sufficiently large r; and it is not hard to see that this condition is also sufficient for convergence. Examples of sequences having n as limit are $n + q, n + q^2, n + q^3, n + q^4, \ldots$, and $n - q, n + 2q^2, n - 3q^3, n + 4q^4, \ldots$. It will be noticed that numerical value has nothing to do with this notion of convergence; in the sense of ordinary analysis the first sequence given here diverges steadily away from n and the second oscillates infinitely.

(3) Let E be the set of all bounded real valued functions of the real variable x defined for $0 \leqslant x \leqslant 1$. The topology to be introduced on E will be defined by first introducing a notion of distance. The distance between two functions f and g belonging to the set E will be defined to be the upper bound of $|f(x) - g(x)|$ for all x between 0 and 1; this upper bound exists since f and g are both bounded. The distance function so defined satisfies the conditions given in Exercise 1, §1, and so neighbourhoods may be defined in E, by saying that the subset U of E is a neighbourhood of f if U contains all functions whose distance from f is less than some positive number ε. Suppose now that the sequence of points (that is bounded real valued functions) $f_1, f_2, f_3, \ldots$ of E converges to the limit f in E, in the sense of this topology. A preassigned neighbourhood U of f can, in particular, be taken as the set of all points of E at distance less than ε from f for a preassigned positive number ε. And so the convergence condition (sufficiency is easily checked) becomes: given a positive number ε there is an integer N such that the distance of f from f_n is less than ε for all $n > N$; in other words, $|f(x) - f_n(x)| < \varepsilon$ for $n > N$. But this is just the condition for uniform convergence as usually defined in analysis. This example illustrates a situation which often arises in the application of topology to analysis; namely special types of convergence can be defined by making a family of functions into a topological space by some suitable definition of neighbourhoods, and then using the notion of a convergent sequence of points in this space.

Exercises

1. Prove that any metric space (Exercise 1, §1) is Hausdorff.

2. Prove that a subspace of a Hausdorff space is Hausdorff.

3. If E and F are Hausdorff spaces prove that the product space $E \times F$ (Exercise 4, §1) is Hausdorff.

4. Let E and F be two topological spaces. Prove that the necessary and sufficient condition that a sequence $\{a_n, b_n\}$ in $E \times F$ should converge to the limit (a, b) is that the sequences $\{a_n\}$ and $\{b_n\}$ should converge to a and b in E and F respectively.

5. Show that the topological space of Exercise 1, §3, namely the real numbers with the complements of finite sets defined as open, is not Hausdorff. Show that a sequence in this space converges to every point as a limit provided that no number appears infinitely often in the sequence. What happens in the case of infinite repeats?

6. In Example (3) of §3, the set of real numbers was made into a topological space by defining as open sets the whole set, the empty set, and every set satisfying an inequality of the form $x > a$. Show that this space is not Hausdorff. Show that a sequence $\{x_n\}$ in this space has a limit if and only if it is bounded below, and show that x is a limit of $\{x_n\}$ if and only if $x \leqslant \underline{\lim} \, x_n$ (the lower limit in the ordinary sense of analysis).

6. Limit points

As in the case of limits of a sequence, the notion of limit point of a set in a topological space is modelled on the corresponding idea in analysis. The formal definition is as follows.

DEFINITION 8. Let A be a set of points in a topological space E. Then a point p of E will be said to be a *limit point of A* if every neighbourhood of p contains a point of A different from p.

The last phrase "different from p" in this definition ensures that it is not enough for p simply to belong to A. If E is taken as the set of real numbers with the usual topology, then the definition just given becomes the one usually given in analysis. Now in this special case one can take a decreasing sequence of intervals with p as mid-point, of lengths, say, $1, \frac{1}{2}, \frac{1}{3}, \frac{1}{4}, \ldots$. If p is a limit point of the set of numbers A, each of these intervals will contain a number $x_1, x_2, x_3, x_4, \ldots$, respectively, different from p and belonging to A. If U is any neighbourhood of the number p, U will contain every interval of length $1/n$ and mid-point p for sufficiently large n. Thus the sequence $x_1, x_2, x_3, \ldots$ has p as its limit. And it follows from this incidentally that every neighbourhood of p contains infinitely many points of A. One must beware, however, of extending the statements just made for this special case to arbitrary topological spaces, as will be shown by the following examples.

Examples. (1) Let E be the set of all points of the (x, y)-plane, with the topology already used in the example preceding Definition 7; that is, a set U is a neighbourhood of a point p if and only if U contains a strip parallel to the y-axis with p on its central line. Let A consist of the single point (x_0, y_0). Then for any $y \neq y_0$ (x_0, y) is a limit point of the set A, for every neighbourhood of (x_0, y) contains (x_0, y_0). Thus it is possible for every neighbourhood of a limit point to contain only a finite number of points of the set, in contrast to the situation arising in the case of the real numbers.

The space of this example is not Hausdorff, and the situation arising here can only arise in a non-Hausdorff space. For let E be a

Hausdorff space, A a set of points in E and p a limit point of A, and suppose that a neighbourhood V of p contains only a finite number of points of A, say $p_1, p_2, p_3, \ldots, p_n$. Since E is Hausdorff there is, for each i, a neighbourhood U_i of p_i and a neighbourhood V_i of p such that $U_i \cap V_i = \emptyset$. Then in particular, $V_0 = V_1 \cap V_2 \cap \ldots \cap V_n \cap V$ is a neighbourhood of p and contains none of the points $p_1, p_2, p_3, \ldots, p_n$. But these are the only points of A in V other than p, and so V_0 contains no points of A other than p contrary to the supposition that p is a limit point of A.

An immediate corollary of what has just been proved is that, in a Hausdorff space, only infinite sets of points are capable of having limit points at all.

(2) The construction of an example to show that a limit point of a set A in a topological space need not be the limit of any sequence of points of A is a bit more complicated. Let E be the set of all real valued functions of the real variable x, defined for all values of x. If f is any point of E (that is a function of x) the $(\varepsilon, x_1, x_2, \ldots, x_n)$-neighbourhood of f will be defined to be the set of all points ϕ of E such that $|\phi(x_i) - f(x_i)| < \varepsilon, i = 1, 2, \ldots, n$; a neighbourhood of f of this type can be defined for every positive number ε, and every finite collection of numbers $x_1, x_2, \ldots, x_n$. The topology of E will now be defined by saying that U is a neighbourhood of f if and only if U contains an $(\varepsilon, x_1, x_2, \ldots, x_n)$-neighbourhood of f for some $\varepsilon, x_1, x_2, \ldots, x_n$. It must be verified, of course, that this assignment of neighbourhoods satisfies the conditions in the definition of a topological space; this will be left as an exercise. A further exercise is to check that this space is a Hausdorff space.

Now let f_0 be the function of x which is identically zero, and define a subset A of E as follows. Let $x_1, x_2, \ldots, x_n$ be any finite collection of real numbers and let $f_{x_1 x_2 \ldots x_n}$ be the function of x defined by setting $f_{x_1 \ldots x_n}(x_i) = 0 \; (i = 1, 2, \ldots, n)$ and $f_{x_1 \ldots x_n}(x) = 1$ for all other values of x. Let A be the set of all $f_{x_1 \ldots x_n}$ for all possible finite sets $x_1, x_2, \ldots, x_n$ of real numbers. f_0 certainly does not belong to A, since it is zero everywhere, while each member of A is zero at a finite number of values of x only. But f_0 is a limit point of A in the topological space E. For let U be a neighbourhood of f_0. Then U contains the $(\varepsilon, x_1, x_2, \ldots, x_n)$-neighbourhood of f_0 for some ε and $x_1, x_2, \ldots, x_n$, and the function $f_{x_1 \ldots x_n}$ belongs to this $(\varepsilon, x_1, x_2, \ldots x_n)$-neighbourhood, since $|f_{x_1 \ldots x_n}(x_i) - f_0(x_i)| < \varepsilon$, both terms of the difference being zero, for $i = 1, 2, \ldots, n$. That is to say, $f_{x_1 \ldots x_n}$, a member of the set A, belongs to the given neighbourhood U of f_0. This proves that f_0 is a limit point of A.

But f_0 is not the limit of any sequence selected from A. For suppose $f_1, f_2, \ldots$ is a sequence belonging to A and having f_0 as limit. By the definition of A each f_n is a function of x equal to zero for a finite set S_n of values of x and equal to 1 for all others. The union of all the S_n for $n = 1, 2, 3, \ldots$ is at most a denumerable set of points, and so there is a real number x_0 not belonging to any of the S_n. Let V be the (ε, x_0)-neighbourhood of f_0 for some $\varepsilon < 1$. By the choice of $x_0, f_i (x_0) = 1$ for all i, and so none of the members of the sequence $f_1, f_2, \ldots$ belongs to V; it follows at once that f_0 cannot after all be the limit of this sequence.

It should be noted in passing that the topological space used in this example appears in rather a natural way in analysis. In fact, to say that a sequence $f_1, f_2, \ldots$ of points of this space converges to the limit f means exactly that the functions $f_1, f_2 \ldots$ converge pointwise to f; that is to say, for every fixed value of x, the sequence $f_1(x), f_2(x), \ldots$ of real numbers converges to $f(x)$.

Exercises

1. Verify the statement made at the end of the section; namely that in the space E of Example (2), the sequence $\{f_i\}$ converges to f if and only if the sequence $\{f_i\}$ of functions converges pointwise to f.

2. Suppose that a topological space E satisfies the following condition:

For each point $p \in E$ there is a sequence $V_1(p), V_2(p), \ldots$ of neighbourhoods of p such that $V_{n+1}(p) \subset V_n(p)$ for each n, and such that, given any neighbourhood U of p there is an n such that $V_n(p) \subset U$.

Prove that in this case, if p is a limit point of a set A in E, p is the limit of some sequence of points of A.

The condition imposed on E here is sometimes called the first countability axiom (the second being a condition on the family of open sets).

3. Prove that a Euclidean space satisfies the first countability axiom. More generally, show that the axiom holds for any metric space.

4. Let E be the space of Example (3) of §1 consisting of the integers with a neighbourhood of n defined as any set containing all the integers $n + mq^r (m = 0, \pm 1, \pm 2, \ldots)$ for some r, q being a fixed prime. Let k be an integer not divisible by q, and let A be the set of all integers divisible by k. Show that every point of E is a limit point of A. If k is divisible by q^s what are the limit points of A? [Hint: Use the fact that if k is not divisible by q the H.C.F. of k and q^r is 1.]

7. Closure of a set

One sometimes wants to consider, along with a given set, the collection of all its limit points. The process of adding these limit points is given a special name in the following definition.

DEFINITION 9. Let A be a set in a topological space E. Then the *closure of A* is defined to be the set in E consisting of all the points of A along with all the limit points of A. The closure of A will be denoted by $\bar{A}$.

Examples. (1) If E is the set of real numbers in the usual topology, and A the set of numbers satisfying the inequality $a < x < b$, then $\bar{A}$ is the set satisfying the inequality $a \leqslant x \leqslant b$.

(2) If E is a Euclidean space and A is the set of points at distance less than r from some fixed point p, then $\bar{A}$ is the set of points whose distances from p are less than or equal to r.

(3) If E is the space of real numbers and A is the set of rational numbers then $\bar{A} = E$.

It is convenient to distinguish those sets in a topological space which already include all their limit points:

DEFINITION 10. A set A in a topological space E with the property $\bar{A} = A$ will be called a *closed set of E*.

Examples. (4) If E is the set of real numbers, the set of numbers satisfying $a \leqslant x \leqslant b$ is closed. Remembering that the set satisfying the inequality $a < x < b$ is an open set of E, it will be noticed that open and closed intervals, as usually employed in analysis, are open and closed sets respectively, in the sense of the topology of the real line.

(5) It is not hard to see that any finite set on the real line is closed, since such a set has no limit points at all.

(6) There are other closed sets on the real line besides finite sets and closed intervals. For example the set consisting of the numbers $0, 1, \frac{1}{2}, \frac{1}{3}, \ldots$ is closed. Note that this set with 0 omitted is not closed.

(7) Example (5) above can be generalized to any Hausdorff space. For if E is a Hausdorff space and A is a finite set of points, A has no limit points (Example (1) §6) and so A is closed.

(8) There are, however, examples of non-Hausdorff spaces in which finite sets are not closed. For instance, if E is the (x, y)-plane with the topology already used in Example (1), §6, a single point (x_0, y_0) is not closed, because all the points (x_0, y) are limit points of the set consisting of (x_0, y_0).

The following theorem gives one of the most important properties of closed sets, one which is sometimes used in defining them. The theorem is preceded by a lemma which translates the definition given here of closure into an easily usable criterion.

LEMMA. *Let A be a set in a topological space E. Then a point p of E belongs to $\bar{A}$ if and only if every neighbourhood of p meets A.*

PROOF. Suppose first that $p \in \bar{A}$. It may happen that p belongs to A, itself, in which case every neighbourhood of p certainly meets A, namely in p at least. If, on the other hand, $p \in \bar{A}$, but $p \notin A$, then p must be a limit point of A. And so, by the definition of limit point, every neighbourhood of p must meet A.

Conversely, suppose that every neighbourhood of p meets A. If $p \in A$ this condition does not really say anything, and p is certainly in $\bar{A}$. But if $p \notin A$, the assumed condition says that every neighbourhood of p meets A in a point which must necessarily be different from p. By definition, p is then a limit point of A, and so belongs to $\bar{A}$.

THEOREM 8. *A set A in a topological space E is closed if and only if the complement of A in E is an open set.*

PROOF. Suppose A is closed. Let p be a point of the complement of A. Then since $\bar{A} = A$, p is not in the closure of A, and so by the above lemma there will be a neighbourhood U of p not meeting A. But this means that U is contained in the complement of A. That is to say, each point p of the complement of A has a neighbourhood contained in the complement of A; the complement of A is therefore, by definition, an open set.

Suppose, to prove the converse, that the complement of A is an open set. It must be shown that $\bar{A} = A$; that is, since in any case $A \subset \bar{A}$, it must be shown that $\bar{A} \subset A$. Suppose on the contrary that p is a point of $\bar{A}$ but that $p \notin A$. Then p is in the complement of A; since the complement of A is open there is a neighbourhood U of p contained in the complement of A, that is, not meeting A. But by the above lemma this is contrary to the supposition that $p \in \bar{A}$. This contradiction shows that a point p in $\bar{A}$ but not in A cannot be found, and so $\bar{A} = A$, and the proof is completed.

An important consequence of this theorem is that one can translate

Theorem 1 into a theorem about closed sets by taking the complements of all the open sets mentioned there, and noting that the formation of a union is complementary to the formation of an intersection. The result obtained is the following:

THEOREM 9. *In a topological space E* (1) *the intersection of an arbitrary collection of closed sets is closed,* (2) *the union of a finite collection of closed sets is closed,* (3) *the empty set is closed and* (4) *the. whole space E is closed.*

In conclusion to this section it should be noted carefully that, if one is considering a subspace F of a space E as well as E itself, the notions of closure and closed sets, like those of neighbourhoods and open sets, are relative. That is to say, a set may be closed in F, in the sense of the induced topology on F, but not closed in E, and the closure of a set in F may not be the same as its closure in E. This will be illustrated by some examples:

Examples. (9) Let E be the set of real numbers in the usual topology, and let F be the set of rational numbers in the induced topology. Then the set A of rational numbers satisfying the inequality $0 \leqslant x \leqslant 1$ is closed in F, but is not closed in E, for in order to close it in E one must add all the irrational numbers between 0 and 1.

(10) Let E and F be as in Example (9) and let A be the set of rational numbers satisfying $0 < x < 1$. This set is not closed in F nor in E. The closure of A in F consists of the *rational* numbers such that $0 \leqslant x \leqslant 1$, but the closure in E consists of *all real* numbers such that $0 \leqslant x \leqslant 1$.

There is, however, a special case in which closed sets in F are also closed in the larger space E, namely when F is a closed set in E in the topology of E (cf. Exercise 5, below).

Exercises

1. Let A and B be sets in a topological space E. Prove the following properties of the operation of closure:

(a) $\bar{\bar{A}} = \bar{A}$;

(b) $\overline{A \cup B} = \bar{A} \cup \bar{B}$;

(c) $\overline{A \cap B} \subset \bar{A} \cap \bar{B}$.

Taking E to be the space of real numbers and A and B to be suitable subsets, show that $\overline{A \cap B}$ and $\bar{A} \cap \bar{B}$ may be different.

2. Let E be a topological space and A a set in E. Prove that $\bar{A}$ is the smallest closed set in E containing A (that is, a closed set contained in every closed set which contains A).

3. It may be noticed that there is a sort of duality between the two previous exercises and the results of Exercise 5, §2, and Theorem 2. This is due to the complementary nature of interior and closure about to be proved. Prove, namely, that, for any set A in a topological space E, $\overline{\complement A} = \complement \overset{\circ}{A}$ and $\overset{\circ}{\complement A} = \complement \overline{A}$. Hence deduce the results of Exercises 1 and 2 above from Exercise 5, §2, and Theorem 2.

4. The properties of closure in Exercise 1 are sometimes taken as the basis of yet another definition of a topological space, as follows:

Let E be an abstract set and let an operation be defined on the subsets of E which assigns to each subset A a subset $\bar{A}$ containing A. This operation is to satisfy (a), (b), (c) of Exercise 1 and also the conditions $\bar{\emptyset} = \emptyset$ and $\bar{E} = E$. Prove that there is one and only one way of making E into a topological space in such a way that $\bar{A}$ is the closure of A.

[Hint: Define U to be open if and only if $\overline{\complement U} = \complement U$ and use Theorem 5 to show that E is thus made into a topological space. Then note that the definition just given for open sets in E ensures that the closed sets are those for which $\bar{A} = A$, and finally check that $\bar{A}$ is the closure of A by showing that it is the smallest closed set containing A.]

5. Let E be a topological space and F a subspace. Prove that $A \subset F$ is closed in the space F if and only if $A = B \cap F$ where B is closed in E.

[Hint: Use Theorem 6.]

In particular, if F is closed as a set in E, prove that $A \subset F$ is closed in F if and only if it is closed in E.

6. Note that, by Theorem 8, open and closed are complementary properties but they are not opposite to one another. A set may be neither open nor closed or it may be both. For example:

(a) Prove that if E is the space of real numbers and A is the set of rational numbers then A is neither open nor closed.

(b) Prove that if E is the space of rational numbers (with topology induced by that of the real numbers) and A is the set $\sqrt{2} < x < \sqrt{3}$ then A is both open and closed. (cf. Chapter III, §4, Exercise 4 for more information on this situation).

7. Prove that each individual point of a topological space E is closed if and only if the following condition holds:

Given any pair of distinct points of E there is a neighbourhood of each which does not contain the other.

Note that this condition is a separation condition for pairs of points similar to but weaker than the Hausdorff condition. Note also that in a space satisfying this condition any finite set is closed, thus generalising Example (7) above.

8. Let E be the set of real numbers with open sets defined as the empty set and complements of finite sets. Prove that E satisfies the separation condition of the last exercise but is not a Hausdorff space. Thus every finite set in E is closed. If A is an infinite set in E prove that $\bar{A} = E$.

9. Let E be a Hausdorff space and let $\{p_i\}$ be a sequence in E having p as its limit. If A is the set of points p_i (for all i) prove that $\bar{A} = A \cup p$. Is this necessarily true in a non-Hausdorff space?

8. Frontier of a set

Frontier points of a set in a topological space have already been mentioned in contrast to interior points. One wants, however, the frontier of a set to be something which, in some sense, separates the points of the set from points not in the set. That the non-interior points of a set are not themselves sufficient for this can be seen from the following example. Let the space E to be considered be the (x, y)-plane in the usual topology, and let A be the set consisting of all points satisfying the inequality $x^2 + y^2 < 1$ along with all the points on the upper half of the circumference of this circular disc. Then the only points of A which are not interior are the points on the upper half circumference; but it would seem natural to say that the frontier of A consists of the whole circumference $x^2 + y^2 = 1$. Now it may be noticed that the points of this circumference are not only not interior to A, but they also fail to be interior points of the complement of A in E. This gives a topological characterization of the set $x^2 + y^2 = 1$ and in doing so suggests a suitable definition for the frontier of a set in any topological space.

DEFINITION 11. Let E be a topological space and A a set in E. Then the *frontier of A* is the set of all points of E which are neither in the interior of A nor in that of $\complement A$.

An alternative definition of frontier is given by the following theorem:

THEOREM 10. *Let A be a set in a topological space E. Then the frontier of A is the set $\bar{A} \cap \overline{\complement A}$.*

PROOF. Let p be in the frontier of A and write $A' = \complement A$; then by definition p is not an interior point of A. This means that there is no neighbourhood of p contained in A, or in other words that every neighbourhood of p must meet A'. It then follows from the lemma of §7 that $p \in \bar{A}'$. Similarly, since p is in the frontier of A it is not an interior point of A', and so every neighbourhood of p meets A; in other words $p \in \bar{A}$. Combining these results, $p \in \bar{A} \cap \bar{A}'$, and since p is any point of the frontier of A, it follows that the frontier of A is contained in $\bar{A} \cap \bar{A}'$.

To get this containing relation in reverse, let $p \in \bar{A} \cap \bar{A}'$. Then by the lemma in §7 every neighbourhood of p meets both A and A'; that is, no neighbourhood of p is contained in A nor in A'. p is therefore not in the interior of A nor in that of A', and so is in the frontier of A. Hence $\bar{A} \cap \bar{A}'$ is contained in the frontier of A. Thus $\bar{A} \cap \bar{A}'$ has been shown both to contain and to be contained in the frontier of A, and so the theorem is proved.

Exercises

1. If A is a set in any topological space prove that the frontier of $\mathring{A}$ is contained in that of A. Give an example of a set in A the space of real numbers for which $\mathring{A}$ and A have different frontiers.

2. If A is any set in a topological space prove that the frontier of $\bar{A}$ is contained in that of A. Give an example of a set A in the space of real numbers for which $\bar{A}$ and A have different frontiers.

3. Let A and B be sets in a topological space. Prove that the frontier of $A \cup B$ is contained in the union of the frontiers of A and of B, and give an example to show that it may be different from this union.

[Hint: Write down the definition of the frontier of $A \cup B$, namely $\overline{A \cup B} \cap \overline{\complement(A \cup B)}$ and use Exercise 1 of §7 above, along with the rules for calculating with the operations $\cup, \cap, \complement$.]

4. If A is a closed set and B an open set in a topological space and A' is the frontier of A, prove that $B \cap A'$ is contained in the frontier of $A \cap B$.

[Hint: It is to be shown that $A \cap B \cap \overline{\complement A} \subset \overline{A \cap B} \cap \overline{\complement(A \cap B)}$; do this by showing that $\complement(A \cap B) = \complement A \cup \complement B$.]

5. Let E and F be two topological spaces and let $A \subset E$, $B \subset F$. Let A' and B' be the frontiers of A and B in E and F respectively. Prove that the frontier of $A \times B$ in $E \times F$ is $(\bar{A} \times B') \cup (A' \times \bar{B})$.

CHAPTER III

TOPOLOGICAL PROPERTIES OF SPACES

1. Continuous mappings and homeomorphisms

THE definition of continuous mappings about to be given has already been discussed in Chapter I. The notion of neighbourhood, however, on which this definition rests, was at that stage entirely intuitive. By means of the definition of topological space given in Chapter II the idea of neighbourhood has been given an abstract formulation, and the properties to be attributed to neighbourhoods have been clearly laid down, and on this foundation the definition of continuity may be securely set up.

DEFINITION 12. Let E and F be two topological spaces. A mapping f of E into F is a law which assigns to each point p of E a well defined point $f(p)$ of F. The mapping f is said to be *continuous at p* if, for each neighbourhood U of $f(p)$ in F, there is a neighbourhood V of p in E such that $f(V) \subset U$. The mapping f of E into F is called *continuous* if it is continuous at all points of E.

There are a number of remarks which should be made concerning this definition. In the first place, it covers the notion of continuity used in analysis. To say that f is a continuous real-valued function of a real variable in analysis means that f is a continuous mapping of the real numbers into themselves, in the sense of the above definition, the real numbers being now taken as a topological space with a neighbourhood of a number taken as any set containing an interval with that number as mid-point. Similarly this definition covers the case of mappings of one Euclidean space into another as discussed from the intuitive point of view in Chapter I.

A second point which should be noted is of the greatest importance and should be borne in mind whenever any question of mappings (continuous or otherwise) is under consideration. Namely, it is essential to name the spaces E and F when a mapping of E into F is being defined, and the mapping is to be regarded as changed if either E or F is replaced by a subspace or by a bigger space. One is misled in this matter by the fact that in elementary work functions are usually given by explicit formulae, something which can in fact be done only in very special cases. The formula $y = x^2$ for example, is usually regarded as sufficient in elementary analysis to define y as a function of x. Here, however, this formula is to be regarded as defining a function or mapping only when the range of values of x to be considered is specified, and also only when it has been stated whether the values of the function are to be thought of as in the set of all real numbers or only in some subset. The following are, for example, four different mappings all defined by the same formula $y = x^2$:

(1) a mapping of the set of all real numbers into itself;

(2) a mapping of the set of all real numbers into the set of non-negative real numbers;

(3) a mapping of the set of real numbers in the closed interval from 0 to 1 into the set of all real numbers;

(4) a mapping of the set of real numbers in the closed interval from 0 to 1 into the closed interval from 0 to 1.

The difference between maps (1) and (3) is that in (3) one is only applying the formula $y = x^2$ to a subset of the set of real numbers, without even considering the numbers outside this subset. In general one often wants to consider the effect of a given mapping on a subspace, and the process of doing so is given a name in the following definition:

DEFINITION 13. Let f be a mapping (not necessarily continuous) of a topological space E into a topological space F, and let E' be a subspace of E. Then f induces a mapping f' of E' into F, defined by setting $f'(p) = f(p)$ for all p in E'. f' is called the *restriction of f to E'*.

The fact that f and f' are different mappings is brought out most clearly by noting that if f' only is known, f is by no means uniquely determined. For example, the mapping (3) above is the restriction of (1) to the closed interval from 0 to 1. But exactly the same restriction is obtained from the mapping g of the real numbers into themselves defined by setting $g(x) = 0$ for $x < 0$, $g(x) = x^2$ for $0 \leqslant x \leqslant 1$, and $g(x) = 1$ for $x > 1$.

In the above list of four mappings, the difference between (1) and (2) or between (3) and (4) lies in the fact that the mappings, although defined on the same set, are regarded as mappings into different sets. The importance of this distinction will not become apparent until Chapter IV when the question will again be brought up in connection with certain operations involving continuous mappings.

It has already been pointed out (§3, Chapter II) that a topological space can be defined in terms of open sets instead of in terms of neighbourhoods of individual points. The usefulness of this mode of definition rests principally on the fact that continuity can be defined in a very simple way in terms of open sets, as shown by the following theorem.

THEOREM 11. *A mapping f of a topological space E into a topological space F is continuous if and only if the inverse image of every open set in F is open in E.*

PROOF. First let f be given as a continuous mapping of E into F, and let U be an open set of F. It is to be shown that $\overset{-1}{f}(U)$ is open in E. Let p be any point of $\overset{-1}{f}(U)$; then $f(p) \in U$, and U, being open in F, is a neighbourhood of $f(p)$ in F (cf. Theorem 4). From the definition of continuity it follows that there is a neighbourhood V of p in E such that $f(V) \subset U$. This inclusion relation implies, however, that $V \subset \overset{-1}{f}(U)$. Thus each point p of $\overset{-1}{f}(U)$ has a neighbourhood contained in $\overset{-1}{f}(U)$, and so $\overset{-1}{f}(U)$ is open in E.

To prove the converse, suppose that $\overset{-1}{f}(U)$ is open in E whenever U is open in F. Let p be any point of E; it must be shown that f is continuous at p. To do this, let U be a neighbourhood of $f(p)$ in F. By Theorem 3 there is an open set W in F such that $f(p) \in W \subset U$. By hypothesis, $\overset{-1}{f}(W)$ is open in E. Since $f(p) \in W$, $\overset{-1}{f}(W)$ certainly contains p, and being open it is a neighbourhood of p. Thus for any given neighbourhood U of $f(p)$ in F there is a neighbourhood, namely $\overset{-1}{f}(W)$, of p in E such that $f(\overset{-1}{f}(W)) = W \subset U$. And so f is continuous at p and the proof is complete. ∎

It should be noted incidentally that the direct image of an open set under a continuous mapping need not be open. For example, let f be the mapping of the space of real numbers into itself given by $f(x) = x^2$. The open set $-1 < x < 1$ is carried onto the set $0 \leq x < 1$ which is not open.

The inverse image symbol $\overset{-1}{f}$ is not in general a mapping. If it is to be a mapping f must in the first place be one-one. That is to say, f being a mapping of E into F, two points p and q of E are mapped on the same point of F if and only if $p = q$. In the second place, in order that $\overset{-1}{f}$ may be defined at all points of F as a mapping of F into

E, it is necessary and sufficient that every point of F should be the image of some point (in fact only one, since f is one-one) of E under f. Another way of stating this second condition is to say that $f(E) = F$, or to say that f is a mapping of E onto F.

Mappings which are one-one and onto are always of special interest because of the possibility of constructing an inverse mapping. In topology however, particular importance is attached to those mappings which are not only one-one and onto but which have also the property that both the mapping and its inverse are continuous.

DEFINITION 14. Let E and F be two topological spaces and let f be a one-one mapping of E onto F. Then if both f and $\overset{-1}{f}$ are continuous f is said to be a *homeomorphism of E onto F*, and E and F are said to be *homeomorphic* under f.

Clearly, if f is a homeomorphism of E onto F then $\overset{-1}{f}$ is a homeomorphism of F onto E since, if $g = \overset{-1}{f}$, $\overset{-1}{g} = f$. One sometimes says of two spaces related in this way that they are homeomorphic, without mentioning the mapping: this terminology will turn out to be sufficient in many contexts, but not always, and so one should develop the habit of noting, at least mentally, the mapping involved when one states that two spaces are homeomorphic.

In view of Theorem 11 and the definition just given it follows that a homeomorphism of E onto F sets up a one-one correspondence between the open sets of E and those of F; for the continuity of $\overset{-1}{f}$ implies that f carries each open set of E into an open set of F, and the continuity of f implies that $\overset{-1}{f}$ carries each open set of F into an open set of E. Also, since, by Theorem 3, every neighbourhood of a point contains an open set containing the point, it follows that a homeomorphism between two topological spaces E and F sets up a one-one correspondence between the neighbourhoods of each point of E and the neighbourhoods of the corresponding point of F. Now a topological space is defined simply by means of a set of points and the family of neighbourhoods of each point. And so it is clear that two spaces in which not only the points are in one-one correspondence but also the neighbourhoods of corresponding points will be very similar to one another.

The statement at the end of the last paragraph can be made rather more precise as follows. There is a wide class of properties of a topological space E which depend only on the definition of E as a topological space, that is, depend only on the knowledge of which sets in E are neighbourhoods (or which sets are open if the other definition is used), but depend in no way on any other properties the elements of E may happen to have. Such properties will in general be defined in terms of the open sets or neighbourhoods of E and continuous mappings of other spaces into E and of E into other spaces. And so it is clear that these properties will also belong to any space homeomorphic to E, since the open sets and neighbourhoods in such a space are in one-one correspondence with those of E, and continuous mappings may be recognized by looking at open sets. For the sake of having a satisfactory definition it is better to take the statement made in the last sentence as characterizing the type of property under consideration.

DEFINITION 15. A property of a topological space E will be called a *topological property of E* if it also belongs to every space homeomorphic to E. *The subject of topology is concerned with the study of topological properties of topological spaces.*

In descriptive expositions on the subject, topology is often described as rubber-sheet-geometry, the implication being that it is the study of properties of figures, curves and surfaces, etc., which remain unchanged under continuous deformations involving stretching and compressing, but without cutting or tearing or sticking points together. This gives quite a good intuitive picture of what is going on, in the sense that two figures which can be deformed into one another as just described can usually be shown fairly easily to be homeomorphic spaces, regarding both as subspaces of Euclidean space.

For example, the surface of a sphere can be deformed into that of a cube simply by taking hold of it at eight points and stretching it tight. And, regarding both of these surfaces as subspaces of Euclidean 3-space they can easily be proved to be homeomorphic as follows. Join the middle point of the cube to a point p on its surface, thus obtaining a directed line segment l. From the centre of the sphere draw a directed line segment l' parallel to l; l' will meet the surface of the sphere in exactly one point $f(p)$. It is not hard to see that the mapping f of the cube onto the sphere is a homeomorphism.

On the other hand there are two respects in which this notion of topology over-simplifies the issue. In the first place the intuitive nature of this notion restricts one to subspaces of Euclidean 3-space, while in fact one often wants to consider sets of a more general nature. And in the second place, even subspaces of Euclidean 3-space which are homeomorphic are not necessarily obtainable from one another by continuous deformation. For example, let E be the circumference of a circle, and let E' be a knotted curve, as shown in Fig. 2, and for simplicity assume that the curves E and E' are of the same length. Fix a point p on E and a point p' on E', and mark a direction of rotation along each curve (shown by the arrows in Fig. 2). Now if q is any point on E, define $f(q)$ to be that point on E' whose distance from p' along E' in the direction marked is the same as the distance of q from p measured along E in the direction marked. f is clearly a homeomorphism of E onto E'. But E cannot be deformed

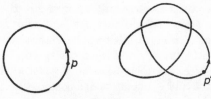

FIG. 2.

continuously into E', unless one extends this term to allow the first curve to cut across itself. Although it might be possible to make such an extension of the notion of continuous deformation in simple cases, such an attempt would be impracticable in more elaborate situations and would certainly make the rubber-sheet-geometry point of view unworkable in practice.

Before proceeding in the next few sections to give examples of topological properties, it had better be explained here just why such properties are interesting and important. Two homeomorphic spaces are to be regarded as having the same topological structure, for there is an exact correspondence between the neighbourhoods in the two spaces, and the topology in a space is defined by means of the neighbourhoods and nothing else. Homeomorphism thus plays a part in topology analogous to that played by isomorphism in algebra. The natural question to ask then is whether one can tell if two given spaces are homeomorphic or not; in other words is it possible to classify all spaces so that homeomorphic spaces appear in the same class. It turns out that this is too ambitious a task to attempt, but it can be thought of as an ideal towards which one strives. The best classifications which have actually been obtained group spaces into classes of spaces bearing relations to one another which are considerably weaker than homeomorphism.

In the meantime, consider how one would try to find out whether two given spaces are homeomorphic or not. If two spaces E and F are homeomorphic and one suspects them to be so, then in order to prove one's suspicions a homeomorphic mapping of E onto F must be constructed. And if one has already reached the stage of thinking, from intuitive grounds or otherwise, that E and F are homeomorphic, the actual construction of this mapping is likely to be more or less a matter of sufficient resourcefulness and ingenuity. On the other hand, if one suspects that two spaces E and F are not homeomorphic, one is up against much greater difficulties in constructing a proof. For one cannot expect to carry out the proof directly. That is, one cannot usually prove directly that every attempt to construct a homeomorphism of E onto F is bound to fail, since such a direct proof would require the writing down and inspection of all mappings of E into F. Of course there are simple cases when one can see at a glance that E and F cannot be homeomorphic, as, for example, when one of the spaces contains only a denumerable number of points and the other is non-denumerable. But in general one has to rely on indirect methods to prove that E and F are not homeomorphic, and this is where topological properties have their use. For if one can find a topological property belonging, say, to E but not to F, then E and F cannot be homeomorphic, since if they were, F would have all topological properties belonging to E.

Topological properties vary greatly in the interest to be attached to them. For example, the fact that in any topological space the whole space is an open set is a topological property. But it is not specially interesting, not only because it is simply a matter of definition, but because it belongs to all topological spaces. Properties which belong only to some spaces but not to others are of interest, because, as observed at the end of the last paragraph, such properties help to distinguish between spaces which are not homeomorphic. Thus the more non-trivial topological properties one has at one's disposal the more chance one has of distinguishing between spaces which are not homeomorphic to one another. It should be emphasized again that this use of topological properties will never show that two spaces *are* homeomorphic to one another; the fact that two given spaces both have a certain topological property is quite inconclusive, and the spaces may or may not be homeomorphic.

In the following three sections examples of some elementary topological properties will be given, while Chapters IV-IX will have as their subject some rather elaborate topological properties of great importance. The latter properties consist essentially of the assignment of a collection of groups to a space, the groups assigned to homeomorphic spaces being isomorphic. This sort of situation is usually described by saying that these groups are topological invariants.

Exercises

1. Let F be a topological space and E a subspace. The inclusion mapping $i: E \to F$ is defined by $i(p) = p$ for all $p \in E$. Prove that i is continuous.

[Hint: Use Theorems 6 and 11].

2. Let E, F, G be three topological spaces and $f: E \to F$, $g: F \to G$ two continuous mappings. Prove that the composition $g \circ f$ is a continuous mapping of E into G.

In particular if E is a subspace of F and f is taken to be the inclusion mapping, deduce that if $g: F \to G$ is continuous then so is the restriction of g to E.

3. Show that a mapping $f: E \to F$ is continuous if and only if the inverse image of every closed set in F is closed in E.

4. Let E, F be two topological spaces and f a mapping of E into F. Prove that f is continuous if and only if $f(\bar{A}) \subset \overline{f(A)}$ for every set $A \subset E$.

If p is a limit point of A, is $f(p)$ necessarily a limit point of $f(A)$?

[Hint: Use Exercise 3.]

5. Let f be a continuous mapping of a topological space E into a topological space F, and let $\{p_n\}$ be a sequence of points in E converging to p as a limit. Prove that $\{f(p_n)\}$ converges to $f(p)$.

6. Let E and F be two topological spaces and $E \times F$ their topological product (Chapter II, §1, Exercise 4). Define f_1: $E \times F \to E$ and $f_2: E \times F \to F$ by $f_1(p, q) = p$ and $f_2(p, q) = q$ for all $p \in E$ and $q \in F$. Prove that f_1 and f_2 are continuous.

Also if G is a topological space and $f: G \to E \times F$ a given mapping, prove that f is continuous if and only if the compositions $f_1 \circ f$ and $f_2 \circ f$ are continuous.

7. Let E be the (x, y)-plane in its usual topology and let I be the set of real numbers t such that $0 \leqslant t \leqslant 1$ (a subspace of the space of real numbers). Let $x(t)$ and $y(t)$ be two real valued functions of t for

$t \in I$. Deduce from the last exercise that the mapping $f{:}I \to E$ defined by $f(t) = (x(t), y(t))$ is continuous if and only if $x(t)$ and $y(t)$ are continuous functions in the ordinary sense of analysis.

8. In connection with Definition 14 it should be noted that a mapping can be one-one and onto and continuous in one direction but not in the other; and such a mapping is, of course, not a homeomorphism. For example, let F be the topological space whose points are the real numbers, open sets being the empty set and complements of finite sets. And let E be the space whose points are the real numbers with the ordinary topology. Define $f{:}E \to F$ by $f(x) = x$ for all real numbers x. Prove that f is one-one, onto and continuous but that $\overset{-1}{f}$ is not continuous.

9. Show that the property of being a Hausdorff space is a topological property.

10. Construct an explicit mapping to show that a closed rectangle in the plane is homeomorphic to a closed circular disc.

Generalize this to the proof that an n-dimensional closed rectangular block and a closed solid n-dimensional sphere are homeomorphic.

11. Let E be a solid n-dimensional sphere, that is, the set of points satisfying $\sum\limits_{i=1}^{n} x_i{}^2 \leqslant 1$ in Euclidean space of n dimensions, and let S be its surface, defined by $\sum\limits_{i=1}^{n} x_i{}^2 = 1$. Let F be a Euclidean space of any dimension. Prove that a continuous mapping $f{:}S \to F$ can always be extended to a mapping $g{:}E \to F$. That is to say, prove that there is a mapping g whose restriction to S coincides with f.

[Hint: Take any point q in F as the image of the centre of E under g, and then let g map the segment joining the centre of E to p on S onto the segment joining q and $f(p)$ in F.

It should be noted that if E is any space and S a subspace, it is not always possible to extend mappings given on S to mappings on E. For example, if the Euclidean space F were replaced by the sphere S and f were taken as the identity mapping the extension would be impossible; this will be proved in Chapter VIII, §3, Exercise 1.]

2. Compact spaces

The subject of this and the two following sections is a discussion of some elementary topological properties which are of considerable importance throughout topology. The first of these properties arises from the attempt to generalize the notion of a closed bounded set in a Euclidean space to other topological spaces. This notion requires some modification, since boundedness, involving as it does the idea of distance, is not itself a topological property. The translation of the property of being closed and bounded into an equivalent topological property of sets in Euclidean space is given by the following theorem, the Heine-Borel Theorem of analysis generalized to a Euclidean space of any dimension.

THEOREM 12. *A set A in a Euclidean space E of dimension n is closed and bounded if and only if, whenever A is contained in the union of an arbitrary collection of open sets in E, then it is also contained in the union of a finite number of open sets chosen from the given collection.*

PROOF. First suppose that A is closed and bounded, and let F be a family of open sets in E whose union contains A, and suppose that A is not contained in the union of any finite number of open sets taken from F; this will be shown to lead to a contradiction. Since A is bounded, it is contained in some closed rectangular block B defined by inequalities of the form $a_i \leqslant x_i \leqslant b_i$, $i = 1, 2, \ldots, n$, where $(x_1, x_2, \ldots, x_n)$ are the coordinates of a variable point in E. Subdivide B by marking in the bisecting hyperplanes with the equations $x_i = \frac{1}{2}(a_i + b_i)$, $i = 1, 2, \ldots, n$. Since it is assumed that A cannot be contained in the union of a finite number of sets chosen from F, it follows that there is at least one of the subdivisions of B, say B_1, containing a portion A_1 of A such that A_1 cannot be contained in the union of a finite number of sets chosen from F. Repeat the bisection process with B_1. That is, mark in the n hyperplanes bisecting B_1 in each coordinate direction. Then, as before, one of the resulting subdivisions B_2 of B_1 will contain a portion A_2 of A_1 such that A_2 cannot be contained in the union of a finite number of sets chosen from F. Then subdivide B_2 in the same way, and so on. Thus a sequence of rectangular blocks $B_1, B_2, B_3, \ldots$ is constructed with the property that each B_i contains a portion A_i of A which cannot be contained in the union of a finite number of open sets selected from F. On the other hand it is not hard to see that there is exactly one point common to all the B_i; namely a point p with coordinates $(c_1, c_2, \ldots c_n)$ where c_j is the common limit of the upper and lower bounds of the j-th coordinates of points in B_i as i tends to infinity. Now if U is any neighbourhood of p, it is clear that, for i large enough, $B_i \subset U$. But B_i contains points of A, namely the set A_i, and so U meets A. Since U is any neighbourhood of p it follows that $p \in \bar{A}$ (Lemma of Chapter II, §7) and so $p \in A$, since A is closed. p is therefore contained in some set V belonging to the family F. But V, being open, is a neighbourhood of p, and so contains B_i for some i. And this gives the required contradiction since it implies that A_i is contained in the set V chosen from F whereas it should not be possible to find any finite number of sets of F whose union contains A_i. The Theorem is thus proved in one direction.

To prove the converse, consider first the family F of open sets consisting of an open sphere of radius 1 about each point of A as centre. By hypothesis, A is contained in the union of some finite subcollection of these spheres, and so A is certainly bounded. It remains to be shown that A is closed. To do this, suppose that there is a point p in $\bar{A}$ but not in A. Let q be any point of A. Since $p \notin A$, p and q are certainly different, and so there are open spheres $U(q)$ and $V(q)$ of centres q and p, respectively, having no point in common. The family of $U(q)$ obtained by letting q vary throughout A clearly contains A in its union, and so, by hypothesis, there is a finite collection q_1, $q_2, \ldots, q_n$ of points of A such that $A \subset U(q_1) \cup U(q_2) \cup \ldots \cup U(q_n)$. On the other hand $V(q_i)$, for $i = 1, 2, \ldots, n$, is an open sphere of centre p; let V be the smallest of these spheres. Then V does not meet $\bigcup_{i=1}^{n} U(q_i)$; for if it did it would have some point in common with $U(q_j)$, say, and since $V \subset V(q_j)$ it would follow that $U(q_j) \cap V(q_j) \neq \emptyset$, which contradicts the definition of the $U(q)$ and $V(q)$. Since, then, V has no point in common with $\bigcup_{i=1}^{n} U(q_i)$, it certainly does not meet A. This is a contradiction, however. For p, being in $\bar{A}$, should have the property that every one of its neighbourhoods meets A. This contradiction shows the impossibility of finding a point $p \in \bar{A}$ and not in A. And so A is closed as required.

One can avoid the explicit mention of the open sets of the Euclidean space in the statement of this theorem by using the concept of induced topology (Chapter II, §4). Regarding A as a subspace of E, the intersections of A with open sets of E are open sets of A; thus in the statement of the above theorem, instead of saying that A is contained in the union of a collection of open sets of E, one can say that A is equal to the union of a collection of open sets of A. The wording of the theorem may also be tidied up with the aid of the following definition.

DEFINITION 16. Let E be any topological space, and let F be a family of sets in E such that E is their union. Then F is said to be a *covering of E*. If, in particular, all the sets in the family F are open sets, then F is called an *open covering of E*. And if F and F' are two coverings of E such that every set belonging to F' also belongs to F, then F' is called a *subcovering of F*.

Using the terminology just introduced Theorem 12 may be reformulated as follows:

A set A in a Euclidean space is closed and bounded if and only if every open covering of A, A being regarded as a subspace of E in its induced topology, contains a finite subcovering.

This generalized Heine-Borel theorem just proved shows that the property of being closed and bounded in a Euclidean space is equivalent to a topological property. This topological property can now be formulated for any topological space, and, combined with the Hausdorff separation condition, leads to the following definition:

DEFINITION 17. A topological space E is called a *compact space* if it is, in the first place, a Hausdorff space, and if also every open covering of E contains a finite subcovering. If A is a set in a topological space, then A is called a *compact set* if A, regarded as a subspace of E, is a compact space.

For example, Theorem 12 says that a set A in a Euclidean space is compact if and only if it is closed and bounded.

Compactness has just been referred to as a topological property, on the grounds that it is defined entirely in terms of open sets. But the topological nature of compactness must still be formally verified; that is, it must be checked that a space homeomorphic to a given compact space is also compact. In fact a rather stronger result will be obtained in the following theorem:

THEOREM 13. *Let f be a continuous mapping of a topological space E onto a topological space F. Then if E is compact and F is Hausdorff F is compact.*

PROOF. Let G be a given open covering of F. Then the inverse image under f of each set of G is open in E (Theorem 11), and the inverse images of all the sets in G form a covering G' of E. G' is thus an open covering of the compact space E, and so it contains a finite subcovering of E. And finally the images under f of the sets in this finite subcovering of E are already known to be sets of the covering G (because of the definition of G') and form a covering of F, since f is onto. Thus the given covering of F contains a finite subcovering, and F is given as a Hausdorff space, and so it is compact.

COROLLARY 1. *If E and F are homeomorphic spaces and E is compact, then so is F.*

PROOF. In the first place it is almost trivial that the Hausdorff separation condition is a topological property, and so F is a Hausdorff space. Thus E is compact and is mapped continuously (by a homeomorphism in fact) onto the Hausdorff space F; and so by the above theorem F is compact.

COROLLARY 2. *If $f:E \to F$ is a continuous mapping of a compact space E into a Hausdorff space F then $f(E)$ is a compact set.*

Exercises

1. Deduce from Theorem 13 that if f is a continuous function of the real variable x for $a \leqslant x \leqslant b$ then $f(x)$ has a maximum and a minimum which it attains at points in the closed interval (a, b).

2. Prove that a compact set in a Hausdorff space is closed.
[Hint: Imitate the second part of the proof of Theorem 12.]

3. Prove that a closed set A in a compact space E is compact.
[Hint: Given an open covering of A construct a covering of E by taking $E-A$ along with open sets intersecting A in the sets of the given covering.]

4. If A is an infinite set of points in a compact space E show that A has at least one limit point.
[Hint: Otherwise A would be closed and so compact; obtain a contradiction by constructing an open covering of A each set of which contains just one point of A.]

5. Let f be a one-one continuous mapping of a compact space E onto a Hausdorff space F. Prove that f is a homeomorphism (that is, prove $\overset{-1}{f}$ continuous).
[Hint: Use Exercises 2 and 3 above and Exercise 3 of §1.]

6. Let E be a Hausdorff space, A a compact set in E and p a point of E not in A. Prove that there is a neighbourhood U of p and an open set V such that $A \subset V$ and $U \cap V = \emptyset$.

7. Let A, B be two disjoint compact sets in a Hausdorff space. Prove that there are open sets U and V such that $A \subset U$, $B \subset V$, $U \cap V = \emptyset$.

8. Let E be a compact metric space, F any topological space and f a continuous mapping of E into F. Let C be an open covering of F. Prove that there is a positive number ε such that any sphere of radius ε in E is mapped by f into some set of the covering C. (A sphere of centre p and radius r in a metric space is the set of points q whose distance from p is less than or equal to r).
[Hint: Suppose that, for each integer n, there is a point p_n of E such

that a sphere of centre p_n and radius $1/n$ is not mapped into any set of C. The set of points p_n has a limit point p; obtain a contradiction by showing that f cannot be continuous at p.]

3. Arcwise connected spaces

The idea which is to be made precise in this section is based on the intuitive observation that certain sets of points, in the plane, say, have the property that any two of their points can be joined by a curve lying entirely in the set, while certain other sets fail to satisfy this condition. For example, if A is a circular disc, open or closed, it is clear that every pair of points of A can be joined by a curve (in fact by a straight line segment) lying entirely in A. On the other hand let A' be a set consisting of two disjoint circular discs; then any path joining a point of one of these discs to a point of the other must certainly cross the gap between the discs, and so must pass through points outside A'.

The first step in giving a rigorous topological meaning to the idea just illustrated is to give a proper definition of a path or curve. In analysis or analytical geometry when one speaks of a curve one is usually thinking of a set of points in which the coordinates are expressed as functions of a single parameter, and it is usually assumed at least that these functions are continuous. For example a curve in the plane would be specified by a pair of equations $x = f(t)$, $y = g(t)$ where f and g are continuous functions of t. If one is specially interested in the part of this curve joining two points p and q in the plane, the parameter t can always be adjusted so as to take the value 0 at p and 1 at q. t having been chosen in this way, it is not hard to see that the two real valued functions f and g define a continuous mapping of the unit interval $0 \leqslant t \leqslant 1$ into the (x, y)-plane. The idea of a continuous mapping of this interval into the plane as representing a curve in the plane lends itself readily to generalization and suggests the following definition for a path in any topological space.

DEFINITION 18. Let E be a given topological space, and let I denote the unit interval $0 \leqslant t \leqslant 1$, regarded as a subspace of the space of real numbers in the usual topology. Then a *path in E joining two points p and q of E is* defined to be a continuous mapping f of I into E such that $f(0) = p$ and $f(1) = q$. The path will be said to *lie in a subset A of E* if $f(I) \subset A$.

The most important thing to be noticed about this definition is that the *path is the mapping*; in elementary geometry one is inclined to think of a path as being a point set, whereas here it is not the point set image $f(I)$ which is the path but the mapping f itself. Thus a path will always be named by the mapping which defines it; the path described in the above definition being called the path f from p to q.

The definition just given can now be used to describe properly the idea mentioned at the beginning of this section.

DEFINITION 19. A topological space E is said to be *arcwise connected* if, for every pair of points p and q of E there is a path in E joining p and q. If A is a set in a topological space E, then A is *arcwise connected* if every pair of points of A can be joined by a path in A.

For example, if E is a Euclidean space of any dimension n it is arcwise connected. For let p and q be two points of E with coordinates $(y_1, y_2, \ldots, y_n)$ and $(z_1, z_2, \ldots, z_n)$ respectively, and define a mapping f of I into E by setting $f(t)$ equal to the point with coordinates $(x_1(t), x_2(t), \ldots, x_n(t))$ where $x_i(t) = (1 - t)y_i + tz_i$, $i = 1, 2, \ldots, n$. This mapping is clearly continuous and $f(0) = p$, $f(1) = q$. Thus f is a path from p to q in E and since p and q are any points of E the arcwise connectedness of E follows.

It will now be shown that arcwise connectedness is a topological property, this result depending on the following theorem:

THEOREM 14. *Let E and F be two spaces and f a continuous mapping of E onto F. Then if E is arcwise connected so is F.*

PROOF. Let p and q be any points of F. Since the mapping f is onto there are points p' and q' in E such that $f(p') = p$ and $f(q') = q$. Since E is arcwise connected there is a path g in E joining p' and q'; that is, there is a continuous mapping g of the interval I into E such that $g(0) = p'$ and $g(1) = q'$. Then the composition $f{\circ}g$ is a continuous mapping of I into F (Exercise 2, §1) such that $(f{\circ}g)(0) = p$ and $(f{\circ}g)(1) = q$; that is to say, $f{\circ}g$ is a path in F joining p and q. Since p and q are any points of F, the existence of this path proves the arcwise connectedness of F.

COROLLARY 1. *If E and F are two homeomorphic spaces, then E is arcwise connected if and only if F is; that is to say, arcwise connectedness is a topological property.*

PROOF. If E and F are homeomorphic there is a continuous mapping of each onto the other, and so by the above theorem, if one of the spaces is arcwise connected, so is the other.

COROLLARY 2. *If f is a continuous mapping of an arcwise connected space E into a space F, then f(E) is an arcwise connected set in F.*

PROOF. f is a mapping onto $f(E)$, and so the result follows from the theorem.

Exercises

1. Let p, q, r be points of a topological space E and let f be a path in E joining p and q, g a path in E joining q and r. Show that there is a path in E joining p and r.

[Hint: Define a path h by $h(t) = f(2t)$ for $0 \leqslant t \leqslant \frac{1}{2}$ and $h(t) = g(2t - 1)$ for $\frac{1}{2} \leqslant t \leqslant 1$.]

2. If A and B are arcwise connected sets in a topological space and $A \cap B \neq \emptyset$ prove that $A \cup B$ is arcwise connected.

3. Prove that if E and F are arcwise connected spaces so is the product $E \times F$.

[Hint: To join (p, q) and (p', q') join each to (p, q').]

4. Prove that the circumference of a circle is arcwise connected. More generally if S is a sphere of dimension r prove that S is arcwise connected.

[Hint: Do the second part by induction on r, noting that the section of an r-dimensional sphere by a hyperplane through its centre is an $(r - 1)$-dimensional sphere.]

5. Prove that the surface of a torus (cf. Fig. 21) is arcwise connected.

4. Connected spaces

For many purposes the property of arcwise connectedness is too restrictive a condition to impose on a space. The property about to be described is rather weaker, and has the additional advantage of being simpler, in that it is defined directly in terms of open sets without the intervention of the idea of a path in a space.

DEFINITION 20. A topological space is said to be *connected* if it cannot be expressed as the union of two disjoint non-empty open sets. A set A in a topological space is called *connected* if, when regarded as a subspace of E in the induced topology, A is a connected space.

Examples. (1) Let A consist of two circular discs in the plane such that the distance between their centres is strictly greater than the sum of their radii. Then A is not a connected set. For let the discs be called A_1 and A_2. Then there is an open set in the plane containing A_1 but not meeting A_2, namely an open disc U whose centre is that of A_1 and whose radius is greater than that of A_1, but not large enough for U to meet A_2. Thus $A_1 = A \cap U$, and so in the induced topology of A, A_1 is an open set. Similarly A_2 is an open set in A, and so A is expressed as the union of the disjoint sets A_1 and A_2, both open in A.

(2) Let A be the set of rational numbers, in the induced topology as a subspace of the real numbers. Then A is not connected. For the set U_1 of rational numbers less than $\sqrt{2}$ and the set U_2 of rational numbers greater than $\sqrt{2}$ are both open sets in A, and are disjoint, and $A = U_1 \cup U_2$.

(3) The space E of all real numbers is connected. For suppose $E = U \cup V$ where U and V are non-empty, disjoint and are both open in E. Since U is not empty it contains some real number u, and since V is not empty there must either be numbers greater than u or less than u belonging to V (possibly both); for the sake of definiteness suppose that there is a set W of all numbers greater than u and belonging to V. Since all the numbers in W are greater than u, W must have a lower bound v, and since $E = U \cup V$, v must be either in U or in V. Suppose $v \in U$; then since U is open there is a positive number ε such that the interval $(v - \varepsilon, v + \varepsilon)$ is contained in U. But this means that the interval $(v, v + \varepsilon)$ contains no points of W, which is impossible if v is the lower bound of W but does not lie in W. Hence v must be in V. But V is open, and so there is a positive number ζ such that the interval $(v - \zeta, v + \zeta)$ is contained in V. This interval cannot contain u, which is in U, and it contains numbers in W, namely between v and $v + \zeta$ since v is the lower bound of W. Hence the interval $(v - \zeta, v + \zeta)$ lies to the right of u, and so is in W. But this implies that there are numbers smaller than v belonging to W which is impossible. Thus it turns out that v cannot lie in U nor in V, which contradicts $E = U \cup V$. This contradiction shows that E is in fact connected.

It will now be shown that connectedness is a topological property, and in fact, as in the case of arcwise connectedness, a rather stronger result will be proved.

THEOREM 15. *Let E and F be two topological spaces and f a continuous mapping of E onto F. Then if E is connected so is F.*

PROOF. Suppose F is not connected. Then $F = U \cup V$, where U and V are two non-empty disjoint open sets of F. Then the inverse images U' and V' of U and V respectively under f are open sets in

E (Theorem 11), and are not empty since f is a mapping onto F. Also U' and V' are disjoint and $E = U' \cup V'$. But this contradicts the fact that E is connected; and so F must be connected too.

COROLLARY 1. *If E and F are homeomorphic then E is connected if and only if F is.*

PROOF. This follows at once from the above theorem and the fact that, if E and F are homeomorphic there is a continuous mapping of each onto the other.

COROLLARY 2. *The image of a connected space E under a continuous mapping into F is a connected set in F.*

In the next theorem and also in many other situations it is convenient to have a criterion for the connectedness of a set in a space E expressed directly in terms of the topology of E, rather than by the intervention of the induced topology. This criterion is set up in the following lemma.

LEMMA. *Let A be a set in a topological space E. Then A is a connected set if and only if it is not possible to find two open sets U and V in E such that $A \subset U \cup V$, $A \cap U \neq \emptyset$, $A \cap V \neq \emptyset$, $A \cap U \cap V = \emptyset$.*

PROOF. First suppose that two sets U and V exist as described above. Then $U' = U \cap A$ and $V' = V \cap A$ are two open sets of A in the induced topology, by the definition of this topology, U' and V' are non-empty by the conditions stated in the lemma and they are disjoint since $A \cap U \cap V = \emptyset$; and $A = U' \cup V'$, since $A \subset U \cup V$. Hence A is not connected (by definition). Conversely, suppose that A is not connected. Then there are two disjoint non-empty open sets U' and V' in A (i.e. in the induced topology) such that $A = U' \cup V'$. But, by the definition of the induced topology, there are open sets U and V in E such that $U' = U \cap A$ and $V' = V \cap A$. It is easy to see that U and V are as described in the statement of the lemma. It has thus been shown that A is not connected if and only if two open sets as specified in the statement of the lemma can be found, and this is equivalent to the lemma as stated.

THEOREM 16. *Let A be a connected set in a topological space E, and let B be a set such that $A \subset B \subset \bar{A}$. Then B is a connected set.*

PROOF. Suppose B is not connected; then by the above lemma there are two open sets U and V in E such that $B \subset U \cup V$, $B \cap U \neq \emptyset$, $B \cap V \neq \emptyset$, $B \cap U \cap V = \emptyset$. Since $A \subset B$ it follows from the first and fourth of these conditions that $A \subset U \cup V$, and $A \cap U \cap V = \emptyset$. It will now be shown that $A \cap U$ and $A \cap V$ are both non-empty. To do this take a point $p \in B \cap U$; such a point exists since $B \cap U$ is not empty. Since U is open it is a neighbourhood of each of its points, by Theorem 4, and in particular it is a neighbourhood of p. But $p \in B$ and $B \subset \bar{A}$, and so $p \in \bar{A}$, whence, by the Lemma in §7, Chapter II, the neighbourhood U of p meets A. Thus $U \cap A$ is not empty; and similarly $V \cap A$ is not empty. Thus $A \subset U \cup V$, $A \cap U \neq \emptyset$, $A \cap V \neq \emptyset$, $A \cap U \cap V = \emptyset$, and by the above lemma this contradicts the fact that A is connected. Hence U and V cannot exist as supposed, and B is connected as was to be shown.

As an application of the last theorem, along with the topological nature of connectedness, it will now be shown that *the following sets of real numbers are all connected*:

(1) a semi-infinite interval $x > a$ for some fixed a; (or, similarly, $x < a$);

(2) a semi-infinite closed interval $x \geqslant a$ (or $x \leqslant a$) for some fixed a;

(3) an open interval $a < x < b$ for fixed a and b;

(4) a semi-open interval $a \leqslant x < b$ or $a < x \leqslant b$ for fixed a and b;

(5) A closed interval $a \leqslant x \leqslant b$ for fixed a and b.

(1) The mapping which assigns to each real number x the number $a + e^x$ is clearly a homeomorphism of the set of all real numbers onto the set satisfying $x > a$. Since the set of all real numbers is connected (Example 3, above) it follows that the semi-infinite interval $x > a$ is connected.

(2) In Theorem 16 let A be the semi-infinite interval $x > a$, B the semi-infinite closed interval $x \geqslant a$. The conditions of the theorem are satisfied, since $B = \bar{A}$ and A is connected; hence B is connected.

(3) The mapping which carries x into $(b - a)/(b - x)$ maps the open interval $a < x < b$ onto the open semi-infinite interval $x > 1$, and the mapping is a homeomorphism. The semi-infinite interval is known to be connected, and so, by Corollary 1 to Theorem 15, the interval $a < x < b$ is connected.

(4) and (5) are proved by using Theorem 16 with A taken as the open interval $a < x < b$ and B taken as each of the semi-open intervals and as the closed interval in turn.

An important consequence of the connectedness of a line interval is the following theorem which establishes a relation between connectedness and arcwise connectedness.

THEOREM 17. *An arcwise connected space is connected.*

PROOF. Let E be an arcwise connected topological space and suppose that E is not connected. Then $E = U \cup V$ where U and V are two non-empty disjoint opens sets of E. Take a point p in U and a point q in V; this can be done since U and V are not empty. Since E is arcwise connected there is a continuous mapping f of the unit interval I into E such that $f(0) = p$ and $f(1) = q$. The conditions $f(0) = p$ and $f(1) = q$ imply that $f(I) \cap U$ and $f(I) \cap V$ are not empty; and since $U \cap V = \emptyset$ it follows that $f(I) \cap U \cap V = \emptyset$. Thus $f(I)$ is contained in the union $U \cup V$ (namely E), and $f(I) \cap U \neq \emptyset$, $f(I) \cap V \neq \emptyset$, $f(I) \cap U \cap V = \emptyset$. And so, by the lemma proved above, $f(I)$ is not connected. On the other hand I is connected and so by Theorem 15, Corollary 2, $f(I)$ is a connected set in E. This contradiction shows that the assumption that E is not connected is false, and so the theorem is proved.

The converse of the above theorem is *not* true, as is shown by the following example:

Let E be the set in the (x, y)-plane such that $y = \sin(1/x)$ for $0 < x \leqslant 1$ along with the points $(0, y)$ for $-1 \leqslant y \leqslant 1$. E is connected; for the set E' of points such that $y = \sin(1/x)$ for $0 < x \leqslant 1$ is a continuous image of the connected interval $0 < x \leqslant 1$ and E is the closure in the plane of E'. But E is not arcwise connected; for any mapping f of the interval $0 \leqslant t \leqslant 1$ into E such that $f(0)$ is a point of E with $x \neq 0$ and $f(1)$ is a point with $x = 0$ is necessarily discontinuous at $t = 1$.

Exercises

1. After Theorem 16 five types of connected sets were found in the space of real numbers. Prove now that a connected set in this space is necessarily of one of these five types or is the whole space.

2. Deduce from Exercise 1 that if f is a continuous real valued function of the real variable x for $a \leqslant x \leqslant b$, then for every y_0 between $f(a)$ and $f(b)$ there is an x_0 between a and b such that $y_0 = f(x_0)$.
[Hint: Use Theorem 15.]

3. Prove that the following are connected:
(a) Euclidean space of any dimension;
(b) a solid sphere of any dimension;
(c) an r-dimensional sphere for $r > 0$.

4. Prove that a space E is connected if and only if there is no non-empty set in E and different from E which is both open and closed.

5. Prove the following partial converse of Theorem 17: an open connected set A in a Euclidean space is arcwise connected.

[Hint: Show that the set of points of A which can be joined by paths in A to a fixed point of A is open and closed in A.]

6. Let A be a connected set in a topological space E and suppose that A has points in common both with a set B of E and with $\complement B$. Prove that A meets the frontier of B. Hence show that in a connected space E every set different from E or $\emptyset$ has a non-empty frontier.

7. Let A and B be connected sets in a topological space E such that $\bar{A} \cap B \neq \emptyset$. Prove that $A \cup B$ is connected.

Note that the property stated here is similar to that given in Exercise 2, §3, for arcwise connected sets, but slightly weaker. In general $A \cup B$ is not arcwise connected for arcwise connected sets A and B unless $A \cap B \neq \emptyset$; it is not in general sufficient that $\bar{A} \cap B \neq \emptyset$, as is seen, for example, by taking A as the graph $y = \sin(1/x)$, $0 < x \leqslant 1$, in the (x, y)-plane and B as the segment joining $(0, -1)$ and $(0, 1)$.

CHAPTER IV

THE FUNDAMENTAL GROUP

1. Homotopy

The subject of this chapter is a more elaborate topological property than those discussed in §§2, 3, 4 of Chapter III. The property in question will consist in attaching a topologically invariant group to a given space; that is to say, a group will be assigned to each topological space in such a way that the groups assigned to homeomorphic spaces are isomorphic.

The idea involved may be introduced by asking the following question: what topological property of a space can be used to

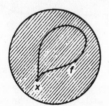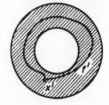

Fig. 3

distinguish between the two spaces shown in Fig. 3, the first being a circular disc and the second an annulus or disc with a hole in it? How, in other words, can one detect the existence of the hole by a criterion which makes no use of non-topological ideas like distance and angle?

A natural answer to this question is obtained by considering the possibility, or otherwise, of shrinking to a point closed loops drawn on the two spaces. Any closed path f on the circular disc starting and ending at a point x can be shrunk to the point x without going outside the disc; at least it certainly appears that this is so from intuitive grounds, and a rigorous proof will be given later. On the other hand, it is possible to draw a closed path such as f' on the annulus which cannot be shrunk to a point within the annulus. One can think of the situation physically by picturing the paths f

and f' as loops of string passing through eyelets at x and x', respectively. The first loop can be drawn tight through the eyelet at x, but the second, if one pulls through the eyelet at x', gets caught around the inner boundary of the annulus, which one can think of as being some sort of barrier.

It is fairly clear that the distinction which has just been drawn relates to a topological property. That is, the property of a space E that every closed loop in E can be shrunk to a point in E is a topological property of E. This is intuitively obvious since, if E' is homeomorphic to E, the shrinking of a given path in E', can be

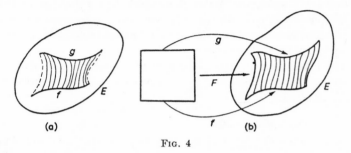

Fig. 4

carried out by copying, step by step, the shrinking of the corresponding path in E. But this reasoning relies too much on some sort of physical intuition to be satisfactory. The essential step to be taken now is the replacement of the shrinking process by an accurately defined topological notion.

Still speaking intuitively, it is clear that shrinking a closed path to a point is a special case of deforming a closed path from one shape to another, and this is itself a special case of deforming any path (not necessarily closed) from one position to another. Pictorially, such a deformation is represented in Fig. 4(a) where f is a given path in a space E and is deformed in E to a new position g. As the path f is moved to the new position g, it traces out in E the shaded curvilinear quadrilateral as shown in the figure. The natural way of describing accurately the idea of a curvilinear quadrilateral in a space is to construct a continuous mapping of a rectangle into the space. In this case one would want a continuous mapping F (Fig. 4(b)) of a rectangle into E such that F restricted to the lower side represents f and restricted to the upper side represents g.

The construction of such a continuous mapping is a precise

topological notion, and will now be taken as the definition of deformation. This idea of deformation, now given a rigorous meaning, is also given a special name in topology, namely homotopy. The formal definition is as follows:

DEFINITION 21. Let f and g be two paths on a topological space E, that is, two continuous mappings of the unit interval I, consisting of real numbers s such that $0 \leqslant s \leqslant 1$, into E. Also let I^2 denote the unit square in the (s, t)-plane; I^2 consists of all points (s, t) such that $0 \leqslant s \leqslant 1$, $0 \leqslant t \leqslant 1$. Then the paths f and g are said to be *homotopic in E*, or simply *homotopic* if there is no possibility of confusion, if there is a continuous mapping F of I^2 into E such that $F(s, 0) = f(s)$ and $F(s, 1) = g(s)$ for all $s \in I$.

The definition is summed up diagrammatically by Fig. 4(*b*).

It is, of course clear that homotopy is a relation between two mappings, a path being a mapping (cf. Chapter III, §3). The definition just given can therefore be generalized to mappings' other than those of I into E. The generalization about to be described will not actually be required until Chapter VI, but this seems the natural place to give the definition.

In the first place, if A and B are any two sets a new set denoted by $A \times B$ and called the product set of A and B can be defined as the collection of all pairs (a, b) where $a \in A$ and $b \in B$. If A and B are topological spaces a neighbourhood of $(a, b) \in A \times B$ can be defined as any subset W of $A \times B$ which contains a set of the form $U \times V$, where U is a neighbourhood of a in A and V is a neighbourhood of b in B. In this way $A \times B$ becomes a topological space (cf. Chapter II, §1, Exercise 4) and is called the product space of A and B. For example I^2 is the product space $I \times I$ of I with itself.

The above definition may now be generalized simply by replacing the first factor in the product $I^2 = I \times I$ by any topological space A.

DEFINITION 22. Let A and E be any two topological spaces and let f and g be two continuous mappings of A into E. f and g will be said to be *homotopic* if there is a continuous mapping F of $A \times I$ into E such that $F(a, 0) = f(a)$ and $F(a, 1) = g(a)$ for all $a \in A$.

Clearly this reduces to the former definition if A is replaced by I.

NOTE. The remark made in Chapter III, §1, on the importance of mentioning both spaces when a mapping is named becomes of significance here and in connection with Definitions 23, 24 and 25. For two mappings f, g of A into E may not be homotopic, but there may be a space $E' \supset E$ such that f and g, regarded as mappings into

E', are homotopic. The point is that by extending the space E to E' one makes available more room for deformation.

Returning now to the special case of homotopy of paths, it turns out that the concept defined above is not of great interest unless some further restriction is imposed. For it is not hard to show that any two paths on an arcwise connected space are homotopic (cf. Exercise 1 below). A non-trivial concept is obtained if one requires in addition that the deformation of one path into another should be carried out without moving the end-points. In this context a path may be thought of as an elastic string with its ends pegged down;

Fig. 5

the only permissible deformations are those in which the pegs are not disturbed. That this is a non-trivial notion may be seen by noting that in Fig. 5 the paths f and g joining the fixed points x and y cannot be deformed into each other. (This statement of impossibility is, of course, based on physical intuition at this stage, but it will appear later that it can be proved.) The notion of deformation or homotopy with fixed end-points is described in detail as follows:

DEFINITION 23. Let f and g be two paths on a topological space E joining the points x and y; that is to say f and g are continuous mappings of I into E such that $f(0) = g(0) = x$ and $f(1) = g(1) = y$. Then f and g are said to be *homotopic with the fixed end-points* x *and* y if there is a continuous mapping $F:I^2 \to E$ such that $F(s, 0) = f(s)$ and $F(s, 1) = g(s)$ for all $s \in I$ and in addition $F(0, t) = x$ and $F(1, t) = y$ for all $t \in I$ (cf. Fig. 6).

The special case of the deformation of a closed loop as described at the beginning of this section is covered by this definition; it corresponds, in fact to taking $x = y$. Explicitly:

DEFINITION 24. Let f and g be two closed paths on a topological space E both beginning and ending at a point x of E. Then f and g are said to be *homotopic with respect to the fixed base-point* x if there is a continuous mapping $F:I^2 \to E$ such that $F(s, 0) = f(s)$ and $F(s, 1) = g(s)$ for all $s \in I$ and also $F(0, t) = F(1, t) = x$ for all $t \in I$.

The particular case of deformation which started off this discussion, namely shrinking to a point, can now be defined:

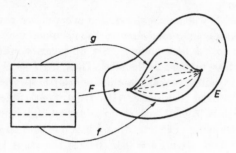

FIG. 6

DEFINITION 25. A closed path f on a topological space E beginning and ending at x will be said to be *shrinkable to x* or to be *homotopic to a constant with respect to the base-point x* if f is homotopic to the mapping $e:I \to E$ defined by $e(s) = x$ for all $s \in I$, with respect to the base-point x.

If this definition is combined with the previous one and the whole

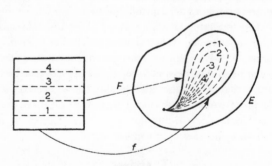

FIG. 7

thing is written out explicitly, it turns out that shrinking a path f to the point x amounts to constructing a continuous mapping F of I^2 into E, whose restriction to the lower side $(t = 0)$ gives the path f, while the other three sides are carried into x. In a simple diagrammatic representation such as Fig. 7 it will be noticed that the horizontal lines, each corresponding to a fixed value of t, are mapped into loops in E which get steadily smaller as t increases. Such a diagrammatic representation gives a very much over-simplified picture of the ideas involved, of course, and should only be regarded as a sort of mechanical aid to the understanding and remembering of the definition.

Example. It will now be shown that every closed path beginning and ending at a point x on a circular disc is homotopic to a constant with respect to the base point x. Set up polar coordinates in the plane of the disc, taking x as the pole. Then, if $f:I \to E$ is the given closed path $f(s)$ will have polar coordinates $(r(s), \theta(s))$. Define $F(s, t)$ as the point with polar coordinates $((1 - t)r(s), \theta(s))$. Since $(r(s), \theta(s))$ is in E all points $(r, \theta(s))$ with $r \leqslant r(s)$ are on E, and so $F(s, t) \in E$. F is thus a mapping of I^2 into E, and it is not hard to see that it is continuous. Also, setting $t = 0$, $F(s, 0)$ is the point $(r(s), \theta(s)) = f(s)$ while the radial coordinate r of $F(s, 1)$ is zero for all s; that is $F(s, 1) = x$. And finally, since $r(0) = r(1) = 0$, it follows that $F(0, t) = F(1, t) = x$ for all t. Thus all the conditions in the definition of the shrinkability of f to the point x are satisfied.

The property just established for a circular disc is sufficiently important to receive a special name:

DEFINITION 26. A topological space E will be said to be *simply connected with respect to the base-point* x if every closed path in E beginning and ending at x is shrinkable to x.

It will turn out later that in certain cases the reference to the base-point is superfluous. When this happens, that is when a space is simply connected with respect to any one of its points as base-point, the space will be said to be *simply connected*. It has just been shown, for example, that a circular disc is simply connected. A similar method of proof would show that a rectangle, or, more generally, a rectangular block of any dimension, is simply connected. Similarly any Euclidean space is simply connected.

Exercises

1. Prove that any two paths on an arcwise connected space are homotopic (no restriction being made on end-points).

[Hint: Let f, g be the paths. E the space and let h be a path joining the initial points of f and g. Map the bottom, top and left-hand edge of I^2 into E by f, g and h respectively. Show that this mapping can be extended to a mapping of I^2 into E by showing that there is a continuous mapping of I^2 into the union of the three mentioned sides (for example by projecting from some point lying to the right of I^2).]

2. Prove that if p and q are two points in the Euclidean plane E and f and g are two paths in E joining p and q, then f and g are homotopic with respect to fixed end-points.

3. Let S be a 2-sphere of centre q in Euclidean 3-space E and let $i: S \to E$ be the inclusion mapping. Let $j:S \to E$ be defined by $j(p) = q$ for all $p \in S$. Prove that i and j are homotopic.
Note that a similar result is also true for higher dimensions.

4. Let E be a solid r-dimensional sphere and q its centre. Let i be the identity mapping of E on itself and let $j:E \to E$ be defined by $j(p) = q$ for all $p \in E$. Prove that i and j are homotopic.

5. Let E be the annulus bounded in the Euclidean plane by two circles of centre q, and let i be the identity mapping of E on itself. Define $j:E \to E$ by setting $j(p) = p'$, where p' is the point where the segment pq meets the inner boundary of E. Prove that i and j are homotopic.

Generalize this result, letting E be the set defined by the inequality $a \leqslant \sum\limits_{i=1}^{n} x_i^2 \leqslant b$ in Euclidean n-space.

2. Homotopy classes

In principle at least, it is not hard to prove that a given simply connected space is simply connected. One has only to proceed as in the case of the circular disc, attempting to construct the necessary homotopies explicitly. This may, of course, require considerable ingenuity in more complicated cases. On the other hand, to show that a space is not simply connected one has to deal with a different type of difficulty, namely that of proving the non-existence of certain homotopies. That is to say, one must construct some closed path on the space and then prove that it is not homotopic to a constant. And, as in the case of trying to show that two spaces are not homeomorphic, a straightforward direct approach to this problem is not likely to succeed.

The solution to this difficulty is to undertake a deeper and more detailed study of closed paths on a topological space. The first thing to notice is that closed paths on a space may be grouped into classes, such that members of the same class can be deformed into one another. This will be proved in Theorem 18, but first some conventions of notation will be introduced. Throughout this section and the next E will be a given topological space and x an arbitrary fixed point of E. The paths considered in this section will all be closed paths beginning and ending at x, and for the sake of verbal economy will be called paths based on x. The statement that two such paths are homotopic with respect to the base-point x will be written as $f \simeq g$; x is not mentioned in this notation, but this does not matter in the present context since the base-point is being kept fixed in the meantime. Also throughout this section and the next, the symbol e will be used to denote the constant mapping of I into E defined by $e(s) = x$ for all $s \in I$.

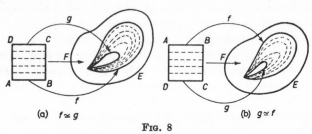

(a) $f \simeq g$ (b) $g \simeq f$

FIG. 8

THEOREM 18. *The relation of homotopy with respect to x of paths based on x is an equivalence relation on the set of all paths in E based on x.*

PROOF. It must be shown that (i) $f \simeq f$ for every path f based on x; (ii) $f \simeq g$ implies $g \simeq f$ for every pair of paths based on x; (iii) if f, g, h are paths based on x such that $f \simeq g$ and $g \simeq h$ then $f \simeq h$.

(i) To prove that $f \simeq f$, define the mapping $F:I^2 \to E$ by setting $F(s, t) = f(s)$. F is clearly a continuous mapping of I^2 into E which carries every horizontal line on I^2 into E in exactly the same way. Thus F restricted to the top or bottom of the square I^2 coincides with f, and the two vertical sides of I^2 are carried into x. This shows that F is a homotopy of f into itself as required.

The proof here has been stated rather informally. The strictly formal proof would run as follows: F as defined above is clearly a continuous mapping of I^2 into E. Setting $t = 0$ and $t = 1$, one obtains $F(s, 0) = f(s)$ and $F(s, 1) = f(s)$; and setting $s = 0$ and $s = 1$, one obtains $F(0, t) = F(1, t) = f(0) = f(1) = x$. Thus F satisfies the required conditions to show $f \simeq f$.

(ii) Let f and g be given such that $f \simeq g$. Then there is a mapping of the unit square I^2 into carrying the vertical sides into x and agreeing with f and g on the bottom and top, respectively. The proof consists simply in turning the square upside down (cf. Fig. 8).

To prove this formally, let $F:I^2 \to E$ be the given continuous mapping such that $F(s, 0) = f(s)$, $F(s, 1) = g(s)$, $F(0, t) = F(1,t) = x$; this is the explicit statement of the given fact that $f \simeq g$. Now define $F' : I^2 \to E$ by setting $F'(s, t) = F(s, 1 - t)$. The conditions just stated on F are translated now into: $F'(s, 0) = g(s)$, $F'(s,1) = f(s)$, $F'(0, t) = F'(1, t) = x$. And this shows that $g \simeq f$.

(iii) Let f, g, h be given such that $f \simeq g$ and $g \simeq h$. The proof that $f \simeq h$ is illustrated by Figs. 9, 10, 11. The given homotopies imply that there are two mappings F' and F'' of I^2 into E, satisfying certain conditions. For the sake of clarity in the diagram, two separate copies $ABCD$ and $PQRS$ of I^2 are shown in Fig. 9. Then the conditions are that F' should agree with f along AB and with g along DC, while F'' agrees with g along PQ and with h along SR. Also both F' and F'' carry the vertical sides of I^2 into x. Now if the two copies of I^2 are stuck together so that DC coincides with PQ it is fairly clear that F' and F'', which agree along DC and PQ, combine to give a continuous mapping of the rectangle $ABRS$ into E (Fig. 10). This mapping carries the vertical sides into x and agrees with f along AB and with h along RS, and so it is almost shown that $f \simeq h$. The catch is that homotopy is defined in terms of a mapping of a square into E, not a rectangle. But this can be remedied by a change of vertical scale (Fig. 11). Allowing for this change of scale, the mapping of the compressed rectangle $ABRS$ (which is a copy now of I^2) should be defined as $F'(s, 2t)$ on the lower half and $F''(s, 2t - 1)$ on the upper half.

The formal proof suggested by the above discussion is as follows: Since $f \simeq g$ and $g \simeq h$ there are continuous mappings F' and F'' of I^2 into E satisfying the following:

$$F'(s, 0) = f(s) \tag{1}$$

$$F'(s, 1) = g(s) \tag{2}$$

$$F''(s, 0) = g(s) \tag{3}$$

$$F''(s, 1) = h(s) \tag{4}$$

$$F'(0, t) = F'(1, t) = F''(0, t) = F''(1, t) = x \tag{5}$$

the first four of these holding for all $s \in I$, and the last for all $t \in I$. Define $F : I^2 \to E$ by the conditions

$$F(s, t) = F'(s, 2t) \quad \text{if} \quad 0 \leqslant t \leqslant \tfrac{1}{2};$$
$$F(s, t) = F''(s, 2t - 1) \quad \text{if} \quad \tfrac{1}{2} \leqslant t \leqslant 1.$$

The first thing to check is that F is in fact properly defined as a mapping, for both parts of its definition apply when $t = \tfrac{1}{2}$ and they

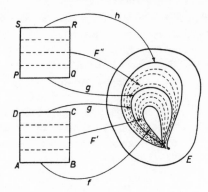

Fig. 9

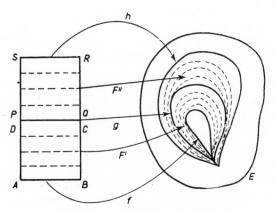

Fig. 10

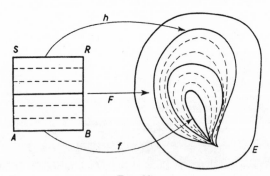

Fig. 11

might contradict one another. Such a contradiction does not, however arise, for. by (2) and (3), $F'(s, 1) = F''(s, 0) = g(s)$, and so $F(s, \frac{1}{2}) = g(s)$ by both parts of the definition. Of course it is more or less obvious from the above discussion with Fig. 11 that F' and F'' fit together properly, but it is nevertheless worth getting into the good habit of checking this kind of point formally, as things are not always as simple as in the present case. The next thing to verify is that F is continuous. It is clear that if $t \neq \frac{1}{2}$ F is continuous, this following directly from the continuity of F' or F'' according as $t < \frac{1}{2}$ or $t > \frac{1}{2}$. Suppose now that U is a neighbourhood in E of $F(s, \frac{1}{2})$ for some $s \in I$. Then the continuity of F' implies that there is a number ζ' such that, if $|s_1 - s| < \zeta'$ and $|2t_1 - 1| < 2\zeta'$, $F'(s_1, 2t_1)$ will lie in the neighbourhood U of $F'(s, 1) = F(s, \frac{1}{2})$. Similarly the continuity of F'' implies that there is a number ζ'' such that if $|s_1 - s| < \zeta''$ and $|(2t_1 - 1) - 0| < 2\zeta''$ then $F''(s_1, 2t_1 - 1)$ will lie in the neighbourhood U of $F''(s, 0) = F(s, \frac{1}{2})$. The inequalities imposed on s_1 and t_1 in the last two sentences are all satisfied if $|s_1 - s| < \zeta$ and $|t_1 - \frac{1}{2}| < \zeta$, where $\zeta = \min(\zeta', \zeta'')$. Thus these two statements combine to show that if $|s_1 - s| < \zeta$ and $|t_1 - \frac{1}{2}| < \zeta$ then $F(s_1, t_1) \in U$. The continuity of F is thus proved for points at which $t = \frac{1}{2}$. This kind of argument will frequently occur in the subsequent working, and will not be given in full again, the understanding being that the full proof is to be done as an exercise.

F has thus been shown to be a continuous mapping of I^2 into E; it will now be shown that it gives the required homotopy of f and h. For $t = 0$ $F(s, 0) = F'(s, 0) = f(s)$ by (1), and for $t = 1$, $F(s, 1) = F''(s, 1) = h(s)$ by (4). Also $F(0, t) = F'(0, 2t)$ or $F''(0, 2t - 1)$ according as $t \leqslant \frac{1}{2}$ or $t \geqslant \frac{1}{2}$, and in either case this is x by (5); similarly $F(1, t) = x$ for all t, and so all the verifications are complete and $f \simeq h$ has been proved.

Since homotopy with respect to a base-point x is an equivalence relation all the paths based on x are divided into equivalence classes.

DEFINITION 27. The equivalence classes of paths based on $x \in E$ corresponding to the relation of homotopy with respect to the base-point x will be called *homotopy classes of paths on E with respect to the base-point x*.

Exercises

1. Let E be a topological space and x, y two points of E. Prove that the relation of homotopy with respect to fixed end-points x and y is an equivalence relation between paths joining x and y.

2. Let A and E be any topological spaces. Show that the relation of homotopy is an equivalence relation between mappings of A into E.

In the case where A is the circumference of a circle, the corresponding equivalence classes are called free homotopy classes of closed paths on E (free because they are not bound to a base-point as in Definition 27).

3. The fundamental group

The mere subdivision of the set of paths based on a point of a topological space into homotopy classes would not be so useful in itself if it were not for the possibility of expressing algebraically

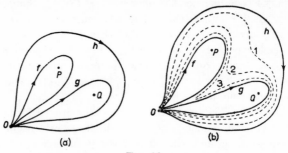

(a)   (b)

Fig. 12

certain relations between closed paths. The type of relation to be considered is illustrated by the following example. Let the space E be the Euclidean plane from which two points P and Q have been removed, and consider closed paths in E based on a third point O (cf. Fig. 12). If f, g, h are the three paths shown in Fig. 12(a) it would be fairly natural to say that h is equivalent (under homotopy with respect to the base-point O) to f followed by g; for intuitively speaking it is clear that h can be deformed into the shape of f followed by g, as illustrated by Fig. 12(b). It is to be understood of course that the deformation is to take place in E, that is in the plane with P and Q removed; if P and Q were not removed the whole thing would become trivial, as f, g, h would all be shrinkable to O.

A natural way of expressing the deformability of h into f followed by g would be to say that h is homotopic to fg, or in symbols, $h \simeq fg$. Of course this notation will have to be justified by the statement of a formal definition of the product fg. Before this is done, however, a further intuitive observation will be made, referring again to Fig. 12. It seems clear that if either f or g is continuously deformed then the path fg obtained by sticking f and g together in succession also sustains a continuous deformation. That is to say it appears that the homotopy class of fg depends only on the homotopy classes of f and g. It should therefore be possible to define a product operation between homotopy classes. If $\bar f$ and $\bar g$ are the homotopy classes of f and g then the product $\bar f\bar g$ would be defined as the homotopy class of fg. If $\bar h$ is the homotopy class of h, the relation of Fig. 12 could then be written as $\bar h = \bar f\bar g$.

The main result of this section, the result which makes it worth while to attempt to translate the situation of Fig. 12 into an algebraic

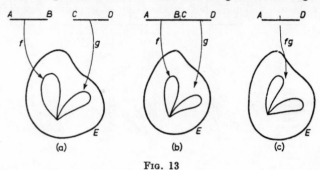

Fig. 13

operation as outlined above, is that the product operation so introduced between homotopy classes turns out to be a group operation.

The formal definitions will now be given, and proofs given for the ideas sketched above. The definition of the product of two paths f and g is illustrated by Fig. 13. E is any topological space and two copies of the unit interval I are shown on which the two mappings f and g are defined. If the two copies of I are joined end-to-end the mappings f and g combine to give a continuous mapping into E of an interval 2 units long. To bring this into the standard form for a path on E, the scale must be reduced by half, and this completes the definition.

DEFINITION 28. Let f and g be two closed paths on a topological space E based on a point x. The symbol fg will denote the following mapping of I into E:

$$(fg)(s) = f(2s), \quad \text{for} \quad 0 \leqslant s \leqslant \tfrac{1}{2},$$
$$(fg)(s) = g(2s - 1), \quad \text{for} \quad \tfrac{1}{2} \leqslant s \leqslant 1.$$

It is easy to verify that fg is continuous ($s = \frac{1}{2}$ is the only point which needs attention) and so defines a path on E; this path is called the *product of f and g*.

It is easy to see from the definition that $(fg)(0) = (fg)(1) = x$, and so the product of two paths based on x is again a path based on x.

The next step is to show that the homotopy class of fg depends only on those of f and g.

THEOREM 19. *If f, f', g, g' are paths in a topological space E based on a point x and if $f \simeq f'$, $g \simeq g'$, then $fg \simeq f'g'$.*

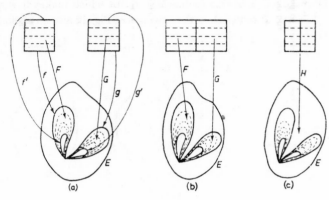

FIG. 14

PROOF. The idea of the proof is shown in Fig. 14. There are mappings F and G of I^2 into E (two copies of I^2 are shown) corresponding to the homotopy of f into f' and of g into g'. F and G are put together by laying the two copies of I^2 side-by-side and halving the horizontal scale. In this way a mapping $H : I^2 \to E$ is obtained which agrees with fg on the lower side and with $f'g'$ on the upper side; H is the required homotopy of fg and $f'g'$.

The details of this sketched proof will now be filled in. Since $f \simeq f'$ and $g \simeq g'$, there are continuous mappings F and G of I^2 into E such that:

$$F(s, 0) \ = f(s) \tag{6}$$

$$F(s, 1) \ = f'(s) \tag{7}$$

$$G(s, 0) \ = g(s) \tag{8}$$

$$G(s, 1) \ = g'(s) \tag{9}$$

$$F(0, t) \ = F(1, t) = G(0, t) = G(1, t) = x. \tag{10}$$

Let H be defined by:

$$H(s, t) = F(2s, t), \qquad 0 \leqslant s \leqslant \tfrac{1}{2},$$
$$H(s, t) = G(2s - 1, t), \quad \tfrac{1}{2} \leqslant s \leqslant 1.$$

It must be checked first that this definition is not self-contradictory for $s = \tfrac{1}{2}$; this follows from the fact that $H(\tfrac{1}{2}, t) = F(1, t) = x$ (by (10)) for all t, and also, using the second part of the definition of H, $H(\tfrac{1}{2}, t) = G(0, t) = x$ (by (10)). Next the continuity of H must be shown. Only the points with $s = \tfrac{1}{2}$ require attention here, and the verification is essentially as in the proof part (iii) of Theorem 18. Finally, to show that H establishes the required homotopy between fg and $f'g'$ it must be shown that the correct boundary conditions hold when s and t are put equal to 0 and 1. Setting $t = 0$ in the definition of H, it follows that $H(s, 0) = F(2s, 0) = f(2s)$ (by (6)) or $H(s, 0) = G(2s - 1, 0) = g(2s - 1)$ (by (8)) according as $0 \leqslant s \leqslant \tfrac{1}{2}$ or $\tfrac{1}{2} \leqslant s \leqslant 1$. If this is compared with Definition 28 it will be seen that $H(s, 0) = (fg)(s)$. Similarly, setting $t = 1$, it can be shown that $H(s, 1) = (f'g')(s)$. To check that H carries the vertical sides of I^2 into x set s equal to 0 and 1 in the definition of H. $H(0, t) = F(0, t) = x$ and $H(1, t) = G(1, t) = x$ (by (10)). Thus all the necessary conditions on H have been verified, and it has been proved as required that $fg \simeq f'g'$.

The theorem just proved now enables the product of homotopy classes to be constructed.

DEFINITION 29. Let $\bar{f}$ and $\bar{g}$ be two homotopy classes of paths based on x with respect to the base-point x, and let f be a path belonging to $\bar{f}$, g a path belonging to $\bar{g}$. The product $\bar{f}\bar{g}$ of $\bar{f}$ and $\bar{g}$ is defined to be the homotopy class to which the path fg belongs.

By Theorem 19 this defines a homotopy class depending only on the classes $\bar{f}$ and $\bar{g}$ and not on the representatives f and g. For if f' and g' are two more paths belonging to $\bar{f}$ and $\bar{g}$, respectively, $fg \simeq f'g'$ and so fg and $f'g'$ belong to the same homotopy class.

The main result of the present chapter can now be stated and proved.

THEOREM 20. Let E be a topological space and x a point of E. Then the homotopy classes with respect to the base-point x of paths based on x are the elements of a group having the product just defined in Definition 29 as group operation.

PROOF. The proof of this theorem consists of three parts: (i) to show that the product operation between homotopy classes is associative, (ii) to prove the existence of an identity element, (iii) to prove that each homotopy class has an inverse.

(i) Let f, g, h be three paths based on x and $\bar{f}$, $\bar{g}$, $\bar{h}$ their homotopy classes. It is to be shown that $(fg)h \simeq f(gh)$, or, what is the same thing, by the definition of the product of homotopy classes, that $(\bar{f}\bar{g})\bar{h} = \bar{f}(\bar{g}\bar{h})$. By definition fg is a continuous mapping of I into E such that $(fg)(s) = f(2s)$, $0 \leqslant s \leqslant \frac{1}{2}$, and $(fg)(s) = g(2s - 1)$, $\frac{1}{2} \leqslant s \leqslant 1$. Applying this definition again, to the product of fg and h, it turns out that $((fg)h)(s) = (fg)(2s)$, $0 \leqslant s \leqslant \frac{1}{2}$, and $((fg)h)(s) = h(2s - 1)$ $\frac{1}{2} \leqslant s \leqslant 1$. Combining these statements it follows that $(fg)h$ is a continuous mapping of I into E such that:

$$\left.\begin{array}{ll} ((fg)h)(s) = f(4s), & 0 \leqslant s \leqslant \frac{1}{4}, \\[2mm] ((fg)h)(s) = g(4s - 1), & \frac{1}{4} \leqslant s \leqslant \frac{1}{2}, \\[2mm] ((fg)h)(s) = h(2s - 1), & \frac{1}{2} \leqslant s \leqslant 1. \end{array}\right\} \tag{11}$$

Similarly, $f(gh)$ is a continuous mapping of I into E such that:

$$\left.\begin{array}{ll} (f(gh))(s) = f(2s), & 0 \leqslant s \leqslant \frac{1}{2}, \\[2mm] (f(gh))(s) = g(4s - 2), & \frac{1}{2} \leqslant s \leqslant \frac{3}{4}, \\[2mm] (f(gh))(s) = h(4s - 3), & \frac{3}{4} \leqslant s \leqslant 1. \end{array}\right\} \tag{12}$$

Now if equations (11) are examined it will be noticed that I is divided into three parts of lengths $\frac{1}{4}$, $\frac{1}{4}$, $\frac{1}{2}$, and $(fg)h$ is constructed by applying f to the first of these subintervals, g to the second and h to the third, the appropriate change of scale being made in each case. For example, the first interval is of length $\frac{1}{4}$, and $(fg)h$ is identified with f with the scale increased by 4; the scale increase is expressed by taking $4s$ as the argument of f. Similarly the scale is increased by 4 in the second interval, $4s - 1$ being a variable going from 0 to 1 as s goes from $\frac{1}{4}$ to $\frac{1}{2}$, while in the third interval, which is of length $\frac{1}{2}$, the scale is increased by 2.

$f(gh)$ is constructed in an exactly similar manner, except that the subdivisions are in this case of lengths $\frac{1}{2}$, $\frac{1}{4}$, $\frac{1}{4}$.

The idea now is to make a continuous transition from $(fg)h$ to $f(gh)$ by changing the three subintervals of lengths $\frac{1}{4}$, $\frac{1}{4}$, $\frac{1}{2}$ into those of lengths $\frac{1}{2}$, $\frac{1}{4}$, $\frac{1}{4}$ simply by stretching the first, compressing the third, and sliding the second sideways, as indicated, for example, by the arrows in Fig. 15. Now $ABCD$ in Fig. 15 can be taken as I^2. PQ, representing stage t of the transition from the subdivisions $\frac{1}{4}$, $\frac{1}{4}$, $\frac{1}{2}$ to $\frac{1}{2}$, $\frac{1}{4}$, $\frac{1}{4}$, is divided into three intervals of lengths $\frac{1}{4}(1 + t)$, $\frac{1}{4}$, $\frac{1}{4}(2 - t)$.

Just as $(fg)h$ and $f(gh)$ are defined on AB and DC, a mapping of PQ into E will be constructed by applying f, g, h to the three intervals PR, RS, SQ with suitable changes of scale, the arguments of f, g, h being chosen so that they vary from 0 to 1 as s varies along the corresponding subinterval. This mapping, which will be called $F(s, t)$, will be equal to $f(4s/(1+t))$ on PR, to $g(4s-t-1)$ on RS, and to $h((4s-t-2)/(2-t))$ on SQ.

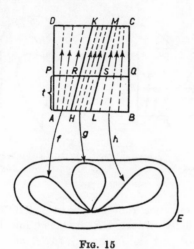

FIG. 15

It is hoped, of course, that the mapping $F(s, t)$ will yield the required homotopy of $(fg)h$ and $f(gh)$. Since it can be defined for each t from 0 to 1 it is certainly a mapping of I^2 into E, and the fact that it is continuous follows at once from the continuity of f, g, h (special attention is required along the lines HK and LM in Fig. 15; the situation is similar to that of Theorems 18 and 19 and the details should be filled in as an exercise). Also it is easy to verify that F coincides with $(fg)h$ on the lower side of I^2 and with $f(gh)$ on the upper side, and that $F(0, t) = F(1, t) = x$ for all t. And so the proof of part (i) of the theorem is complete.

(ii) The second part of the theorem will be proved by showing that the homotopy class $\bar{e}$ of the constant mapping e (cf. p. 70) acts as identity. That is to say it will be shown that, for any path f based on x, $ef \simeq fe \simeq f$.

The definition of ef is a continuous mapping of I into E such that $(ef)(s) = x$ for $0 \leqslant s \leqslant \frac{1}{2}$ and $(ef)(s) = f(2s-1)$ for $\frac{1}{2} \leqslant s \leqslant 1$.

Thus I is divided in half, the first half being mapped on x, while f is applied to the second half with the scale doubled. The idea now is to shrink steadily the part mapped on x while extending the part to which f is applied. In Fig. 16 $ABCD$ is I^2, AB is bisected at P and PD is joined. The horizontal line QR at height t is divided into intervals of lengths $\frac{1}{2}(1 - t)$ and $\frac{1}{2}(1 + t)$, and as t varies from 0 to 1 it is clear that these lengths change continuously from $\frac{1}{2}$, $\frac{1}{2}$ to 0, 1.

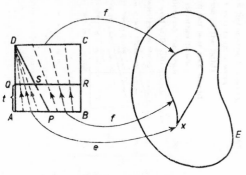

FIG. 16

The continuous transition from ef applied to AB into f applied to DC should be possible by mapping QR, at stage t, into E in such a way that QS is mapped on x and f is applied to SR with the appropriate change of scale. Then define $F(s, t)$ to be x for points on QS and to be equal to $f((2s + t - 1)/(t + 1))$ on SR.

$F(s, t)$ defined in this way is clearly a mapping of I^2 into E agreeing with ef on AB and with f on DC, and also carrying the vertical sides AD, BC into x. It remains to show that F is continuous in the pair of variables s, t. For any point (s, t) not on the line PD the continuity is obvious; for if (s, t) is in the triangle APD then F carries it into x and also carries a neighbourhood of (s, t), namely the whole triangle APD, into x; while, if (s, t) is in $PBCD$ but not on PD the continuity of F at (s, t) follows from that of f and the fact that $(2s + t - 1)/(t + 1)$ is continuous in s and t. Finally, consider points (s, t) on PD. F carries such a point into x. Now it is not hard to see that, if (s', t') is sufficiently near to the line PD and to the right of it, then $(2s' + t' - 1)/(t' + 1)$ can be made as small as one pleases. It follows thus from the continuity of f and the definition of F, that points sufficiently near to (s, t) and to the right of PD will be carried by F into a preassigned neighbourhood of x; all points to the left of PD are carried into x itself, and so the continuity of F at a point of PD is proved.

F thus satisfies all the conditions necessary to show that $ef \simeq f$. The proof that $fe \simeq f$ is carried out in exactly the same manner.

(iii) To complete the proof of the theorem it must now be shown that every homotopy class has an inverse. That is to say, if f is any given path based on x, it must be shown that there is a path g based on x such that $fg \simeq e$ and $gf \simeq e$. A path fulfilling this condition is obtained by taking f in reverse. Explicitly this means defining a mapping g of I into E by setting $g(s) = f(1 - s)$. The

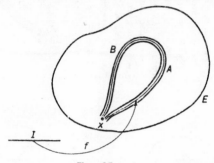

Fig. 17

idea of the proof that $fg \simeq e$ is based on the following mechanical analogy. Think of the path f as being marked by means of a thin curved tube (cf. Fig. 17). f should actually be represented by threading a piece of string (representing I) through the tube in the direction $xABx$; and then g would be represented by threading the string through the tube in the opposite direction $xBAx$. Now the product fg is defined by applying f to the first half PQ of I and g to the second half QR, the scale being doubled in each case (cf. Fig. 18). In the mechanical model this would be represented by stretching PQR to twice its length, folding it over so that QR lies along QP and then threading the doubled string through the tube in the direction $xABx$. The doubled string thus forms a loop inside the tube, and the deformation which will shrink fg to the point x is represented by pulling the free ends of this loop so that it slides out of the tube; successive stages of this operation are shown in Fig. 19. To represent even better the mapping to be defined presently, the string, as it is withdrawn from the tube, should be wrapped up and compressed into the point x.

The operation described here now has to be formulated properly. It will be noted that, at stage t of the withdrawal of the string loop from the tube, a length $t/2$ at each end of the original unit interval has actually been withdrawn, and the remainder lies along only

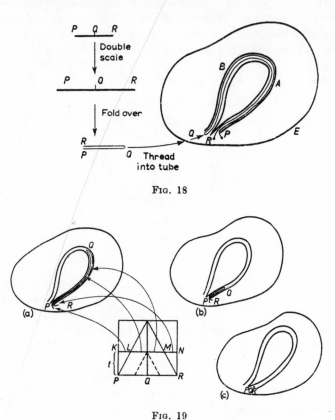

FIG. 18

FIG. 19

a part of the tube. Now, if PQR (see Fig. 19) is taken as the lower side of the square I^2, this statement corresponds to the condition that on a horizontal line KN at height t above the base a length $t/2$ at each end should be mapped into x, while the first half of the segment LM should be mapped into E in the same way as fg maps the interval from 0 to $\frac{1}{2} - t/2$ on PR and the second half of LM in the same way as fg maps the interval from $\frac{1}{2} + t/2$ to 1 on PR. Thus the analogy of drawing the loop through the tube suggests that $fg \simeq e$ can be established by defining a mapping $F:I^2 \to E$ as follows:

$$F(s, t) = x, 0 \leqslant s \leqslant t/2$$

$$F(s, t) = f(2s - t), t/2 \leqslant s \leqslant \tfrac{1}{2},$$

$$F(s, t) = g(2s + t - 1), \tfrac{1}{2} \leqslant s \leqslant 1 - t/2,$$

$$F(s, t) = x, 1 - t/2 \leqslant s \leqslant 1.$$

That this mapping does in fact satisfy the required conditions, namely that it is continuous, agrees with fg for $t = 0$ and with e for $t = 1$ and carries the vertical sides of I^2 into x, should now be verified as an exercise; the method is similar to that already illustrated in other homotopy proofs.

DEFINITION 30. The theorem just proved shows that, in a given topological space E, the homotopy classes of closed paths with respect to a base-point x form a group. This group will be called the *fundamental group of E relative to the base-point* x, and will be denoted by $\pi(E, x)$.

Exercises

1. Definition 28 can be generalized as follows: Let x, y, z be three points of a topological space E, f a path in E joining x and y, and g a path in E joining y and z. Let the mapping $fg:I \to E$ be defined by setting $(fg)(s) = f(2s), 0 \leqslant s \leqslant \tfrac{1}{2}$, and $(fg)(s) = g(2s - 1), \tfrac{1}{2} \leqslant s \leqslant 1$. Check that fg is a path joining x and z.

Prove the following generalization of Theorem 19. If f and f' are homotopic with respect to the fixed end-points x and y and g and g' are homotopic with respect to the fixed end-points y and z, then fg and $f'g'$ are homotopic with respect to the fixed end-points x and z.

2. Let w, x, y, z be points of a topological space E and let f, g, h be paths on E joining the pairs w, x and x, y and y, z respectively prove that (using the product operation defined in Exercise 1) $f(gh)$ and $(fg)h$ are homotopic with respect to the fixed end-points w and z.

[Hint: Imitate the proof of Theorem 20, (i).]

Note that the result proved here permits the use of the notation fgh without brackets provided that one is interested in the homotopy class only. A similar remark holds for any sequence of paths joined end to end.

3. Let x, y be two points of a topological space E and let f be a path in E joining x and y. Let e_x, e_y be the mappings of I into E defined by setting $e_x(s) = x$, $e_y(s) = y$ for all $s \in I$. Prove that $e_x f$ and $f e_y$ are homotopic to f with respect to the fixed end-points x and y.

[Hint: Imitate the proof of Theorem 20, (ii).]

4. Let f be a path on a topological space E joining x and y and define f^{-1} by the equation $f^{-1}(s) = f(1 - s)$. Prove that ff^{-1} is homotopic to e_x (cf. the last exercise) with respect to the base-point x.

[Hint: Imitate the proof of Theorem 20, (iii).]

5. Let E be a simply connected space (Definition 26 and the remarks following it) and let x and y be two points of E. Prove that any two paths f and g in E joining x and y are homotopic with respect to the fixed end-points x and y.

[Hint: Use the notation of Exercises 1–4 above. Prove f homotopic to $f(g^{-1}g)$ and so to $(fg^{-1})g$ with respect to the fixed end-points x and y. Note that fg^{-1} is a closed path based on x and then use Exercises 1 and 3 above.]

6. Let f be a closed path based on a point x of a topological space E. Prove that, if f is freely homotopic to a constant mapping, then it is homotopic to the constant mapping e_x with respect to the base-point x. (The converse is, of course, trivially true).

[Hint: To say that f is freely homotopic to a constant mapping means that there is a mapping $F: I^2 \to E$ such that $F(s, 0) = f(s)$, $F(0, t) = F(1, t)$ for all t and $F(s, 1) = y$ for some point y independent of s (this is essentially the same as the definition indicated in Exercise 2 of §2). Write $g(t) = F(0, t)$; then g is a path joining x and y. Show first that f is homotopic with respect to the fixed base-point x to gg^{-1}, and then use Exercise 4 above.]

7. Deduce from the last exercise that a topological space E is simply connected if and only if every closed path on E is freely homotopic to a constant mapping.

8. Let f be a closed path on a sphere S, based on a point x. Prove that f is homotopic with respect to the base-point x to a product, $f_1 f_2 f_3 \ldots f_r$ (the product being in the sense of Exercise 1, and the insertion of brackets being unnecessary by Exercise 2) where each f_i is a homeomorphism of I onto some arc of a great circle of S.

[Hint: S can be covered by two open sets U and V each homeomorphic to an open circular disc; use the continuity of f to subdivide I into intervals $I_1, I_2, \ldots, I_r$ such that each $f(I_i) \subset U$ or V. Hence show f homotopic to a product $g_1 g_2 \ldots g_r$ each g_i being an open path on U or V. Apply Exercise 5 above to replace each g by an arc of a great circle.]

9. Deduce from Exercise 8 that the sphere S is simply connected.
[Hint: There is some point y not on the path $f_1, f_2 \ldots f_r$ and $S - y$ is homeomorphic to the Euclidean plane.

Note that the step given by Exercise 8 is necessary, for it could happen that the given path f passes through every point of S.]

10. Use the method of Exercises 8 and 9 to show that every r-dimensional sphere is simply connected.

4. Change of base-point

The first step in this section will be to compare the groups $\pi(E, x)$ and $\pi(E, y)$ in the case where x and y can be joined by a path in the topological space E. It is clear in this case that a given path based

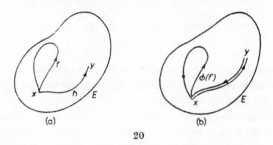

(a)   (b)

20

on x leads by a simple construction to a path based on y. For (cf. Fig. 20) if f is a given path based on x and h is a path from x to y, then a path $\phi(f)$ based on y is obtained by going along h in reverse (i.e. from y to x), then round f and finally back to y along h. It will now be shown that this correspondence between paths based on x and those based on y leads to an isomorphism between the corresponding groups of homotopy classes.

THEOREM 21. *If E is a topological space and x and y are two points of E which can be joined by a path in E, then $\pi(E, x)$ and $\pi(E, y)$ are isomorphic.*

PROOF. Let h be a path in E from x to y, that is to say, a continuous mapping of I into E such that $h(0) = x$ and $h(1) = y$. Let f be any path based on x, that is, a continuous mapping of I into E such that $f(0) = f(1) = x$. Define a path $\phi(f)$ based on y as follows:

$$\phi(f)(s) = h(1 - 3s), \, 0 \leqslant s \leqslant \tfrac{1}{3},$$
$$\phi(f)(s) = f(3s - 1), \, \tfrac{1}{3} \leqslant s \leqslant \tfrac{2}{3},$$
$$\phi(f)(s) = h(3s - 2), \, \tfrac{2}{3} \leqslant s \leqslant 1.$$

It is quite easy to see that $\phi(f)$ is a continuous mapping of I into E and carries 0 and 1 into y.

One would expect that a continuous deformation of f would lead to a corresponding continuous deformation of $\phi(f)$; that is, if f and g are homotopic with respect to the base-point x one would expect $\phi(f)$ and $\phi(g)$ to be homotopic with respect to the base-point y. To check this suppose that the homotopy of f and g with respect to x is given by a continuous mapping $F:I^2 \to E$ such that $F(s, 0) = f(s)$, $F(s, 1) = g(s)$, $F(0, t) = F(1, t) = x$ for all s, t. Define G by setting:

$$G(s, t) = h(1 - 3s), \qquad 0 \leqslant s \leqslant \tfrac{1}{3} \text{ and all } t,$$

$$G(s, t) = F(3s - 1, t), \quad \tfrac{1}{3} \leqslant s \leqslant \tfrac{2}{3} \text{ and all } t,$$

$$G(s, t) = h(3s - 2), \qquad \tfrac{2}{3} \leqslant s \leqslant 1 \text{ and all } t.$$

The verification that G is a continuous mapping of I^2 into E and that it satisfies the correct conditions for s and t equal to 0 and 1 to establish the homotopy of $\phi(f)$ and $\phi(g)$ with respect to y should be carried out as an exercise.

From what has just been shown, it follows that all paths in a given homotopy class with respect to the base-point x are mapped by ϕ into the same homotopy class with respect to y. If $\bar{f}$ is a homotopy class with respect to x and f is a path in this class, then the homotopy class with respect to y of $\phi(f)$ will be denoted by $\bar{\phi}(\bar{f})$. $\bar{\phi}$ is thus a well defined mapping of $\pi(E, x)$ into $\pi(E, y)$.

In exactly the same way a mapping $\bar{\psi}$ of $\pi(E, y)$ into $\pi(E, x)$ can be constructed. To do this let g be a given path based on y, and define $\psi(g)$ as a path based on x, the definition being similar to that of $\phi(f)$ above:

$$\psi(g)(s) = h(3s), \qquad 0 \leqslant s \leqslant \tfrac{1}{3},$$

$$\psi(g)(s) = g(3s - 1), \ \tfrac{1}{3} \leqslant s \leqslant \tfrac{2}{3},$$

$$\psi(g)(s) = h(3 - 3s), \ \tfrac{2}{3} \leqslant s \leqslant 1.$$

Having done this $\bar{\psi}$ is defined as the mapping of $\pi(E, y)$ into $\pi(E, x)$ which maps the homotopy class of g on that of $\psi(g)$.

It will now be shown that the mappings $\bar{\phi}$ and $\bar{\psi}$ are inverse to one another; this will show that both mappings are one-one and onto. In order to do this it will be sufficient to prove that, if f is a given path based on x, then $\psi(\phi(f))$ is homotopic to f with respect to the base-point x, and that if g is a given path based on y then $\phi(\psi(g))$ is homotopic to g with respect to the base-point y.

The full definition of $\psi(\phi(f))$ is as follows:

$$\psi(\phi(f))(s) = h(3s), \qquad 0 \leqslant s \leqslant \tfrac{1}{3},$$

$$\psi(\phi(f))(s) = h(4 - 9s), \quad \tfrac{1}{3} \leqslant s \leqslant \tfrac{4}{9},$$

$$\psi(\phi(f))(s) = f(9s - 4), \quad \tfrac{4}{9} \leqslant s \leqslant \tfrac{5}{9},$$

$$\psi(\phi(f))(s) = h(9s - 5), \quad \tfrac{5}{9} \leqslant s \leqslant \tfrac{2}{3},$$

$$\psi(\phi(f))(s) = h(3 - 3s), \quad \tfrac{2}{3} \leqslant s \leqslant 1.$$

It will be noticed that this definition amounts to dividing I into five subintervals to each of which h or h reversed or f is applied with the appropriate change of scale. Experience with this sort of situation in Theorem 20 should suggest that the deformation of $\psi(\phi(f))$ into f will be carried out by expanding the middle one of these subintervals, to which f is applied, so that it fills the whole of I, while the remaining subintervals are compressed into the end-points of I. And considerations similar to those followed in Theorem 20 suggest that the required homotopy will be given by a mapping $F:I^2 \to E$ defined as follows:

$$F(s, t) = h(3s), \qquad\qquad\qquad 0 \leqslant s \leqslant \tfrac{1}{3}(1-t),$$

$$F(s, t) = h(4-4t-9s), \qquad\qquad \tfrac{1}{3}(1-t) \leqslant s \leqslant \tfrac{4}{9}(1-t),$$

$$F(s, t) = f(9s/(8t+1) - (4-4t)/(8t+1)), \tfrac{4}{9}(1-t) \leqslant s \leqslant \tfrac{1}{9}(5+4t),$$

$$F(s, t) = h(9s-5-4t), \qquad\qquad \tfrac{1}{9}(5+4t) \leqslant s \leqslant \tfrac{1}{3}(t+2),$$

$$F(s, t) = h(3-3s), \qquad\qquad\qquad \tfrac{1}{3}(t+2) \leqslant s \leqslant 1.$$

The details of the proof that this mapping F gives the required homotopy of $\psi(\phi(f))$ and f with respect to the base-point x should be filled in as an exercise. The proof that g and $\phi(\psi(g))$ are homotopic with respect to the base-point y is carried out in a similar manner.

Having now shown that the mapping $\bar{\phi}:\pi(E, x) \to \pi(E, y)$ is one-one and onto, it remains to show that, for any two paths f and g based on x, $\phi(fg)$ is homotopic to $\phi(f)\phi(g)$ with respect to the base-point y. This will show that $\bar{\phi}$ is an isomorphism, as required. If one carries out reasoning similar to that used in Theorem 20, and the earlier part of the proof of this theorem, one will be led to the consideration of a mapping $F:I^2 \to E$ defined as follows:

$$F(s, t) = h(1 - 6s/(2 - t)), \qquad 0 \leqslant s \leqslant \tfrac{1}{6}(2 - t),$$

$$F(s, t) = f(6s + t - 2), \qquad \tfrac{1}{6}(2 - t) \leqslant s \leqslant \tfrac{1}{6}(3 - t),$$

$$F(s, t) = h(6s + t - 3), \qquad \tfrac{1}{6}(3 - t) \leqslant s \leqslant \tfrac{1}{2},$$

$$F(s, t) = h(t + 3 - 6s), \qquad \tfrac{1}{2} \leqslant s \leqslant \tfrac{1}{6}(t + 3),$$

$$F(s, t) = g(6s - 3 - t), \qquad \tfrac{1}{6}(t + 3) \leqslant s \leqslant \tfrac{1}{6}(t + 4),$$

$$F(s, t) = h((6s - t - 4)/(2 - t)), \quad \tfrac{1}{6}(t + 4) \leqslant s \leqslant 1.$$

It is not hard to prove that F gives the required homotopy with respect to the base-point y of $\phi(fg)$ and $\phi(f)\phi(g)$. When this has been done the proof of the present theorem is complete.

COROLLARY. *If E is an arcwise connected space, the group $\pi(E, x)$ is independent of the base-point x.*

PROOF. In this case any pair of points of E can be joined by a path in E and so $\pi(E, x)$ and $\pi(E, y)$ are isomorphic for any x and y in E. Hence $\pi(E, x)$ is the same as $\pi(E, y)$ from the point of view of group theory.

It follows from what has just been said that, if E is an arcwise connected space, one can speak without ambiguity of the fundamental group of E without mentioning any base-point, the understanding being that this group is $\pi(E, x)$ for any arbitrary x in E. The fundamental group of an arcwise connected space will be denoted by $\pi(E)$.

Exercises

1. Prove Theorem 21 by the use of Exercises 1–4 of §3.

2. The proof that the fundamental group of the circumference C of a circle is infinite cyclic cannot be completed at the moment. In the meantime obtain the partial result that $\pi(C)$ is cyclic.

[Hint: Take C as the unit circle in the complex z-plane. Cover C by two overlapping arcs (homeomorphic to line segments) U and V and show that any given path f is homotopic to a product $g_1, g_2 \ldots g_r$, each g_i being a path in either U or V. Use Exercises 1 and 5 of §3 to replace each g_j by a mapping h_j of the form $h_j(s) = e^{ic_j(s - \theta_j)}$. Show next that if the paths h_j and h_{j+1} run in opposite directions round C they may be replaced by a path running directly from the beginning of h_j to the end of h_{j+1}. Hence f is homotopic to a path $g\colon I \to C$ where I is divided into subintervals $I_1, I_2, \ldots, I_m$ and $g(s) = e^{ik_j(s-s_j)}$ on I_j, the k; all > 0 or all < 0. Finally show that this can be adjusted so that the k_j are all equal. Thus prove that $\pi(C)$ is generated by the homotopy class of a path $\phi\colon I \to C$ defined by $\phi(s) = e^{2\pi i s}$. To show that $\pi(C)$ is actually infinite cyclic it will have to be proved (cf. Chapter VIII, §2, Exercise 9) that neither ϕ nor any of its powers is homotopic to a constant mapping.]

3. Show that the fundamental group of a torus is abelian with two generators.

[Hint: As in the previous exercise use a covering of the torus by simply connected open sets. Also use the fact that the torus is obtained from a square by identifying opposite sides. For the complement to this exercise, showing that the fundamental group of the torus is free abelian with two generators, see Chapter VIII, §2, Exercise 9.]

4. Prove that the fundamental group of an annulus is the same as that of the circumference of a circle.

[Hint: Use Exercise 5, §1.]

Note that the result of this exercise, along with the fact (still to be proved) that the fundamental group of a circumference is infinite cyclic, justifies the possibility of finding two paths f and g on the annulus, as in Fig. 5, which are not homotopic with respect to fixed end-points.

5. The last exercise can be generalized as follows: Let E' be a subspace of E, both spaces being arcwise connected, and suppose that there is a continuous mapping $f\colon E \to E$ satisfying the following conditions:

(a) $f(E) = E'$;

(b) the restriction of f to E' is the identity mapping on E';

(c) f is homotopic to the identity mapping of E onto itself, with E' fixed. Prove that $\pi(E) \cong \pi(E')$

Exercise 4 is the special case in which E is the annulus and E' the inner boundary.

5. Topological invariance

It will now be shown that the fundamental group of an arcwise connected space is topologically invariant. In detail, this means that, if E and E' are two homeomorphic arcwise connected spaces, then $\pi(E)$ and $\pi(E')$ are isomorphic. This is highly plausible, since paths themselves and homotopies of paths and the forming of products are all defined in terms of continuous mappings; and one expects concepts defined in this way to be topological in character. It only remains now to give a formal verification.

THEOREM 22. *Let E and E' be homeomorphic and both arcwise connected. Then $\pi(E)$ and $\pi(E')$ are isomorphic.*

PROOF. Since E and E' are homeomorphic there is a homeomorphism f of E onto E'; for convenience the inverse of f will be denoted by g. In the proof of this theorem these mappings will be used to transfer paths and homotopies from one space to the other. Let x be any point of E and write $y = f(x)$. If h is any path in E based on x, it is clear that the composed mapping $f \circ h : I \to E'$ is a path in E' based on y. If k is a second path in E based on x and h and k are homotopic with respect to the base-point x, that is, if there is a continuous mapping $F : I^2 \to E$ agreeing with h on the lower side and with k on the upper and carrying the vertical sides into x, then it is clear that the composed mapping $f \circ F : I^2 \to E'$ agrees with $f \circ h$ on the lower side of I^2 and with $f \circ k$ on the upper side and carries the vertical sides into y. Hence $f \circ h$ and $f \circ k$ are homotopic with respect to the base-point y. This shows that if $\bar{h}$ is a given homotopy class on E with respect to the base-point x, then, for any representative path h of $\bar{h}$, $f \circ h$ always lies in the same homotopy class $\phi(\bar{h})$ of E' with respect to y.

Hence a mapping $\phi : \pi(E) \to \pi(E')$ has been constructed. It will now be shown that ϕ is an isomorphism between the two groups. ϕ is certainly a mapping onto, for any path h on E' based on y can be obtained by composing f with $g \circ h$, and so any homotopy class in E' with respect to y can be obtained as an image under ϕ. Now let h and k be two paths on E based on x. By examining Definition 28, the definition of the product of two paths it is not hard to see that the product of the paths $f \circ h$ and $f \circ k$ on E' is $f \circ (hk)$. And so ϕ is a homomorphism. Finally suppose $\phi(\bar{h})$ is the identity of $\pi(E')$. If h is a path in the class $\bar{h}$, this means that $f \circ h$ is homotopic to the constant mapping in E' with respect to y. That is to say, there is a continuous mapping $F' : I^2 \to E'$ agreeing with $f \circ h$ on the lower side of I^2 and carrying the other three sides into y. It is then easy to see that $g \circ F'$ where g is the inverse of f, is a continuous mapping of I^2 into E agreeing with $g \circ f \circ h = h$ on the lower side and carrying the other three sides into x. That is to say h is homotopic to the constant mapping with respect to x, and so $\phi(\bar{h})$ equal to the identity of $\pi(E')$ implies that $\bar{h}$ is the identity of $\pi(E)$, and so ϕ is an isomorphism. The theorem is thus completely proved.

To conclude this chapter, attention will be drawn to the relation between the fundamental group of a topological space and the property of simple connectivity. It is not hard to see that a space E is simply connected with respect to a point x if and only if $\pi(E, x)$ reduces to the identity element alone. In particular, if E is arcwise connected one can speak of E as being simply connected, without reference to any base-point: E will have this property if and only if $\pi(E)$ reduces to the identity.

CHAPTER V

THE HOMOLOGY GROUPS

1. Geometrical motivation for homology theory

In the last chapter, it was found that the study of closed curves in a topological space gave rise to a topologically invariant group associated with the space. The remainder of this book will be concerned with some other topologically invariant groups which can be attached to a given space; the ideas to be developed will be introduced first by some further remarks on closed curves.

If a simple closed curve, such as an ellipse, or a polygon, is drawn on the plane, then it has an inside and outside. That is to say the curve forms the common boundary of these two portions of the plane. Similarly if a closed curve is drawn on the surface of a sphere, the curve is the boundary of two portions of that surface. Contrast this situation, however, with that obtained by drawing the curve α on the surface of a torus, Fig. 21. α does not divide the surface into two disjoint portions; or, what is the same thing, α is not the boundary of any portion of the surface of the torus. The possibility of drawing a closed curve on a surface without dividing the surface into two disjoint portions is clearly a topological property. That is to say, if F is a surface and C is a curve on it, and if F' is homeomorphic to F and C' is the curve on F' corresponding to C, then C fails to divide F if and only if C' fails to divide F'. This topologically invariant property gives in the usual way a test for distinguishing between topologically distinct surfaces. It is not, of course, a very delicate test, as there are many topologically different surfaces on which a non-bounding closed curve may be drawn.

To illustrate this point further, and to show how this 'bounding test' may be refined, consider the comparison of the torus, Fig. 21, and the double torus, Fig. 22. In the case of the torus two curves α, β are marked such that, if the surface is cut along them, it can be flattened out into a rectangle. Any further cut must necessarily divide the surface into two parts. But if the double torus is cut along the curves marked α, β it cannot be flattened out, and further cuts α', β' may be made without dividing the surface into disjoint parts.

This suggests that a numerical measurement may be attached to the bounding or dividing properties of closed curves on a surface. For the maximum number of closed curves along which the surface may be cut without dividing it into two or more disjoint parts is clearly a topological invariant. This invariant makes more precise the property of the existence or otherwise of curves which bound portions of the surface. It is closely related to the more elaborate invariants which are later to be developed, and already gives some indication that the study of the bounding properties of curves on a

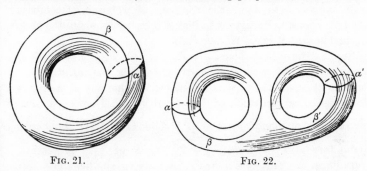

FIG. 21.   FIG. 22.

surface may provide a test which will help considerably in distinguishing between topologically different surfaces. In fact, it will turn out that closed surfaces can be fully classified by this test (Chapter VIII, §2, Exercise 7).

In order to generalize what has been said about surfaces to other spaces, one will have to consider not only whether given closed curves are boundaries or not, but also whether pieces of closed 2-, 3-, . . . r-dimensional surface are boundaries of something or not. The first step in doing this is to make precise what is meant by a piece of r-dimensional surface embedded in a space, and what is meant by being a boundary. These ideas must, of course, be defined so that when $r = 1$ or $r = 2$ the ordinary elementary idea of a curve bounding a surface or surface bounding a solid are obtained. Now a simple closed curve is just a single loop homeomorphic to the circumference of a circle, but already in the case of surfaces there is a much greater variety of possible shapes; and for higher dimensional figures the variety of possible shapes defies classification. It is therefore convenient to adopt a rather special method for specifying the r-dimensional surfaces to be considered. The method will be illustrated by considering first a surface S embedded in a space E.

It will be assumed that S can be subdivided into a finite number of curvilinear triangles; this is a genuine restriction but the subsequent gain in manipulative facility justifies it. S can then be thought of as the sum of these triangles $T_1, T_2, \ldots, T_m$. That is to say, one may write formally $S = T_1 + T_2 + \ldots + T_m$. And so in general one can think of all the triangles embedded in E (infinite in number of course) as being listed in some way, and in order to construct a piece of surface in E one simply picks a finite number of these triangles. It is not necessary to try to say what shape S has; it is only necessary to name the triangles of which it is composed. And this point is important in higher dimensions where the shapes occurring cannot easily be described.

Suppose now that $S = T_1 + T_2 + \ldots + T_m$. How does one know whether S is closed or not? Obviously one can do this by looking at each T_i in turn and checking whether any of them has a free edge. One can think of this as being carried out algebraically by saying that (boundary of S) $= \sum\limits_{i=1}^{m}$ (boundary of T_i), then writing (boundary of T_i) $= T_i^1 + T_i^2 + T_i^3$, where each T_i^j represents a curvilinear arc, namely a side of T_i, and seeing whether all the terms of $\sum T_i^j$ can be paired off with one another.

From this it looks as if the addition of the boundary sides is carried out 'modulo 2' in the sense that anything appearing twice is crossed out. This is not altogether satisfactory; for although one wants the boundary sides of the T to cancel as indicated, it may happen that the surface S is composed of two pieces which have a triangle in common (as, for instance, a bowl with a triangular base sitting on a table). Now one may want to acknowledge the fact that this triangle appears twice in the surface, but certainly not by cancelling it out and so leaving a hole in the surface. The natural way to represent algebraically the double appearance of a triangle would be to attach to it the coefficient 2. Thus it is reasonable to consider surfaces in E which are represented algebraically by linear combinations, with coefficients which are integers, of triangles embedded in E.

The main steps of the generalization to r-dimensional surfaces in a space E can now be indicated:

(1) The idea of a triangle must be generalized first. The tetrahedron is the natural generalization to three dimensions, and the simplexes to be defined in §2 give the extension to any number of dimensions.

(2) The method of embedding simplexes in a space E must be properly specified; it will in fact be done by means of continuous mappings (in §4).

(3) Pieces of r-dimensional surface in E will be considered which are represented algebraically by linear combinations of simplexes with integral coefficients (§5).

(4) The rule for writing down the boundary of a simplex must be set up in such a way that the intuitive idea of a boundary is reproduced in low dimensional cases (§6).

2. Euclidean simplexes

In the rigorous formulation of the ideas described in the above §1, the first step is to define properly the Euclidean simplexes and to work out some of their properties.

DEFINITION 31. Let $x_0, x_1, \ldots, x_p$ denote $p + 1$ points in n-dimensional Euclidean space, and let the coordinates of x_i be $(x_i^1, x_i^2, \ldots, x_i^n)$, $i = 0, 1, \ldots, p$. The points $x_0, x_1, \ldots, x_p$ will be called *linearly independent* if and only if the matrix

$$\begin{pmatrix} x_0^1 \, x_0^2 \ldots x_0^n \, 1 \\ x_1^1 \, x_1^2 \ldots x_1^n \, 1 \\ \vdots \qquad \vdots \\ x_p^1 \, x_p^2 \ldots x_p^n \, 1 \end{pmatrix} \tag{13}$$

has rank $p + 1$.

This definition may be expressed geometrically by considering the hyperplanes in Euclidean n-space containing the points $x_0, x_1, \ldots, x_p$. Such a hyperplane $\sum_{i=1}^{n} a_i X^i = b$ must necessarily satisfy the condition $\sum_{i=1}^{n} a_i x_j^i = b$ $(j = 0, 1, \ldots, p)$, that is, a set of homogeneous linear equations in $a_1, a_2, \ldots, b$ whose matrix, namely (13), has rank $p + 1$. Thus there are at most $(n + 1) - (p + 1)$ linearly independent equations of the form $\sum_{i=1}^{n} a_i X^i = b$ satisfied by the coordinates of $x_0, x_1, \ldots, x_p$. In other words, the smallest linear subspace of the given Euclidean n-space which can contain $x_0, x_1, \ldots, x_p$ is of dimension p.

To illustrate this, suppose four points x_1, x_2, x_3, x_4 in 3-space are linearly independent. Then the smallest linear subspace containing them is of dimension 3, that is, the whole space. Thus four points are linearly independent if and only if they are non-coplanar. Similarly three points in 3-space or in the plane are linearly independent if and only if they are not collinear.

DEFINITION 32. Let $x_0, x_1, \ldots, x_p$ be $(p + 1)$ linearly independent points of Euclidean n-space. Then the *Euclidean p-simplex* $[x_0 x_1 \ldots x_p]$ is defined as the set of all points with coordinates $(z^1, z^2, \ldots, z^n)$ where

$$
\left.
\begin{aligned}
z^i &= \sum_{j=0}^{p} \lambda_j x_j^i \ (i = 1, 2, \ldots, n), \\
\lambda_j &\geqslant 0 \ (j = 0, 1, \ldots, p), \\
\sum_{j=0}^{p} \lambda_j &= 1.
\end{aligned}
\right\} \tag{14}
$$

The points $x_0, x_1, \ldots, x_p$ will be called the *vertices* of $[x_0 x_1 \ldots x_p]$.

The geometrical meaning of this definition will now be examined in the cases $p = 1, 2, 3$. For convenience take $n = 3$. For $p = 1$ one is considering the set of points (z^1, z^2, z^3) with $z^i = \lambda_0 x_0^i + \lambda_1 x_1^i$, $\lambda_0 \geqslant 0$, $\lambda_1 \geqslant 0$, $\lambda_0 + \lambda_1 = 1$. But these are the formulae for the coordinates of the point dividing the join of (x_0^1, x_0^2, x_0^3), (x_1^1, x_1^2, x_1^3) internally in the ratio $\lambda_1 : \lambda_0$. Clearly as the λ's vary all the points of the line segment joining (x_0^1, x_0^2, x_0^3) and (x_1^1, x_1^2, x_1^3) are obtained. And so this line segment is the Euclidean simplex $[x_0 x_1]$ in the sense of the above definition.

Take now $p = 2$. The points to be considered are those with coordinates (z^1, z^2, z^3) such that $z^i = \lambda_0 x_0^i + \lambda_1 x_1^i + \lambda_2 x_2^i$, $\sum \lambda_j = 1$, $\lambda_j \geqslant 0$. And these are the coordinates of the point dividing in the ratio $(\lambda_1 + \lambda_2) : \lambda_0$ the join of x_0 to the point dividing the segment $x_1 x_2$ in the ratio $\lambda_2 : \lambda_1$. It is clear that all points of the triangle $x_0 x_1 x_2$ are obtained in this way, and so this triangle is the Euclidean 2-simplex $[x_0 x_1 x_2]$ of the above definition.

An exactly similar argument may be carried out for the case $p = 3$, showing that the 3-simplex $[x_0 x_1 x_2 x_3]$ is the tetrahedron with x_0, x_1, x_2, x_3 as vertices.

Each point of the Euclidean p-simplex $[x_0 x_1 \ldots x_p]$ is specified by giving a set of values to $\lambda_0, \lambda_1, \ldots, \lambda_p$ in (14). It will now be shown that the correspondence between the points of the simplex and the $(p + 1)$-tuples $(\lambda_0, \lambda_1, \ldots, \lambda_p)$ is one-one.

Suppose then, that $(\lambda_0, \lambda_1, \ldots, \lambda_p)$ and $(\mu_0, \mu_1, \ldots, \mu_p)$ define the same point of the simplex $(x_0 x_1 \ldots x_p)$. In symbols this hypothesis states that:

$$\sum_{j=0}^{p} \lambda_j x_j^i = \sum_{j=0}^{p} \mu_j x_j^i, \quad i = 1, 2, \ldots, n,$$

$$\sum_{0}^{p} \lambda_j = \sum_{0}^{p} \mu_j$$

These equations can be written as;

$$\sum_{j=0}^{p} (\lambda_j - \mu_j) x_j^i = 0, \quad i = 1, 2, \ldots, n,$$

$$\sum_{j=0}^{p} (\lambda_j - \mu_j) = 0$$

namely a set of homogeneous linear equations in $(\lambda_j - \mu_j), j = 0,$ $1, 2, \ldots, p$, with the matrix (13) which is of rank $p + 1$. Hence $\lambda_i = \mu_i$ for each i, as was to be shown.

DEFINITION 33. The numbers $\lambda_0, \lambda_1, \ldots, \lambda_p$ in (14) are called the *barycentric coordinates* of the corresponding point in the simplex.

The reason behind this definition is that, in the cases $p = 1, 2, 3,$ the point of the simplex $[x_0 x_1 \ldots x_p]$ with barycentric coordinates $(\lambda_0, \lambda_1, \ldots, \lambda_p)$ is the barycentre or mass centre of masses $\lambda_0, \lambda_1, \ldots, \lambda_p$ placed respectively at the vertices $x_0, x_1, \ldots, x_p$.

Associated with a given Euclidean p-simplex there are a number of others called its faces and defined as follows:

DEFINITION 34. Let $x_i, x_j, \ldots, x_l$ be $q + 1$ of the vertices of the Euclidean p-simplex $[x_0 x_1 \ldots x_p]$. Then the q-simplex $[x_i x_j \ldots x_l]$ is called a q-*dimensional face of* $[x_0 x_1 \ldots x_p]$.

A p-simplex has only one p-dimensional face, namely itself. The 0-dimensional faces of a simplex are its vertices. The p-simplex $[x_0 x_1 \ldots x_p]$ has $p + 1$ $(p - 1)$-dimensional faces, namely the simplexes $[x_0 x_1 \ldots \hat{x}_i \ldots x_p]$, where the circumflex denotes the omission of the corresponding vertex. The term 'face', without qualification as to dimension, will generally be used to denote these $(p - 1)$-dimensional faces. In particular, the faces of a tetrahedron are its faces in the ordinary sense, those of a triangle are its sides and those of a line segment are its end points. In addition, for example, a tetrahedron has 1-dimensional faces, namely its edges.

If, in the formulae (14), one sets $\lambda_i = 0$, the remaining λ's still add up to 1 and are non-negative. Thus the formulae (14) with $\lambda_i = 0$ define exactly the set of points of the $(p - 1)$-simplex

$[x_0x_1 \ldots \hat{x}_i \ldots x_p]$, that is to say, the i-th face of $[x_0x_1 \ldots x_p]$. Similarly it is not hard to see that the points of any q-dimensional face of $[x_0x_1 \ldots x_p]$ may be obtained from the formulae (14) by setting a suitable selection of barycentric coordinates equal to zero.

An important property of the Euclidean simplexes is their convexity; that is to say, if two points belong to a Euclidean simplex then all points on the line segment joining them also belong to the simplex. This is fairly obvious from a diagram in the cases of simplexes of dimensions $1, 2, 3$, but it requires formal proof in the general case. Let $(y^1, y^2, \ldots, y^n)$ and $(z^1, z^2, \ldots, z^n)$ be two points of $[x_0x_1 \ldots x_p]$ and let $y^i = \sum_{j=0}^{p} \lambda_j x_j^i$, $z^i = \sum_{j=0}^{p} \mu_j x_j^i$, with $\sum_{0}^{p} \lambda_j = \sum_{0}^{p} \mu_j = 1$. Take any point on the line segment joining these points, say the point dividing it internally in the ratio $\alpha : \beta$. The coordinates of this point are $(w^1, w^2, \ldots, w^n)$, where

$$w^i = \frac{\beta y^i + \alpha z^i}{\alpha + \beta} = \frac{\beta \sum \lambda_j x_j^i + \alpha \sum \mu_j x_j^i}{\alpha + \beta} = \frac{\sum (\beta \lambda_j + \alpha \mu_j) x_j^i}{\alpha + \beta}.$$

Set

$$\nu_j = \frac{\beta \lambda_j + \alpha \mu_j}{\alpha + \beta};$$

then since the λ's, μ's, α, β are all non-negative, it follows that $\nu_j \geqslant 0$ for each j. Also $\sum_{0}^{p} \nu_j = 1$. Thus $(w^1, w^2, \ldots, w^n)$ is a point of $[x_0x_1 \ldots x_p]$, namely the point with barycentric coordinates $(\nu_0, \nu_1, \ldots, \nu_p)$. This proves the convexity of $[x_0x_1 \ldots x_p]$.

A further useful property of Euclidean simplexes is that they consist exactly of all the points obtained by joining any one vertex to all the points of the opposite face. More precisely, if $[x_0x_1 \ldots x_p]$ is a given simplex, and x_i a selected vertex, then every point of $[x_0x_1 \ldots x_p]$ lies on some line segment joining x_i to some point of the face $[x_0x_1 \ldots \hat{x}_i \ldots x_p]$. The converse property, that every such point belongs to the simplex $[x_0x_1 \ldots x_p]$, is trivial by the convexity of the simplex. To prove the stated property, let $(z^1, z^2, \ldots, z^n)$ be a point of $[x_0x_1 \ldots x_p]$ different from x_i. In terms of barycentric coordinates let $z^i = \sum_{j=0}^{p} \lambda_j x_j^i$, and let $(y^1, y^2, \ldots y^n)$ be the point with coordinates given by $y^h = \sum_{j \neq i} \lambda_j' x_j^h$, where $\lambda_j' = \lambda_j / \sum_{l \neq i} \lambda_l$. The point $(y^1, y^2, \ldots, y^n)$ belongs to the face $[x_0x_1 \ldots \hat{x}_i \ldots x_p]$, having barycentric coordinates $(\lambda_0', \lambda_1', \ldots, 0, \ldots, \lambda_p')$, with the zero in the i-th place. Also the point $(z^1, z^2, \ldots, z^p)$ divides the join of x_i and $(y^1, y^2, \ldots, y^n)$ in the ratio $(\sum_{j \neq i} \lambda_j):\lambda_i$. Hence $(z^1, z^2, \ldots z^n)$ lies on a segment joining x_i to a point of the opposite face, as required.

Exercises

1. Let ABC be a triangle and P a point in it. Prove that the barycentric coordinates of P in the triangle ABC are the ratios of the areas of the triangles PBC, PCA, PAB to that of triangle ABC. Generalize this result to the case of a tetrahedron.

2. Let S denote the Euclidean p-simplex $[x_0 x_1 \ldots x_p]$ and let $\dot{S}$ be the union of its $(p-1)$-dimensional faces and let q be the point of S with barycentric coordinates

$$\left(\frac{1}{p+1}, \frac{1}{p+1}, \ldots, \frac{1}{p+1}\right).$$

(This point is called the centroid or barycentre of S; note that it is the centroid in the ordinary sense if $p = 2$ or 3). Prove that every directed segment starting from q meets $\dot{S}$ in exactly one point.

3. Use the result of the last exercise to prove that S is homeomorphic to the solid sphere E^p consisting of all points in Euclidean p-space such that $\sum_{i=1}^{p} x_i^2 \leqslant 1$, and that the homeomorphism can be constructed to carry $\dot{S}$ onto the sphere S^{p-1} with the equation $\sum_{i=1}^{p} x_i^2 = 1$.

[Hint: Take S and E^p to be in the same Euclidean space, and map each radius of E^p proportionally on the parallel segment joining the centroid of S to a point of $\dot{S}$.]

4. Prove that, in the notation of Exercise 3, there is a homeomorphism of $\dot{S}$ onto S^{p-1} carrying one face of S onto the hemisphere satisfying $x_p \leqslant 0$ and the rest onto the hemisphere $x_p \geqslant 0$.

[Hint: Place the selected face S_0 of S in the hyperplane $x_p = 0$ with its centroid at the origin. Let f be the projection from the origin of the remaining faces of S onto the set $x_p > 0$ of S^{p-1}; prove that f, so far as defined, is a homeomorphism. Then map the segment joining the origin to each point q on the frontier of S_0 proportionally on the arc of a great circle on S^{p-1} joining $(0, 0, \ldots, 0, -1)$ to $f(q)$.]

Note that this exercise gives an example of the extension of a mapping similar to that seen in Exercise 11, §1, Chapter III.

5. Generalize the result proved in the last paragraph of §2, by showing that, if $[x_0x_1 \ldots x_p]$ is a Euclidean p-simplex and $[x_0x_1 \ldots x_q]$ and $[x_{q+1}x_{q+2} \ldots x_p]$ are opposite faces (in the sense of being defined by complementary sets of vertices), then $[x_0x_1 \ldots x_p]$ consists of all points on all line segments obtained by joining a point on one of these faces to a point of the other. (The result given in §2 is the special case $q = 0$, when one of the pair of opposite faces is a vertex).

6. Let $\sum$ be any convex set in a Euclidean space (that is a set such that if it contains points p and q then it contains all the points of the line segment joining p and q) and let $x_0, x_1, \ldots, x_p$ be linearly independent points belonging to $\sum$. Prove that $[x_0x_1 \ldots x_p] \subset \sum$.
[Hint: Proceed inductively; suppose true for a number of vertices less than $p + 1$, and then use the result stated at the end of §2.]

3. Linear mappings

Using the barycentric coordinates introduced in Definition 33, two different simplexes of the same dimension will now be compared and will be shown to homeomorphic. In fact, a homeomorphism will be constructed which carries q-dimensional faces into q-dimensional faces for each q.

Let $[x_0x_1 \ldots x_p]$ and $[y_0y_1 \ldots y_p]$ be two Euclidean p-simplexes in Euclidean n-space, and let f be a mapping which carries each point of $[x_0x_1 \ldots x_p]$ into the point of $[y_0y_1 \ldots y_p]$ having the same barycentric coordinates. Thus if $(z^1, z^2, \ldots, z^n)$ is a point of $[x_0x_1 \ldots x_p]$ whose coordinates are given by (14), its image under f has coordinates $(w^1, w^2, \ldots, w^n)$ where $w^i = \sum_{j=0}^{p} \lambda_j y_j^i$. f is certainly a one-one mapping, since the correspondence between the points of a simplex and their barycentric coordinates has been shown to be one-one. Also since faces are obtained by setting one or more barycentric coordinates equal to zero, it easily follows that the q-dimensional face $[x_ix_j \ldots x_l]$ of $[x_0x_1 \ldots x_p]$ is mapped by f onto the q-dimensional face $[y_iy_j \ldots y_l]$ of $[y_0y_1 \ldots y_p]$. In particular, the vertex x_i is mapped on the vertex y_i, for each i.

It remains to be shown that f is a homeomorphism. Let $(z^1, z^2, \ldots, z^n)$ be a point of $[x_0x_1 \ldots x_p]$ with coordinates given by (14). The equations (14) may be regarded as linear equations in $\lambda_0, \lambda_1, \lambda_2, \ldots, \lambda_p$. They are certainly consistent so long as $(z^1, z^2, \ldots, z^n)$ is in $[x_0x_1 \ldots x_p]$, for then $(z^1, z^2, \ldots, z^n)$ is, by Definition 32, given by assigning certain values to the λ's in (14). Also the rank of the matrix of the equations (14) namely the matrix (13), is $p + 1$, $x_0, x_1, \ldots, x_p$ being linearly independent points; and so, given $(z^1, z^2, \ldots, z^n)$ in $[x_0x_1 \ldots x_p]$, $p + 1$ of the equations (14) can be solved for $\lambda_0, \lambda_1, \ldots, \lambda_p$ as linear, and hence continuous, functions of the coordinates $z^1, z^2, \ldots, z^i$. But if $(w^1, w^2, \ldots, w^n)$ is the image of $(z^1, z^2, \ldots z^n)$ under f, the w^i are certainly continuous functions of the λ_j, and so, by what has just been proved are continuous functions of the z^i. Hence f is continuous. Similarly f^{-1} is continuous, and so f is a homeomorphism.

DEFINITION 35. The mapping f constructed as above is called a *linear mapping of* $[x_0x_1 \ldots x_p]$ *onto* $[y_0y_1 \ldots y_p]$.

The reason for this definition is that the equations (14) and the similar relations connecting the w^i and the λ_j enable the w^i to be expressed linearly in terms of the z^j. Some generalizations of this idea will now be described in concluding this section.

In the first place, if one simply rearranges the order of the vertices of a simplex and applies the definition of a Euclidean simplex, the same point-set is obtained. That is to say, the point-set $[\bar{x}_0\bar{x}_1 \ldots \bar{x}_p]$ is the same as the point-set $[x_0x_1 \ldots x_p]$ if $\bar{x}_0, \dot{v}_1, \ldots, \bar{x}_p$ is some permutation of $x_0, x_1, \ldots x_p$. But of course the barycentric coordinates of a point with respect to the ordered set of vertices $\bar{x}_0, \bar{x}_1, \ldots, \bar{x}_p$ will not be the same as those with respect to the ordered set $x_0, x_1, \ldots, x_p$. Thus if $[y_0y_1 \ldots y_p]$ is a second p-simplex a new linear mapping of the point-set $[x_0x_1 \ldots x_p]$ onto $[y_0y_1 \ldots y_p]$ may be defined, namely that which is obtained by applying Definition 35 to $[\bar{x}_0\bar{x}_1 \ldots \bar{x}_p]$ and $[y_0y_1 \ldots y_p]$.

Similarly, the y_i could be rearranged in some new order $\bar{y}_0, \bar{y}_1, \ldots, \bar{y}_p$, and one could then construct the linear mapping of $[\bar{x}_0\bar{x}_1 \ldots \bar{x}_p]$ onto $[\bar{y}_0\bar{y}_1, \ldots \bar{y}_p]$, using the above definition. This linear mapping could equally well be specified as the linear mapping of $[x_0x_1 \ldots x_p]$ onto $[y_0y_1 \ldots y_p]$ which carries the vertices of the first simplex in the order $\bar{x}_0, \bar{x}_1, \ldots, \bar{x}_p$ into those of the second in the order $\bar{y}_0, \bar{y}_1, \ldots \bar{y}_p$. This way of describing a linear mapping will be used in the future, the essential feature being that the mapping is fully defined as soon as the orders of the vertices of the two simplexes are specified.

It should be noted further that there is nothing in the definition of a linear mapping which really requires that the object and image simplexes should lie in the same Euclidean spaces, or even in spaces of the same dimension. The same definition could be applied to a simplex $[x_0 x_1 \ldots x_p]$ in Euclidean n-space E_n and a simplex $[y_0 y_1 \ldots y_p]$ in m-space E_m, the correspondence being as before between points with the same barycentric coordinates.

A more essential generalization of the original definition of a linear mapping is obtained by considering two simplexes $[x_0 x_1 \ldots x_p]$ and $[y_0 y_1 \ldots y_q]$ in Euclidean spaces E_n and E_m respectively, where $q < p$. Let $u_0, u_1, \ldots, u_p$ be a set of points in E_m obtained by taking the vertices $y_0, y_1, \ldots, y_q$ with repetitions. That is to say, y_0 will be taken p_0 times, y_1 p_1 times, and so on, where $p_0 + p_1 + \ldots = p + 1$, and the resulting set, in some order, will be called $u_0, u_1, \ldots u_p$. The points u_i do not of course define a p-simplex because they are not linearly independent, all of them lying in the q-dimensional linear space containing $[y_0 y_1 \ldots y_q]$. But a mapping f (no longer homeomorphic) of $[x_0 x_1 \ldots x_p]$ onto $[y_0 y_1 \ldots y_q]$ which can still justifiably be called linear can be defined as follows.

Let $(z^1, z^2, \ldots, z^n)$ be the point of $[x_0 x_1 \ldots x_p]$ with barycentric coordinates $(\lambda_0, \lambda_1, \ldots, \lambda_p)$. Then let $(w^1, w^2, \ldots, w^m)$ be the point of E_m with coordinates given by

$$w^i = \sum_{j=0}^{p} \lambda_j u_j^i, \ i = 1, 2, \ldots, m, \tag{15}$$

where $(u_j^1, u_j^2, \ldots, u_j^m)$ are the coordinates of u_j. Now if each u_j is replaced by the y_i to which it is equal, it can be seen at once that w^i is a linear combination of $y_0^i, y_1^i, \ldots, y_q^i$ with non-negative coefficients adding up to unity. This means that $(w^1, w^2, \ldots, w^m)$ is a point of the simplex $[y_0 y_1 \ldots y_q]$. Also every point of this simplex can be obtained in this way. For any point of $[y_0 y_1 \ldots y_q]$ has coordinates $(v^1, v^2, \ldots, v^m)$ such that $v^i = \sum_{j=0}^{q} \mu_j y_j^i$ and $\sum_{j=0}^{q} \mu_j = 1$, and each of the y_j is the same as some one of the u_h.

Thus the mapping f which maps the point $(z^1, z^2, \ldots, z^n)$ of $[x_0 x_1 \ldots x_p]$ with coordinates given by (14) onto the point $(w^1, w^2, \ldots, w^m)$ of $[y_0 y_1 \ldots y_q]$ given by (15) is a mapping of $[x_0 x_1 \ldots x_p]$ onto $[y_0 y_1 \ldots y_q]$. Also, by (15) the w^i are linear functions of the λ_j, and by solving (14), the latter are linear functions of the z^h. Thus the w^i are linear functions of the z^h. This justifies the name 'linear mapping' for f and also shows that f is continuous.

Such a linear mapping, where the image simplex is of lower dimension than the original, will be called *degenerate*. Clearly it is fully specified when the images of the vertices of $[x_0 x_1 \ldots x_p]$ are given.

Exercises

1. Let S_1, S_2, S_3 be Euclidean simplexes (not necessarily of the same dimension) and let $f:S_1 \to S_2$ and $g:S_2 \to S_3$ be linear mappings (possibly degenerate). Prove that the composition mapping $g \circ f$ is a linear mapping.

2. Let $[x_0 x_1 \ldots x_p]$ and $[y_0 y_1 \ldots y_q]$ be simplexes in Euclidean spaces E_1 and E_2 respectively, with $q \leqslant p$. Let f be a linear mapping of $[x_0 x_1 \ldots x_p]$ onto $[y_0 y_1 \ldots y_q]$ for some arrangement of the vertices. Let x_{p+1} be a point of E_1 linearly independent of $x_0, x_1, \ldots x_p$ and let y_{q+1} be a point of E_2 linearly independent of $y_0, y_1, \ldots, y_q$. Define the mapping g of $[x_0 x_1 \ldots x_{p+1}]$ onto $[y_0 y_1 \ldots y_{q+1}]$ as follows: if $q \in [x_0 x_1 \ldots x_{p+1}]$ is on a line segment joining x_{p+1} to $q' \in [x_0 x_1 \ldots x_p]$ and divides this segment in the ratio $c : 1$ then $g(q)$ is to divide the join y_{q+1} and $f(q')$ in the ratio $c{:}1$. Prove that g is a linear mapping.

4. Singular simplexes on a space

The concept now to be introduced to give formal rigour to the idea of embedding a simplex in a given space E is that of the singular simplex. As a preparation for this definition, for each dimension p, a definite p-simplex will be chosen in some Euclidean space. This fixed choice is really just a matter of convenience, and could be made in many ways. The choice actually to be made is as follows:

DEFINITION 36. *The standard Euclidean p-simplex* Δ_p *will be the* simplex in $(p+1)$-space E_{p+1} whose vertices are the points $(0, 0, \ldots, 1, \ldots, 0)$ with the unit in the i-th place, for $i = 1, 2, \ldots, p + 1$.

If $(z^1, z^2, \ldots, z^{p+1})$ is any point of Δ_p and if $(\lambda_0, \lambda_1, \ldots, \lambda_p)$ are its barycentric coordinates, then inspection of the formulae (14) shows that $\lambda_i = z^{i+1}$ $(i = 0, 1, \ldots, p)$. Thus $z^1 + z^2 + \ldots z^{p+1} = 1$. Conversely, take any point in E_{p+1} with coordinates $(z^1, z^2, \ldots, z^{p+1})$ such that $z^i \geqslant 0$ for each i and $\sum\limits_{i=1}^{p+1} z^i = 1$. Then z^i may be expressed by the formulae (14) provided λ_j is taken as z^{j+1} for each j and $x_0, x_1, \ldots, x_p$ are taken as the vertices of Δ_p as defined above. In other words, Δ_p is precisely the set of points with non-negative coordinates on the hyperplane $\sum\limits_{i=1}^{p+1} z^i = 1$ in E_{p+1}.

DEFINITION 37. The above choice of standard Euclidean simplexes having been made, a *singular p-simplex*, or *singular simplex of dimension p*, on a space E is defined as a continuous mapping σ of Δ_p into E.

There are two points to be carefully noted here:

(a) The singular simplex *is the mapping* into E, and is not a set of points in E. This point is emphasized by the notation; a singular simplex defined as above by the mapping σ is called the singular simplex σ.

(b) In further emphasis of (a), the set of points $\sigma(\Delta_p)$, that is the image of the mapping σ, does not even need to look like a simplex (except for $p = 0$, when both Δ_0 and $\sigma(\Delta_0)$ are single points). The definition of a singular simplex makes no reference to the shape of $\sigma(\Delta_p)$. This may seem rather strange, as the idea of a singular simplex is supposed to be based on the intuitive idea of a simplex embedded in a space. But a little reflection shows that the situation is no stranger than that arising from the contrast between the intuitive idea of a path and the rigorous definition. The intuitive reasoning which motivates the work to be carried out later may still be based on some sort of pictorial notion of curvilinear triangles and tetrahedra in the space; but the actual proofs must be based only on Definition 37.

It will be useful to have a special notation for a particular type of singular simplex on a space E which is either a Euclidean space or a subspace of a Euclidean space. Suppose that E contains a Euclidean p-simplex $[x_0x_1 \ldots x_p]$. Then the linear mapping of Δ_p onto $[x_0x_1 \ldots x_p]$ which carries the vertex $(0, 0, \ldots, 1, \ldots 0)$, with 1 in the ith place, onto x_{i-1} is a continuous mapping of Δ_p into E and so is a singular simplex on E.

DEFINITION 38. The singular simplex on E just described will be denoted by $(x_0x_1 \ldots x_p)$.

Note that $[x_0x_1 \ldots x_p]$ with square brackets denotes a point-set, while $(x_0x_1 \ldots x_p)$ with round brackets is a mapping. Rearrangement of the x_i does not affect the former, but does change the latter.

5. Chains on a space

In §1, addition was suggested as the algebraic expression for the geometrical process of sticking together simplexes to form pieces of p-dimensional surface in a space E. But, algebraically speaking, addition does not make much sense unless it appears as the operation in some sort of algebraic system. The natural thing to do, then, is to construct an additive abelian group whose generators are the singular p-simplexes on E. This is, of course, a group with an infinite number of generators.

DEFINITION 39. The additive abelian group whose generators are the singular p-simplexes on E is called the *group of p-chains on E*, and will be denoted by $C_p(E)$. Its elements will be called *p-chains* or *p-dimensional chains on E*.

Each p-chain so defined will be a linear combination $\sum a_i \sigma^i$ of singular p-simplexes σ^i on E with coefficients a_i which are integers (positive, negative or zero), and it is understood that only a finite number of coefficients are non-zero in any such expression. A chain group is to be constructed for each dimension p. In particular, each element of $C_0(E)$ is specified by simply giving a finite collection of points on E with positive or negative multiplicities, for in this case, and in this case alone, a singular 0-simplex is defined fully by the image of the mapping defining it.

6. The boundary of a simplex

It has already been suggested that, speaking geometrically, the boundary of a piece of surface divided into triangles should be made up of the boundaries of the triangles put together in some way. But since one does not want to add together simplexes 'modulo 2', some rule must be evolved for writing down the boundary of a triangle in such a way that, for example, the common side of two triangles put together to form a quadrilateral will not count as part of the boundary of the quadrilateral.

Of course, since the sticking together of triangles is now to be represented algebraically by forming linear combinations of singular simplexes, the operation which will have to be defined now is the formation of the boundary of a singular simplex. The procedure will be introduced by considering singular simplexes in a Euclidean space E, in particular the type defined by linear mappings (Definition 38).

Consider the singular simplex $(x_0 x_1 \ldots x_p)$, where $[x_0 x_1 \ldots x_p]$ is a p-simplex in E. The aim is to define an operation on $(x_0 x_1 \ldots x_p)$ which will express first of all the geometrical fact that the point-set boundary of $[x_0 x_1 \ldots x_p]$ consists of the union of its faces, and will, secondly, have the form of a simple algebraic rule which can be easily worked with. One would expect that the geometrical faces of

$[x_0 x_1 \ldots x_p]$ would be represented, in terms of singular simplexes, by singular simplexes which are linear mappings of Δ_{p-1} onto these faces. For each such face there are, of course, $p!$ choices of singular simplex, but the requirement of algebraic simplicity suggests that one should try first the singular simplexes $(x_0 x_1 \ldots \hat{x}_i \ldots x_p)$ for $i = 0, 1, 2, \ldots, p$. In addition, one would expect each singular simplex $(x_0 x_1 \ldots \hat{x}_i \ldots x_p)$ to appear just once in the boundary of $(x_0 x_1 \ldots x_p)$. Thus, denoting the operation of forming the boundary by the letter d, it seems reasonable to put forward as a tentative definition of $d(x_0 x_1 \ldots x_p)$ a formula of the type $\sum_{i=0}^{p} \pm (x_0 x_1 \ldots \hat{x}_i \ldots x_p)$.

To see whether a formula like this can be used as a definition, it is necessary to investigate whether a simple rule can be devised for fixing the sign of each term in such a way that the resulting definition expresses algebraically the intuitive geometrical properties of boundaries. Now the perimeter of a triangle and the surface of a tetrahedron are closed, that is have no boundary. One therefore naturally requires that the definition of the boundary operation on singular simplexes should satisfy the condition that the boundary of a boundary should reduce to zero. A bit of experimentation with low dimensional cases (say $p = 1, 2, 3$) shows that this can be arranged if the signs in the above tentative definition are taken alternately $+$ and $-$, giving the formula:

$$d(x_0 x_1 \ldots x_p) = \sum_{i=0}^{p} (-1)^i (x_0 x_1 \ldots \hat{x}_i \ldots x_p). \qquad (16)$$

It will be proved presently that

$$d^2(x_0 x_1 \ldots x_p) = \sum_{i=0}^{p} (-1)^i d(x_0 x_1 \ldots \hat{x}_i \ldots x_p) = 0$$

for all p, and so the requirements of intuition are fully satisfied in this respect. The further justification for accepting (16) as a definition of the boundary operation arises from the elegance and power of the theory which can be based on it. The formal statement of the definition will now be given.

DEFINITION 40. Let E be a subspace of a Euclidean space containing a Euclidean p-simplex $[x_0 x_1 \ldots x_p]$ and let $(x_0 x_1 \ldots x_p)$ be the singular simplex on E defined in Definition 38. Then the *boundary of* $(x_0 x_1 \ldots x_p)$ will be denoted by $d(x_0 x_1 \ldots x_p)$ and will be defined by the formula (16). Moreover, if $\sigma_1,\ \sigma_2, \ldots, \sigma_m$ are singular simplexes on E defined by linear mappings of Δ_p into E, such that, for each i, $d\sigma_i$ is defined by a formula like (16), and if α is the chain $\sum\limits_{i=1}^{m} a_i \sigma_i$, the a_i being integers, then $d\alpha$ is defined as $\sum\limits_{i=1}^{m} a_i d\sigma_i$. In particular, set $d\alpha = 0$ for any 0-chain α.

The second part of the definition in which $d\alpha$ is defined is, of course, designed to express algebraically the geometrical idea stated in the first sentence of this section, namely on the nature of the boundary of a surface made of triangles placed edge to edge.

THEOREM 23. *If $(x_0 x_1 \ldots x_p)$ is as in Definition 40, $d^2(x_0 x_1 \ldots x_p)$ $= 0$, where d^2 denotes the operation of d twice in succession.*

PROOF. The formula (16) expresses $d(x_0 x_1 \ldots x_p)$ as a $(p-1)$-chain on E, a linear combination of singular simplexes defined by linear mappings. And so the second part of Definition 40 says that

$$d^2(x_0 x_1 \ldots x_p) = \sum_{i=0}^{p} (-1)^i d(x_0 x_1 \ldots \hat{x}_i \ldots x_p)$$

$$= \sum_{j<i} (-1)^{i+j}(x_0 x_1 \ldots \hat{x}_j \ldots \hat{x}_i \ldots x_p)$$

$$+ \sum_{j>i} (-1)^{i+j-1}(x_0 x_1 \ldots \hat{x}_i \ldots \hat{x}_j \ldots x_p)$$

$$= 0,$$

since each term appears twice, once in each summation, with opposite signs.

7. Boundaries and cycles on any space

The definition of the last section shows how to form the boundary of a special type of singular simplex on a portion of Euclidean space. In particular let x_i be the vertex $(0, 0, \ldots, 1, \ldots, 0)$, with the unit in the $(i+1)$-th place, of Δ_p, and let $(x_0 x_1 \ldots x_p)$ be the singular p-simplex on Δ_p defined by the identity mapping of Δ_p on itself. Then the above definition gives $d(x_0 x_1 \ldots x_p)$ as a $(p-1)$-chain on Δ_p. The idea now is that, if σ is a given singular p-simplex on a space E, the mapping σ of Δ_p into E should be made to carry $d(x_0 x_1 \ldots x_p)$ into a singular $(p-1)$-chain on E which will be called the boundary of the singular simplex σ, to be denoted by $d\sigma$.

This is the natural extension of the geometrical idea that, if a triangle, say, is embedded in E by some continuous mapping, then the boundary of the embedded triangle is obtained by restricting this mapping to the sides of the original plane triangle. But of course, whereas one speaks in this geometrical statement of point-sets, namely the triangle and its sides, the rigorous definition of the boundary of a singular simplex must be expressed entirely in terms of singular simplexes and chains.

The method of carrying $d(x_0 x_1 \ldots x_p)$ into E to define $d\sigma$ can best be described by considering a more general situation, which will in any case be of importance later. Let E, E' be two spaces and let f be a continuous mapping of E into E'. Then, in geometrical language, any simplex embedded in E is also automatically embedded in E' because E is mapped by f into E'. To express this idea properly, let σ be a singular simplex of dimension p on E, that is, by definition, a continuous mapping $\sigma : \Delta_p \to E$. Then the composition $f \circ \sigma$ is a continuous mapping of Δ_p into E', in other words, a singular p-simplex on E'. Thus to each singular p-simplex σ on E there is assigned a singular p-simplex $f_1(\sigma) = f \circ \sigma$ on E'. That is to say, a mapping f_1 has been set up of the collection of generators of $C_p(E)$ into the collection of generators of $C_p(E')$. It therefore follows at once from the definition of $C_p(E)$, $C_p(E')$ that f_1 can be extended to a homomorphism of $C_p(E)$ into $C_p(E')$ by setting $f_1(\sum a_i \sigma_i)$ equal to $\sum a_i f_1(\sigma_i)$.

DEFINITION 41. The homomorphism $f_1 : C_p(E) \to C_p(E')$ constructed as above from the continuous mapping $f : E \to E'$ is called the *homomorphism induced by f* on the chain group $C_p(E)$. The transition from a continuous mapping to the induced homomorphism on the chain group will always be denoted by the attachment of the suffix unity. It is, of course, clear that an induced homomorphism may be constructed as above for each value of p, but it is convenient to use the same notation, namely f_1, for it independently of the value of p.

An essential property of the induced homomorphism which has to be proved is the following:

THEOREM 24. *Let E, E', E'' be three spaces, f a continuous mapping of E into E', g a continuous mapping of E' into E''. Then* $(g \circ f)_1 = g_1 \circ f_1$.

If one attempts to see the geometrical meaning of this theorem it appears rather trivial, for geometrical intuition sees a simplex as a point-set, a triangle or a tetrahedron, say, embedded in the space E

And from this point of view, the theorem simply says that, if a simplex is given embedded in E and is carried into E' by f and thence into E'' by g, then the final result is the same as would be obtained by carrying the original simplex straight into E'' by $g_\circ f$. That this is so for a point-set simplex embedded in E is simply a matter of the definition of $g_\circ f$. But of course a singular p-simplex on E is not a point-set; it is a mapping of Δ_p into E. And so the above theorem does require a formal proof.

PROOF. To prove Theorem 24 it is sufficient to show that, for any singular p-simplex σ on E, the image of σ under $(g_\circ f)_1$ is the same as its image under $g_{1\circ} f_1$. Now the image of σ under $(g_\circ f)_1$ is, by Definition 41 applied to $g_\circ f$, the composition of the mappings σ and $g_\circ f$, that is to say $g_\circ f_\circ \sigma$. On the other hand, the image of σ under $g_{1\circ} f_1$ is obtained by operating first with f_1 on σ, the result being $f_\circ \sigma$ (Definition 41), and then operating with g_1 on $f_\circ \sigma$, the result being $g_\circ f_\circ \sigma$ (Definition 41 applied to g). Thus $(g_\circ f)_1 (\sigma) = (g_{1\circ} f_1)(\sigma) = g_\circ f_\circ \sigma$, and the theorem is proved.

The idea of the induced homomorphism now enables the boundary of a singular simplex σ on a space E to be defined. The situation is that $(x_0 x_1 \ldots x_p)$ is a singular simplex on Δ_p (cf. the beginning of this section) and $d(x_0 x_1 \ldots x_p)$ has already been set up as a $(p-1)$-chain on Δ_p, that is, an element of $C_{p-1}(\Delta_p)$. On the other hand, σ is a continuous mapping of Δ_p into E, and so the induced homomorphism $\sigma_1 : C_{p-1}(\Delta_p) \to C_{p-1}(E)$ is defined.

DEFINITION 42. In the notation already introduced, $d\sigma$ is defined as $\sigma_1(d(x_0 x_1 \ldots x_p))$. The operator d is then to be extended to any p-chain on E by setting $d(\sum a_i \sigma_i) = \sum a_i d\sigma_i$. d thus becomes a homomorphism of $C_p(E)$ into $C_{p-1}(E)$. A similar homomorphism is defined for each value of p, but no distinction in notation will be made.

An essential property of the boundary operator d just defined is the following:

THEOREM 25. *Let E and E' be two spaces and let f be a continuous mapping of E into E'. Then $f_{1\circ} d = d_\circ f_1$.*

Translated into geometrical terms and applied to the case $p = 2$, this theorem means that, if one has a triangle T embedded in a space E and then one embeds it in E' by the further mapping f of E into E', then the boundary of the image triangle in E' can either be found directly in E', or by first marking the boundary of T in E and mapping it into E' by means of f.

PROOF. The proof of the theorem is a simple formal verification:

$$(f_1 \circ d)(\sigma) = f_1(d\sigma) \text{ (definition of the composition of } f_1 \text{ and } d),$$
$$= f_1(\sigma_1(d(x_0 x_1 \ldots x_p))) \text{ (definition of } d\sigma),$$
$$= (f_1 \circ \sigma_1)(d(x_0 x_1 \ldots x_p)) \text{ (definition of the composition of } f_1 \text{ and } \sigma_1),$$
$$= (f \circ \sigma)_1(d(x_0 x_1 \ldots x_p)) \text{ (Theorem 24)},$$
$$= d(f \circ \sigma) \text{ (definition of the boundary of the singular simplex } f \circ \sigma),$$
$$= (d \circ f_1)(\sigma) \text{ (definition of } f_1, \text{ along with the definition of the composition of } d \text{ and } f_1),$$

where σ is any singular p-simplex on E. Applying this result to linear combinations of singular p-simplexes it follows that $(f_1 \circ d)(\alpha) = (d \circ f_1)(\alpha)$ for any element α of $C_p(E)$ and this proves the theorem.

The definition of $d(x_0 x_1 \ldots x_p)$ in §6 was constructed exactly so that the boundary of the boundary of a singular p-simplex of the form $(x_0 x_1 \ldots x_p)$ on a portion of Euclidean space would be zero. This result will now be carried over to any singular simplex on any space.

THEOREM 26. For any space E and each value of p the boundary operator d satisfies $d^2 = 0$.

PROOF. The symbol d^2 means, of course, the operation of d twice successively. As in the proofs of Theorems 24 and 25, it is enough to show that $d^2\sigma = 0$ for any singular p-simplex σ on E. Now

$$d^2\sigma = d(d\sigma) = d(\sigma_1(d(x_0 x_1 \ldots x_p))) \text{ (definition of } d\sigma),$$
$$= \sigma_1(d(d(x_0 x_1 \ldots x_p))) \text{ (Theorem 25, applied to the mapping } \sigma),$$
$$= \sigma_1(d^2(x_0 x_1 \ldots x_p))$$
$$= 0 \text{ (Theorem 23)},$$

and this completes the proof.

To conclude this section, a name will be given to those chains on a space which, in this theory, play the part of generalized closed curves and surfaces.

DEFINITION 43. A *p-cycle on a space* E is a p-chain α such that $d\alpha = 0$.

If α and β are p-cycles on E then $d(\alpha - \beta) = d\alpha - d\beta = 0$, and so $\alpha - \beta$ is a p-cycle. This implies that the p-cycles on E form a subgroup of $C_p(E)$. This subgroup will be denoted by $Z_p(E)$. It is clearly the kernel of the homomorphism $d : C_p(E) \to C_{p-1}(E)$.

DEFINITION 44. If α is a p-chain on E such that there is a $(p + 1)$-chain β on E satisfying $\alpha = d\beta$, then α will be called a *p-boundary on E*.

If α and β are p-boundaries on E then $\alpha = d\gamma$, $\beta = d\delta$ for suitable $(p + 1)$-chains γ and δ. Thus $\alpha - \beta = d(\gamma - \delta)$ and so $\alpha - \beta$ is a p-boundary. Thus the p-boundaries on E form a subgroup of $C_p(E)$ which will be denoted by $B_p(E)$. $B_p(E)$ is clearly the image of the homomorphism $d : C_{p+1}(E) \to C_p(E)$.

Let α be a p-boundary on E. Then $\alpha = d\beta$ for some chain β, and $d\alpha = d^2\beta = 0$ (Theorem 26). Thus a p-boundary is a p-cycle, or in other words $B_p(E)$ is a subgroup of $Z_p(E)$.

8. Homologous cycles and homology groups

The remarks made in §1 of this Chapter on the bounding properties of curves on a surface indicate that attention should now be directed to the distinction between cycles which are boundaries and those which are not. But the obviously infinite variety of cycles on a space E makes this impracticable until some sort of classification has been carried out. An indication of what is wanted may be had by considering two closed curves α and β on a space E. Clearly if α and β taken together form the boundary of a piece of surface S in E, then α is a boundary if and only if β is. For if α bounds a piece of surface S', then β bounds the piece of surface obtained by sticking S and S' together.

To express this idea algebraically, let α and β be two p-cycles on E, and let γ be a $(p + 1)$-chain such that $\alpha - \beta = d\gamma$; that is, α and β together form the boundary of γ. The use of the minus sign between α and β is an arbitrary choice made for future convenience; the formula can be made to appear in this form by suitable choice of the signs of the simplexes making up α and β. Then if α is a boundary, say $\alpha = d\gamma'$ it follows that $\beta = \alpha - d\gamma = d(\gamma' - \gamma)$, and so β is a boundary. Similarly if $\alpha - \beta = d\gamma$ and β is a boundary, then so is α.

The relation $\alpha - \beta = d\gamma$ will now be given a name:

DEFINITION 45. If α and β are two p-cycles on E such that $\alpha - \beta = d\gamma$ for some $(p + 1)$-chain γ, then α and β will be called *homologous cycles of E*, and α will be said to be *homologous to β*. This relation will be written $\alpha \sim \beta$. In particular if β is zero and $\alpha = d\gamma$ then α is said to be *homologous to zero*, written $\alpha \sim 0$.

The relation of homology just introduced is an equivalence

relation on the set of p-cycles on E. To prove this, note first that $\alpha - \alpha = d0$ and so $\alpha \sim \alpha$; second, if $\alpha \sim \beta$ then $\alpha - \beta = d\gamma$ for some γ, and so $\beta - \alpha = -d\gamma = d(-\gamma)$, that is $\beta \sim \alpha$; third, if $\alpha \sim \beta$, $\beta \sim \gamma$, then $\alpha - \beta = d\lambda$, $\beta - \gamma = d\mu$ for some λ and μ, and so $\alpha - \gamma = d(\lambda + \mu)$, that is, $\alpha \sim \gamma$. Thus homology is reflexive, symmetric and transitive, in other words is an equivalence relation.

DEFINITION 46. The equivalence classes of p-cycles on E under the relation of homology are called *p-dimensional homology classes on E*.

The usefulness of these homology classes is due in one respect to the fact that, while one certainly cannot count up the cycles on E and say how many are or are not boundaries, one can often make a simple list of representatives of the various homology classes. For example, in the case of the torus (cf. Fig. 21) if α and β are taken as 1-cycles, each consisting of a 1-simplex with the ends joined, then every 1-cycle on the torus is homologous to a cycle of the form $m\alpha + n\beta$, where m and n are integers, and such a cycle is homologous to zero only if $m = n = 0$. (cf. Chapter VIII, §2, Exercise 4 for the proof of this statement.) Thus the one-dimensional homology classes of the torus are labelled by pairs of integers m, n.

But the principal value of the idea of homology classes appears from algebraic considerations. Namely, the group $Z_p(E)$ of p-cycles on E is an additive abelian group and the relation of homology actually splits it up into cosets modulo the subgroup $B_p(E)$ of p-boundaries on E. For α and β, elements of $Z_p(E)$, are in the same coset modulo $B_p(E)$ if and only if $\alpha - \beta$ is in $B_p(E)$, and this is precisely the relation of homology. It follows that the homology classes of p-cycles on E can be regarded as the elements of the quotient group $H_p(E) = Z_p(E)/B_p(E)$.

DEFINITION 47. The group $H_p(E)$ is called the *p-dimensional*, or simply the *p-th*, *homology group of E*.

Thus the homology classes of p-cycles on E form a group, two classes being added by adding representative cycles. And the information one wants on possible bounding relations in E is to be obtained by studying the structure of this group for each p, finding how many generators there are, if this number is finite, and what relations hold between them. For example, it will eventually be shown that the 1-dimensional homology group of the torus is a group with two generators, represented by α, β in Fig. 21, and no relations (cf. Chapter VIII, §2, Exercise 4).

9. Relative homology

The idea of homology was evolved from the consideration of the way in which a surface was or was not divided by closed curves. A somewhat similar situation arises from the consideration of a surface which already has boundaries, using open curves this time. Consider, for example, a sphere with two holes cut in it (Fig. 23). While any closed curve on this surface will certainly divide it into two parts, open arcs such as α joining two points on the boundaries of the holes can be drawn without dividing the surface. On the other hand, two arcs α, β of this type will divide the surface into two

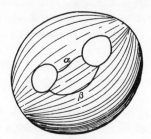

Fig. 23.

parts. If, however, there were more holes in the sphere it would be possible to draw a larger number of open arcs joining boundary points of the holes without cutting the surface in two.

Now, just as the homology groups of a space were designed to generalize and make more precise the bounding properties of closed curves on a surface, a further type of group will be introduced here to deal with the more general situation outlined above. The sphere of Fig. 23 with two holes cut in it is a space E, and the edges of the holes form a subspace F. A system of open cuts joining points of F will divide E if the cuts, along with portions of the boundaries of the holes, form a boundary on E. The type of open cut considered here must, in a more precise treatment, be replaced by a 1-chain whose boundary is a 0-chain on F, and so the last sentence may be rephrased by saying that a 1-chain α with boundary in F represents a cut dividing E if $\alpha + \beta$, where β is some 1-chain on F, forms a boundary on E. The two ideas just introduced, namely 1-chains representing cuts joining points of F, and the making up of a boundary with a given 1-chain along with other chains on F, will now be extended to any space.

In what follows E will be a space and F a subspace.

DEFINITION 48. A p-chain α on E will be called a *relative p-cycle on E modulo F* if $d\alpha$ is a $(p-1)$-chain on F.

If α and β are relative p-cycles on E modulo F, $d(\alpha - \beta) = d\alpha - d\beta$, and, since $d\alpha$ and $d\beta$ are both chains on F so is $d\alpha - d\beta$. Thus $\alpha - \beta$ is also a relative p-cycle on E modulo F. It follows at once that the relative p-cycles on E modulo F form a subgroup of $C_p(E)$. This subgroup will be denoted by $Z_p(E, F)$.

DEFINITION 49. A p-chain α on E will be called a *relative p-boundary of E modulo F* if there is a p-chain β on F and a $(p+1)$-chain γ on E such that $\alpha + \beta = d\gamma$.

If α and β are relative p-boundaries on E modulo F then there are p-chains γ and δ on F and $(p+1)$-chains λ and μ on E such that $\alpha + \gamma = d\lambda$, $\beta + \delta = d\mu$; and so $(\alpha - \beta) + (\gamma - \delta) = d(\lambda - \mu)$. Thus $\alpha - \beta$ is a relative p-boundary on E modulo F, and so the relative p-boundaries form a subgroup of $C_p(E)$. This subgroup will be denoted by $B_p(E, F)$.

If α is an element of $B_p(E, F)$ then $\alpha + \beta = d\gamma$ for suitable chains γ on E and β on F. Hence $d\alpha = -d\beta$, a $(p-1)$-chain on F. Thus α is a relative p-cycle on E modulo F. That is to say, $B_p(E, F)$ is a subgroup of $Z_p(E, F)$.

The definitions of this section are already bearing a formal resemblance to those of §7. This similarity will be pushed further by the definition of relative homology.

DEFINITION 50. Two relative p-cycles α, β on E modulo F will be said to be *relatively homologous modulo F* or simply *homologous modulo F* if their difference is a relative p-boundary. This relation will be written $\alpha \sim \beta$ mod F. In particular the relative p-boundaries themselves will be said to be *(relatively) homologous to* 0 *modulo F*.

Reasoning as in §8, it is easy to see that this relation of relative homology is an equivalence relation on $Z_p(E, F)$, and that the equivalence classes are the cosets of this group with respect to the subgroup $B_p(E, F)$.

DEFINITION 51. The cosets of $Z_p(E, F)$ with respect to $B_p(E, F)$ are called *p-dimensional relative homology classes of E modulo F*, and the quotient group $H_p(E, F) = Z_p(E, F)/B_p(E, F)$ is called the *p-th relative homology group of E modulo F*.

Exercises

1. Let E be the circumference of a circle, say the circle of centre

$(0, 0)$ and radius 1 in the (x, y)-plane. The standard Euclidean simplex Δ_1 is the set of points in the (x_1, x_2)-plane such that $x_1 + x_2 = 1, x_1 \geqslant 0,\ x_2 \geqslant 0$, and its points are fully specified by the parameter x_1. The mapping σ which carries the point (x_1, x_2) on Δ_1 into $(\cos 2\pi x_1,\ \sin 2\pi x_1)$ on E is a singular simplex on E. Prove that it is a cycle.

2. Continuing with the notation of Exercise 1, define two further singular simplexes σ_1 and σ_2 on E as follows: σ_1 carries (x_1, x_2) on Δ_1 into $(\cos \pi x_1, \sin \pi x_1)$ and σ_2 carries (x_1, x_2) into $(\cos \pi (1 + x_1),$ $\sin \pi(1 + x_1))$. Prove that the chain $\sigma_1 + \sigma_2$ is a cycle on E and prove that it is homologous to the cycle σ of Exercise 1.

[Hint: To prove the homology relation, map Δ_2 into E in such a way that one side is wrapped round the whole circumference, while the others are carried onto the upper and lower semicircles.]

3. Let E be a line segment, F the set consisting of its two endpoints x_0 and x_1 and let α and β be the relative homology classes in E modulo F represented by the singular simplexes $(x_0 x_1)$ and $(x_1 x_0)$ respectively. (Check that these singular simplexes are relative cycles.) Prove that $\alpha = -\beta$.

[Hint: Map Δ_2 on E in such a way that two of the sides are mapped along E and the third is mapped on one of the end-points, and note that if σ_1 and σ_2 are singular simplexes which map Δ_1 and Δ_2 respectively on a single point in any space then $\sigma_1 = d\sigma_2$.]

4. A torus E can be constructed by sticking together the opposite sides of a square E' with vertices x_1, x_2, x_3, x_4. Thus there is a continuous mapping f of E' onto E which is a homeomorphism on the interior of E' but which is such that $f(p) = f(q)$ if p and q are opposite to one another on a pair of opposite sides of E'. Let α be the chain $(x_1 x_2 x_4) - (x_2 x_4 x_3)$ on E', the two singular simplexes being defined by linear mappings. Prove that $f_1(\alpha)$ is a cycle on E. (f_1 is the homomorphism on chain groups induced by f).

5. Let two circles be given in the (x, y)-plane E with centres (a, b), (a', b') and radii r and r' respectively. Using the notation of Exercise 1 for points of Δ_1, define the two singular simplexes σ and σ' on E by the formulae:

$$\sigma(x_1, x_2) = (a + r \cos 2\pi x_1,\ b + r \sin 2\pi x_1),$$
$$\sigma'(x_1, x_2) = (a' + r' \cos 2\pi x_1,\ b' + r' \sin 2\pi x_1).$$

Prove that σ and σ' are homologous cycles of E.

[Hint: Map the square E' of Exercise 4 onto a cylinder by identifying points lying opposite one another on one pair of opposite sides. α goes into a chain β on this cylinder such that $d\beta = \tau - \tau'$, where τ and τ' are cycles obtained by mapping Δ_1 round the cylinder's circular ends. Then map the cylinder into E so that its ends go into the given circles.]

6. Prove that if a space E consists of just one point, $H_0(E)$ is infinite cyclic and $H_r(E)$ is zero for $r \geqslant 1$.

[Hint: Start by showing that there is exactly one singular simplex σ_p on E for each dimension p, and that, for $p > 1$, $d\sigma_p = 0$ or σ_{p-1} according as p is odd or even.]

7. Let E be a non-arcwise connected space and let $E = E_1 \cup E_2 \cup \ldots \cup E_m$ where no point of E_i can be joined by a path in E to a point of E_j for $i \neq j$. Prove that $H_p(E)$ is the direct sum of the groups $H_p(E_i)$ for each p.

8. Let E be an arcwise connected space; prove that $H_0(E)$ is infinite cyclic, with a generator represented by $\sigma: \Delta_0 \to E$ such that $\sigma(\Delta_0) = x$, where x is an arbitrary point of E.

9. Prove that, if E is arcwise connected and $F \subset E$, then $H_0(E, F)$ is zero, provided that F is not empty.

CHAPTER VI

CONTINUOUS MAPPINGS AND THE HOMOLOGY GROUPS

1. The induced homomorphism

In Chapter V, §7, it was shown that a continuous mapping f of a space E into a space E' induces a homomorphism f_1 of $C_p(E)$ into $C_p(E')$ for each p, and that $f_1 \circ d = d \circ f_1$. The last equation means that, if f_1 carries a p-chain α on E into the p-chain α' on E' then it carries $d\alpha$ onto $d\alpha'$. This is in agreement with the geometrical statement that, if S is a piece of surface embedded in E and $f(S) = S'$, a piece of surface in E', then f carries the boundary curve of S into that of S'. Looking at this geometrical statement from another point of view, let α and β be two closed curves in E together forming the boundary of S. Then f carries α, β into closed curves which together form the boundary of S'.

Experience already gained in the last chapter in translating intuitive results into theorems on homology suggests that the above statement should be put in the form: if α and β are homologous cycles on E then $f_1(\alpha)$ and $f_1(\beta)$ are cycles on E' and are homologous. Rather than attempt to prove this result as it stands, it seems worth while to ask a more general question on relative homology. In this context the following definition will be useful:

DEFINITION 52. Let E, E' be two spaces, F a subspace of E and F' a subspace of E'. If a continuous mapping of E into E' carries F into F', f will be called *a continuous mapping of the pair (E, F) into the pair (E', F')*. Two such mappings f, g of the pair (E, F) into the pair (E', F') will be called *homotopic* if there is a continuous mapping H of the pair $(E \times I, F \times I)$ into (E', F') such that $H(p, 0) = f(p)$, $H(p, 1) = g(p)$ for all $p \in E$.

The second part of the definition is a natural extension of the idea of homotopy (Definition 22); the geometrical idea is that the mapping f is to be deformed into the mapping g in such a way that *at each stage* of the deformation F is carried into F'.

As in the case of single spaces, the notation $f\colon(E, F) \to (E', F')$ will be used as a shorthand for "f is a mapping of (E, F) into (E', F')".

A particular case of a mapping $f:(E, F) \to (E', F')$ is obtained if $E \subset E'$ and $F \subset F'$, and f is defined by $f(p) = p$ for all $p \in E$. This mapping is called the inclusion mapping of (E, F) into (E', F'); it is not hard to see that it is continuous.

Following the lead of the geometrical consideration (at the beginning of this section) of the effect of a mapping f on closed curves of E, it seems reasonable to ask: (1) if f is a continuous mapping of the pair (E, F) into the pair (E', F'), does f carry relative p-cycles of E modulo F into relative p-cycles of E' modulo F'; (2) if so, are relatively homologous relative p-cycles carried into relatively homologous relative p-cycles? The answer is given by:

THEOREM 27. *Let f be a continuous mapping of the pair (E, F) into the pair (E', F'). Then f_1 carries $Z_p(E, F)$ into $Z_p(E', F')$ and $B_p(E, F)$ into $B_p(E', F')$ and so each relative homology class of E modulo F into a relative homology class of E' modulo F'.*

PROOF. Let α be an element of $Z_p(E, F)$. Then $d\alpha$ is in $C_{p-1}(F)$. If $\alpha' = f_1(\alpha)$ then $d\alpha' = d_\circ f_1(\alpha) = f_1(d\alpha)$ by Theorem 25. Since $d\alpha$ is a chain on F and $f(F) \subset F'$, $f_1(d\alpha)$ is a chain on F'. That is to say, $d\alpha'$ is a chain on F', and so α' is in $Z_p(E', F')$. Since α is any element of $Z_p(E, F)$ it follows that f_1 carries this group into $Z_p(E', F')$.

Next let α be an element of $B_p(E, F)$. Then there is a p-chain β on F and a $(p + 1)$-chain γ on E such that $\alpha + \beta = d\gamma$. Applying the homomorphism f_1 to this equation, $f_1(\alpha) + f_1(\beta) = f_1(d\gamma) = d(f_1(\gamma))$, by Theorem 25. Since f carries F into F', $f_1(\beta)$ is a chain on F', and so $f_1(\alpha)$ added to a chain on F' is a boundary on E', that is to say, $f_1(\alpha)$ is in $B_p(E', F')$. This holds for any α in $B_p(E, F)$, and so the second part of the theorem has been proved.

Finally, if α and β are two elements of some relative homology class in $Z_p(E, F)$, then $\alpha - \beta$ is, by definition, in $B_p(E, F)$, and so, by what has just been proved, $f_1(\alpha - \beta) = f_1(\alpha) - f_1(\beta)$ is in $B_p(E', F')$. That is to say, $f_1(\alpha)$ and $f_1(\beta)$ are in the same relative homology class of $Z_p(E', F')$. This proves the last part of the theorem.

The last part of the above theorem shows that the continuous mapping f induces an operation on homology classes. For, let $\bar{\alpha}$ be a relative homology class of relative p-cycles of E modulo F, and let α be a relative cycle belonging to this class. Then Theorem 27 shows that the relative homology class of $f_1(\alpha)$ depends only on the class $\bar{\alpha}$ and not on the particular representative α chosen. For if α and β are both in the class $\bar{\alpha}$ they are relatively homologous, and so $f_1(\alpha) \sim f_1(\beta)$, modulo F'. Write $f_*(\bar{\alpha})$ for the relative homology class in $Z_p(E', F')$ of $f_1(\alpha)$, α being any representative of $\bar{\alpha}$. Then the remark just made means that f_* is a mapping of p-dimensional relative homology classes of E modulo F into those of E' modulo F'. But these relative homology classes are the elements of the relative homology groups, and so f_* maps $H_p(E, F)$ into $H_p(E', F')$. Moreover, f_* is a homomorphism. For let $\bar{\alpha}$ and $\bar{\beta}$ be elements of $H_p(E, F)$. Then:

$$f_*(\bar{\alpha} + \bar{\beta}) = \text{the relative homology class of } f_1(\alpha + \beta) \text{ (definition}$$
$$\text{of } f_*, \; \alpha + \beta \text{ being a representative of the class}$$
$$\bar{\alpha} + \bar{\beta})$$
$$= \text{the class of } f_1(\alpha) + f_1(\beta) \text{ (since } f_1 \text{ is a homomorphism)}$$
$$= f_*(\bar{\alpha}) + f_*(\bar{\beta}) \text{ (definition of } f_*).$$

DEFINITION 53. Given a continuous mapping of the pair (E, F) into the pair (E', F'), the homomorphism f_*, constructed as above is called the *induced homomorphism* on the relative homology groups. A similar homomorphism may, of course, be constructed for each value of p, but no distinction in notation will be made.

In particular, if F is taken to be the empty set one obtains the special result that a continuous mapping f of E into E' induces a homomorphism f_* of $H_p(E)$ into $H_p(E')$ for each value of p. A special case of importance is obtained if $E \subset E'$ and f is taken to be the inclusion mapping (Chapter III, §1, Exercise 1).

Another special case to be noted arises when the pairs (E, F) and (E', F') coincide and f is the identity mapping; then f_* is the identity homomorphism of $H_p(E, F)$ on itself. This apparently trivial remark will be of importance presently.

Exercise

If F is a subspace of E, and E and F are both arcwise connected, prove that the inclusion mapping $F \to E$ induces an isomorphism of $H_0(F)$ onto $H_0(E)$.

2. Topological invariance of the homology groups

In accordance with the general principle stated in §1 of Chapter III that anything defined by means of continuous mappings should be topologically invariant, one would expect the homology groups of a space to be topological invariants. The essential step in the proof that this is so is the following theorem.

THEOREM 28. *Let E, E', E'' be three spaces each with a sub-space F, F', F'', respectively, and let two continuous mappings $f : E \to E'$ and $g : E' \to E''$ be given such that $f(F) \subset F'$, $g(F') \subset F''$. Then the composition $h = g \circ f$ may be constructed and has the property $h(F) \subset F''$, and the induced homomorphisms $f_* : H_p(E, F) \to H_p(E', F')$, $g_* : H_p(E', F') \to H_p(E'', F'')$, $h_* : H_p(E, F) \to H_p(E'', F'')$ satisfy $h_* = g_* \circ f_*$ for each p.*

PROOF. The first point, that $h(F) \subset F''$, is evident, for $h(F) = g(f(F)) \subset g(F') \subset F''$. Thus h_* is defined. Let $\bar{\alpha}$ be an element of $H_p(E, F)$ and α a relative cycle representing the relative homology class $\bar{\alpha}$. Then;

$$h_*(\bar{\alpha}) = \text{the relative homology class of } h_1(\alpha) \text{ (Definition 53)},$$
$$= \text{the class of } (g_1 \circ f_1)(\alpha) \text{ (Theorem 24)}.$$

But $(g_* \circ f_*)(\bar{\alpha})$ is, by definition of g_*, the relative homology class obtained by operating with g_1 on a representative of the class $f_*(\bar{\alpha})$, while, by the definition of f_*, $f_1(\alpha)$ is a representative of $f_*(\bar{\alpha})$. And so $(g_* \circ f_*)(\bar{\alpha})$ is the relative homology class of $(g_1 \circ f_1)(\alpha)$, which has just been proved equal to $h_*(\bar{\alpha})$. This holds for all $\bar{\alpha}$ in $H_p(E, F)$ and so the theorem is proved.

This theorem will now be applied to the case of two homeomorphic spaces E, E', with homeomorphisms $f : E \to E'$ and $g : E' \to E$ such that $f \circ g$ and $g \circ f$ are the identity mappings on E' and E respectively. Also let F be a subspace of E and write $F' = f(F)$. Since the homomorphism induced on the homology groups by the identity mapping is the identity, Theorem 28, along with the statement $f \circ g =$ identity, implies $f_* \circ g_* =$ identity; similarly $g_* \circ f_* =$ identity. Thus f_* and g_* are isomorphisms, and so the following has been proved:

THEOREM 29. *The relative homology groups are topological invariants of a pair of spaces.*

This holds, of course, in the particular case where F is empty, giving the result *that the homology groups $H_p(E)$ are topological invariants of E.*

3. Homotopic mappings and the homology groups

Consider a 1-cycle α on a space E, and for simplicity suppose it to be represented geometrically by a single loop. If this loop is subjected to some deformation in E, carrying it to a new position α', it is intuitively obvious that α traces out a path γ, a piece of surface embedded in E, and that the boundary of γ consists of α and α'

(cf. Fig. 24). What one naturally wants to say here is that α and α' are homologous cycles, and that $\alpha - \alpha' = d\gamma$. But the situation is not quite so simple as this. For while α may be considered as a curve made up of line segments (i.e. 1-simplexes) in E, γ appears then as made up of a number of curvilinear quadrilaterals, namely the paths of these 1-simplexes in the deformation of α. But if γ is to be considered as a 2-chain it has to be made up of 2-simplexes. Briefly, the path of a cycle cannot be considered as a chain unless some further operation is carried out.

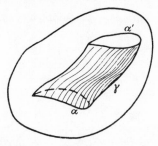

FIG. 24.

Before going further into this question, it will be phrased in a different way. For a cycle on a space is actually a linear combination of singular simplexes on the space, that is to say, a collection of mappings with associated coefficients. Thus the picture of a 1-cycle in Fig. 24 as a simple loop, that is the continuous image of the circumference of a circle, is not generally valid. And consequently the idea of deformation of a cycle, which in the description of Fig. 24 simply takes the form of a homotopy of the mapping embedding the loop α in E, does not make sense as it stands.

One can, however, replace the crude concept of the deformation of a cycle by the following considerations. Let f and g be two homotopic mappings of a space X into E. Let α be a p-cycle on X and let $f_1(\alpha)$ and $g_1(\alpha)$ be its images in $Z_p(E)$ under the homomorphisms induced by f and g. The image of X in E has a path of deformation because of the homotopy from f to g, and the cycle $f_1(\alpha)$ can be thought of as being pulled along this path into the new position $g_1(\alpha)$. The question to be asked in this section and the next two is whether the successive positions of $f_1(\alpha)$ as the mapping f is deformed into g can be thought of as making up in some way a $(p + 1)$-chain having $f_1(\alpha)$ and $g_1(\alpha)$, with suitable signs, as its boundary.

In order to tackle this question, note first that a homotopy of f into g means an embedding of $X \times I$, where I is the interval $0 \leqslant t \leqslant 1$, in E. And so to begin with some homological properties of the product $X \times I$ will be examined. In effect this amounts to considering a special case of the general problem which has just been posed. For there are two naturally homotopic mappings of X into $X \times I$, namely those given by $f(q) = (q, 0)$ in $X \times I$ and $g(q) = (q, 1)$ in $X \times I$. The question to be tackled first is whether, when α is a p-cycle on X, $f_1(\alpha)$ and $g_1(\alpha)$ are homologous in $X \times I$.

To illustrate the method to be adopted, consider first the case $p = 2$, with the aid of the accompanying Fig. 25. A singular 2-simplex on X, that is, a continuous mapping $\sigma : \Delta_2 \to X$, induces a mapping $\sigma' : \Delta_2 \times I \to X \times I$ if one sets $\sigma'(x, t) = (\sigma(x), t)$. Forgetting for a moment the strict definition of a singular simplex on a space as a certain mapping into the space, think of $f_1(\sigma)$ as being the curvilinear triangle on the base $X \times \{0\}$ of $X \times I$, and $g_1(\sigma)$ as being that on the top $X \times \{1\}$ (cf. Fig. 25). These two triangles are joined by a curvilinear prism in $X \times I$ obtained by embedding, by means of the mapping σ', the prism $\Delta_2 \times I$ in $X \times I$. Intuitively, one clearly wants the boundary of this prism in $X \times I$ to consist of $g_1(\sigma)$, $f_1(\sigma)$ and the three surfaces obtained by embedding in $X \times I$ the vertical sides of $\Delta_2 \times I$. But in homology theory boundaries are defined only for portions of space built up from simplexes, and so the prism in $X \times I$ must be broken up in some way into tetrahedra. Now the prism $\Delta_2 \times I$, with its vertices named as in Fig. 25, can be split up in a natural way into the three tetrahedra $[x_0 y_0 y_1 y_2]$, $[x_0 x_1 y_1 y_2]$, $[x_0 x_1 x_2 y_2]$, and so the embedded prism in $X \times I$ may be thought of as decomposed into the images of these tetrahedra under σ'.

Reverting to the rigorous notion of singular simplexes and chains on $X \times I$, it is clear that the idea of a curvilinear prism in $X \times I$ broken into tetrahedra will have to be replaced by a chain consisting of a linear combination of three singular 3-simplexes on $X \times I$. The natural way to do this, following the geometrical picture as closely as possible, will be to form a 3-chain on $\Delta_2 \times I$ from the singular simplexes $(x_0 y_0 y_1 y_2)$, $(x_0 x_1 y_1 y_2)$, $(x_0 x_1 x_2 y_2)$ defined by linear mappings (Definition 38) and then to map this chain into $C_3(X \times I)$ by means of the induced homomorphism $\sigma_1' : C_3(\Delta_2 \times I) \to C_3(X \times I)$. If the resulting chain on $X \times I$ is called $P\sigma$, the essential feature of its construction must be that its boundary should be a linear combination of $f_1(\sigma)$, $g_1(\sigma)$ and singular simplexes representing the vertical sides of the prism in $X \times I$ in Fig. 25. That such a construction can be made will appear in §4, below.

Suppose now that $\alpha = \sum a_i \sigma_i$ is a 2-cycle on X, and suppose that a chain $P\sigma_i$, representing as above a curvilinear prism in $X \times I$, is

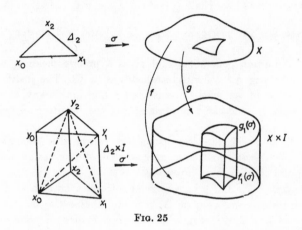

FIG. 25

constructed for each σ_i. The idea is that, when the boundaries of the $P\sigma_i$ are calculated, the singular simplexes representing the vertical sides of the prisms in $X \times I$ should cancel out, so that $d\sum a_i P\sigma_i = g_1(\alpha) - f_1(\alpha)$. This would prove that $g_1(\alpha)$ and $f_1(\alpha)$ were homologous. That a construction can be made to satisfy this further requirement will also appear in §4.

4. Prisms

Consider the product $\Delta_p \times I$. Δ_p is a simplex in Euclidean $(p + 1)$-space, and so it is convenient to embed $\Delta_p \times I$ in $(p + 2)$-space in such a way that, if $(z^1, z^2, \ldots, z^{p+2})$ are the coordinates of a variable point, then $\Delta_p \times \{0\}$ lies in the set $z^{p+2} = 0$, and $\Delta_p \times \{1\}$ in the set $z^{p+2} = 1$, and the coordinates of two points $(q, 0)$ in $\Delta_p \times \{0\}$ and $(q, 1)$ in $\Delta_p \times \{1\}$ differ only in the value of z^{p+2}. In addition, the set $z^{p+2} = 0$ in $(p + 2)$-space is itself a Euclidean $(p + 1)$-space, and it is convenient to identify it with the $(p + 1)$-space containing Δ_p in such a way that Δ_p is identified with $\Delta_p \times \{0\}$.

Let $x_0, x_1, \ldots, x_p$ be the vertices of Δ_p, and so of $\Delta_p \times \{0\}$, and let $y_0, y_1, \ldots, y_p$ be those of $\Delta_p \times \{1\}$. Also let $(x_0x_1 \ldots x_iy_i \ldots y_p)$ denote the singular simplex on $\Delta_p \times I$ defined by the linear mapping of Δ_{p+1} with vertices in the usual standard order onto the simplex with the vertices $x_0, x_1, \ldots x_i, y_i, \ldots, y_p$ in that order (Definition 38).

DEFINITION 54. The chain $\sum\limits_{i=0}^{p} (-1)^i (x_0x_1 \ldots x_iy_i \ldots y_p)$ on $\Delta_p \times I$ will be called the *prism over* $(x_0x_1 \ldots x_p)$ and will be denoted by $P(x_0x_1 \ldots x_p)$.

This definition generalizes and gives a precise meaning to the idea of dividing $\Delta_2 \times I$ into tetrahedra as in §3. The justification for the choice of coefficients in this chain is that in this way, as will be seen presently, one can follow rigorously the intuitive suggestions of §3.

For the sake of facility in working with prisms, it is convenient to extend the above definition at once so that P becomes an operator on singular simplexes on any space.

DEFINITION 55. Let σ be a singular p-simplex on a space E, that is a continuous mapping of Δ_p into E. Define the mapping σ': $\Delta_p \times I \to E \times I$ by setting $\sigma'(z, t) = (\sigma(z), t)$ for each point z of Δ_p and each t in I. Then if σ_1' is the induced homomorphism of $C_{p+1}(\Delta_p \times I)$ into $C_{p+1}(E \times I)$, define the chain $P\sigma$ to be $\sigma_1'(P(x_0x_1 \ldots x_p))$. $P\sigma$ will be called *the prism over* σ.

Since, in the above notation, $(x_0x_1 \ldots x_p)$ is the singular simplex on Δ_p induced by the identity mapping, the definitions of $P\sigma$ and $P(x_0x_1 \ldots x_p)$ agree when σ is taken to be the singular simplex $(x_0x_1 \ldots x_p)$ on Δ_p. It is worth noting that some pictorial significance may be given to the phrase "prism over σ" if E is identified with the subset $E \times \{0\}$ of $E \times I$.

The operator P being now defined on any singular simplex on E, it can at once be extended to a homomorphism of $C_p(E)$ into $C_{p+1}(E \times I)$, by setting $P(\sum\limits_i a_i\sigma_i) = \sum\limits_i a_iP\sigma_i$ for any p-chain $\sum\limits_i a_i\sigma_i$ on E.

THEOREM 30. *Let f be a continuous mapping of E into a space F, and let the mapping $f':E \times I \to F \times I$ be defined by setting $f'(z, t) = (f(z), t)$ for each point z of E and each t in I. Then $P_\circ f_1 = f_1'{}_\circ P$.*

PROOF. In words this theorem states that f_1' carries the prism over σ into the prism over $f_1(\sigma)$, which is just what one would expect geometrically. To prove the theorem let σ be a singular simplex on E.

Then:

$$(P \circ f_1)(\sigma) = P(f_1(\sigma))$$

$$= P(f \circ \sigma) \quad \text{(Definition 41)},$$

$$= (f \circ \sigma)_1'(P(x_0 x_1 \ldots x_p)) \quad \text{(definition of the operator } P)$$

where $(f \circ \sigma)_1'$ is the homomorphism of $C_{p+1}(\Delta_p \times I)$ into $C_{p+1}(F \times I)$ induced by the mapping $(f \circ \sigma)' : \Delta_p \times I \to F \times I$ defined by setting $(f \circ \sigma)'(z, t) = ((f \circ \sigma)(z), t)$ for each z in Δ_p and t in I. Clearly $(f \circ \sigma)' = f \circ \sigma'$, and so, by Theorem 24, $(f \circ \sigma)_1' = f_1' \circ \sigma_1'$. Hence:

$$(f \circ \sigma)_1'(P(x_0 x_1 \ldots x_p)) = f_1' \circ \sigma_1' (P(x_0 x_1 \ldots x_p))$$

$$= f_1'(P\sigma) \quad \text{(definition of } P\sigma)$$

$$= (f_1' \circ P)(\sigma).$$

This holds for any σ and so the theorem is proved.

The next step is the calculation of $dP(x_0 x_1 \ldots x_p)$. The definition of $P(x_0 x_1 \ldots x_p)$ shows that

$$dP(x_0 x_1 \ldots x_p) = \sum_{i=0}^{p} (-1)^i \, d(x_0 x_1 \ldots x_i y_i \ldots y_p).$$

Each $(x_0 x_1 \ldots x_i y_i \ldots y_p)$ is a singular simplex on the subspace $\Delta_p \times I$ of Euclidean $(p + 2)$-space defined by a linear mapping, and so Definition 40 gives:

$$d(x_0 x_1 \ldots x_i y_i \ldots y_p) = \sum_{j \leqslant i} (-1)^j (x_0 x_1 \ldots \hat{x}_j \ldots x_i y_i \ldots y_p)$$

$$+ \sum_{j > i} (-1)^j (x_0 x_1 \ldots x_i y_i \ldots \hat{y}_{j-1} \ldots y_p)$$

It follows that $dP(x_0 x_1 \ldots x_p) =$

$$\sum_{j \leqslant i} (-1)^{i+j} (x_0 x_1 \ldots \hat{x}_j \ldots x_i y_i \ldots y_p)$$

$$+ \sum_{j > i} (-1)^{i+j} (x_0 x_1 \ldots x_i y_i \ldots \hat{y}_{j-1} \ldots y_p).$$

From the first summation, taking $i = j$, for $i = 1, 2, \ldots, p$, one obtains the terms $\sum_{i=1}^{p} (x_0 x_1 \ldots x_{i-1} y_i \ldots y_p)$, and from the second, taking $j = i + 1$, for $i = 0, 1, \ldots, p - 1$, one obtains $-\sum_{i=0}^{p-1} (x_0 x_1 \ldots x_i y_{i+1} \ldots y_p)$. But these two summations are the same with opposite signs, and so cancel. The remaining terms may be written as follows:

$$dP(x_0x_1 \ldots x_p) = (y_0y_1 \ldots y_p) - (x_0x_1 \ldots x_p)$$
$$+ \sum_{\substack{i=1 \\ j<i}}^{i=p} (-1)^{i+j}(x_0x_1 \ldots \hat{x}_j \ldots x_iy_i \ldots y_p)$$
$$+ \sum_{\substack{i=0 \\ j>i+1}}^{i=p-1} (-1)^{i+j}(x_0x_1 \ldots x_iy_i \ldots \hat{y}_{j-1} \ldots y_p) \quad (17)$$

Now, the first two terms in (17) are singular simplexes on the top and bottom of $\Delta_p \times I$ as required. It remains to be shown that the two summations in (17) represent in some way chains on the vertical sides of $\Delta_p \times I$. From the diagram for the case $p = 2$ (cf. Fig. 25) it appears that the upright sides of $\Delta_2 \times I$ are obtained by constructing prisms over the sides of Δ_2. And so it is reasonable to expect that the two summations in (17) should be obtained by applying the operator P to $d(x_0x_1 \ldots x_p)$. This will now be proved.

THEOREM 31. $dP(x_0x_1 \ldots x_p) = (y_0y_1 \ldots y_p) - (x_0x_1 \ldots x_p)$
$$- Pd(x_0x_1 \ldots x_p) \quad (18)$$

PROOF. The method of proof will be to calculate $P(d(x_0x_1 \ldots x_p)$ and then to compare the result with the right hand side of (17). Using the definition of $d(x_0x_1 \ldots x_p)$ (Definition 40) it follows that one must calculate $P(x_0x_1 \ldots \hat{x}_i \ldots x_p)$ for each i. Now one might be tempted to write:

$$P(x_0x_1 \ldots \hat{x}_i \ldots x_p) = \sum_{j<i}(-1)^j(x_0x_1 \ldots x_jy_j \ldots \hat{y}_i \ldots y_p)$$
$$+ \sum_{j>i}(-1)^{j-1}(x_0 \ldots \hat{x}_i \ldots x_jy_j \ldots y_p) \quad (19)$$

this formula being obtained by applying mechanically the defining formula for $P(x_0x_1 \ldots x_p)$ to the case $P(x_0x_1 \ldots \hat{x}_i \ldots x_p)$. But although (19) happens to be the right answer one cannot derive it in this direct fashion. For the definition of $P(x_0x_1 \ldots x_p)$ applies to just one singular simplex on Δ_p, namely $(x_0x_1 \ldots x_p)$. To calculate $P(x_0x_1 \ldots \hat{x}_i \ldots x_p)$ one must use the general definition of the prism over a singular simplex on the space Δ_p, applying this definition to the singular simplex $(x_0x_1 \ldots \hat{x}_i \ldots x_p)$.

To define in detail $P(x_0x_1 \ldots \hat{x}_i \ldots x_p)$ let $\Delta_{p-1} \times I$ have vertices $u_0, u_1, \ldots, u_{p-1}, v_0, v_1, \ldots, v_{p-1}$. $\Delta_{p-1} \times I$ will be embedded in Euclidean $(p + 1)$-space, just as $\Delta_p \times I$ was embedded in

$(p + 2)$-space, the u_i being the vertices of $\Delta_{p-1} \times \{0\}$, the v_j those of $\Delta_{p-1} \times \{1\}$, and the points of $\Delta_{p-1} \times \{0\}$ and $\Delta_{p-1} \times \{1\}$ differing only in the value of the last coordinate. Also, Δ_{p-1} will be identified with $\Delta_{p-1} \times \{0\}$. Let the mapping $\sigma^i : \Delta_{p-1} \to \Delta_p$ be the singular $(p - 1)$-simplex $(x_0 x_1 \ldots \hat{x}_i \ldots x_p)$ on Δ_p, that is to say, the linear mapping carrying $u_0, u_1, \ldots, u_{p-1}$, in that order, into $x_0, x_1, \ldots, \hat{x}_i \ldots x_p$. Let $\sigma^{i'}$ be the mapping of $\Delta_{p-1} \times I$ into $\Delta_p \times I$ defined by setting $\sigma^{i'}(z, t) = (\sigma^i(z), t)$ for each point z in Δ_{p-1} and each t in I. The definition of $P(x_0 x_1 \ldots \hat{x}_i \ldots x_p)$ is then $\sigma_1^{i'}(P(u_0 u_1 \ldots u_{p-1}))$, where $\sigma_1^{i'}$ is the homomorphism on chain groups induced by $\sigma^{i'}$, and

$$P(u_0 u_1 \ldots u_{p-1}) = \sum_{j=0}^{\cdot p-1} (-1)^j (u_0 u_1 \ldots u_j v_j \ldots v_{p-1}).$$ This last formula

for $P(u_0 u_1 \ldots u_{p-1})$ is correct because $(u_0 u_1 \ldots u_{p-1})$ is related to Δ_{p-1} just as $(x_0 x_1 \ldots x_p)$ is related to Δ_p.

Now, if the mapping $\sigma^{i'}$ should induce the linear mapping of the simplex with vertices $u_0, u_1, \ldots, u_j, v_j \ldots v_{p-1}$ onto that with vertices $x_0, x_1, \ldots, \hat{x}_i, \ldots, x_j, y_j, \ldots, y_p$, or $x_0, x_1, \ldots, x_j, y_j, \ldots \hat{y}_i, \ldots, y_p$, according as $j > i$ or $j < i$, it would follow that the induced homomorphism $\sigma_1^{i'}$ would carry the singular simplex $(u_0 u_1 \ldots u_j v_j \ldots v_{p-1})$ into $(x_0 x_1 \ldots \hat{x}_i \ldots x_j y_j \ldots y_p)$, or $(x_0 x_1 \ldots x_j y_j \ldots \hat{y}_i \ldots y_p)$, according as $j > i$ or $j < i$, and so $\sigma_1^{i'}$ would carry $P(u_0 u_1 \ldots u_{p-1})$ into the right hand side of (19). (19) would therefore be the correct formula for $P(x_0 x_1 \ldots \hat{x}_i \ldots x_p)$, and a comparison of (19) with the two summations on the right of (17) would establish the theorem.

Thus, to complete the proof of the theorem, the linearity of the restriction of $\sigma^{i'}$ to the simplex with the vertices $u_0, u_1, \ldots, u_j, v_j, \ldots, v_{p-1}$ must be shown for each j. The simplest way do to this is to let f_i be the linear mapping of the simplex with vertices $u_0, u_1, \ldots, u_j, v_j, \ldots, v_{p-1}$ onto that with vertices $x_0, x_1, \ldots, x_j, y_j, \ldots, \hat{y}_i, \ldots, y_p$ (assuming $j < i$ for the sake of definiteness) and to show that f_i coincides with the appropriate restriction of $\sigma^{i'}$.

Let $(w^1, w^2, \ldots, w^{p+1})$ be the coordinates of a variable point in the $(p + 1)$-space containing $\Delta_{p-1} \times I$, and $(z^1, z^2, \ldots, z^{p+2})$ those in the $(p + 2)$-space containing $\Delta_p \times I$. If $(w^1, w^2, \ldots, w^{p+1})$ is in the simplex with vertices $u_0, u_1, \ldots, u_j, v_j, \ldots, v_{p-1}$ and $(z^1, z^2, \ldots, z^{p+2}) = f_i(w^1, w^2, \ldots, w^{p+1})$ then for f_i to coincide with the restriction of $\sigma^{i'}$ to this simplex it is necessary and sufficient that:

(1) $z^{p+2} = w^{p+1}$,

(2) $(z^1, z^2, \ldots, z^{p+1}, 0) = \sigma^i(w^1, w^2, \ldots, w^p, 0)$,

these statements being simply a reformulation of the definition of $\sigma^{i'}$.

Now, if $\lambda_0, \lambda_1, \ldots, \lambda_p$ are the barycentric coordinates of $(w^1, w^2, \ldots, w^{p+1})$ with respect to the set of vertices $u_0, u_1, \ldots, u_j$, $v_j, \ldots, v_{p-1}$, the fact that $(z^1, z^2, \ldots, z^{p+2}) = f_i(w^1, w^2, \ldots, w^{p+1})$ along with the linearity of f_i implies that $\lambda_0, \lambda_1, \ldots, \lambda_p$ are also the barycentric coordinates of $(z^1, z^2, \ldots, z^{p+2})$ with respect to the vertices $x_0, x_1, \ldots, x_j, y_j, \ldots, \hat{y}_i, \ldots, y_p$. w^{p+1} is the linear combination of the $(p+1)$th coordinates of $u_0, u_1, \ldots, u_j, v_j, \ldots, v_{p-1}$ with $\lambda_0, \lambda_1, \ldots, \lambda_p$ as coefficients, and, by what has just been said, z^{p+2} is the same linear combination of the $(p+2)$th coordinates of $x_0, x_1, \ldots, x_j, y_j, \ldots, \hat{y}_i, \ldots, y_p$. But the last coordinates of $u_0, u_1, \ldots, u_j, x_0, x_1, \ldots, x_j$ are 0 and those of $v_j, v_{j+1}, \ldots, v_{p-1}$, $y_j, y_{j+1}, \ldots, y_p$ are 1, and so it follows at once that $z^{p+2} = w^{p+1}$.

For $h \neq p + 1$, w^h is the linear combination of the h-th coordinates of $u_0, u_1, \ldots, u_j, v_j, \ldots, v_{p-1}$ with $\lambda_0, \lambda_1, \ldots, \lambda_p$ as coefficients; but for $h \neq p + 1$, the h-th coordinate of u_k is the same as that of v_k for all k. Hence w^h is the linear combination of the h-th coordinates of $u_0, u_1, \ldots, u_{p-1}$ with $\lambda_0, \lambda_1, \ldots, \lambda_{j-1}, \lambda_j + \lambda_{j+1}, \lambda_{j+2}, \ldots, \lambda_p$ as coefficients. Similarly z^h, $h \neq p + 2$, is the linear combination of the h-th coordinates of $x_0, x_1, \ldots, \hat{x}_i, \ldots, x_p$ with $\lambda_0, \lambda_1, \ldots, \lambda_{j-1}$, $\lambda_j + \lambda_{j+1}, \lambda_{j+2}, \ldots, \lambda_p$ as coefficients. These coefficients are thus the barycentric coordinates of $(w^1, w^2, \ldots, w^p, 0)$ with respect to the vertices $u_0, u_1, \ldots, u_{p-1}$, and also those of $(z^1, z^2, \ldots, z^{p+1}, 0)$ with respect to $x_0, x_1, \ldots, \hat{x}_i \ldots, x_p$, and so the linearity of σ^i implies that $(z^1, z^2, \ldots, z^{p+1}, 0) = \sigma^i(w^1, w^2, \ldots, w^p, 0)$. The conditions (1), (2) above thus hold and so f_i coincides with the appropriate restriction of $\sigma^{i'}$, and the proof of Theorem 31 is complete.

5. Homotopic mappings and the homology groups (contd.)

Returning now to the topic of §3, let σ be a singular p-simplex on a space X, and, as in §4, let σ' be the mapping of $\Delta_p \times I$ into $X \times I$ given by $\sigma'(z, t) = (\sigma(z), t)$ for z in Δ_p and t in I. Also, f and g will be the mappings of X into $X \times I$ defined by $f(q) = (q, 0)$, $g(q) = (q, 1)$ for each q in X. The principal tool in this discussion will be the following generalization of Theorem 31.

THEOREM 32. $\qquad dP\sigma = g_1(\sigma) - f_1(\sigma) - Pd\sigma.$ $\qquad\qquad$ (20)

PROOF. This will be proved by operating on (18) with the homomorphism σ_1' on the chain groups of $\Delta_p \times I$ induced by σ'.

Applying σ_1' to the left hand side of (18):

$$\sigma_1'(dP(x_0 x_1 \ldots x_p)) = d\sigma_1'(P(x_0 x_1 \ldots x_p)) \qquad \text{(Theorem 25)},$$

$$= dP\sigma \qquad \text{(Definition 55)}.$$

To work out $\sigma_1'(x_0 x_1 \ldots x_p)$, let z be any point of Δ_p. By the definition of f, $(f \circ \sigma)(z) = (\sigma(z), 0)$ in $X \times I$, and this, by the definition of σ', is the same as $\sigma'(z, 0)$. But the singular simplex $(x_0 x_1 \ldots x_p)$ is the identity mapping of Δ_p on itself, or, what is the same thing, since Δ_p is identified with $\Delta_p \times \{0\}$, the mapping which carries z onto $(z, 0)$. $\sigma'(z, 0)$ is therefore the image of z under the composition of the mapping σ' and $(x_0 x_1 \ldots x_p)$, and this composition is $\sigma_1'(x_0 x_1 \ldots x_p)$, by the definition of the induced homomorphism σ_1'. The result just obtained above, that $\sigma'(z, 0) = (f \circ \sigma)(z)$, then shows that $\sigma_1'(x_0 x_1 \ldots x_p)$ operating on z is the same as $(f \circ \sigma)$ operating on z. Hence:

$$\sigma_1'(x_0 x_1 \ldots x_p) = (f \circ \sigma) = f_1(\sigma) \qquad \text{(Definition 41)}$$

similarly,

$$\sigma_1'(y_0 y_1 \ldots y_p) = g_1(\sigma).$$

Finally, $\quad \sigma_1'(Pd(x_0 x_1 \ldots x_p)) = P\sigma_1(d(x_0 x_1 \ldots x_p)) \qquad \text{(Theorem 30)}$

$$= Pd\sigma \qquad \text{(Definition 42)}.$$

(18) has thus been transformed into (20) by the operation of σ_1'.

As a corollary to this theorem it should be noted that P, d, f_1, g_1 are all homomorphisms on chain groups, and so (20) may be applied to chains on X simply by operating term by term. Hence for a chain α on X:

$$dP\alpha = g_1(\alpha) - f_1(\alpha) - Pd\alpha. \qquad (21)$$

Suppose in particular that α is a cycle. Then $d\alpha = 0$, and so $Pd\alpha$ is zero, and so (21) shows that $g_1(\alpha) - f_1(\alpha) = dP\alpha$. That is to say, $f_1(\alpha)$ and $g_1(\alpha)$ are homologous. This proves the result concerning $X \times I$ which was conjectured on intuitive grounds in §3. But before treating homotopic mappings of X into any space E, the ultimate goal of this discussion, the result just proved will be extended to relative homology.

Let Y be a subspace of X. $Y \times I$ is thus a subspace of $X \times I$. Let α be a relative p-cycle of X modulo Y and let f and g be as in Theorem 32. Clearly $f_1(\alpha)$ and $g_1(\alpha)$ are relative p-cycles on $X \times I$ modulo $Y \times I$, for their boundaries are chains on $Y \times \{0\}$ and

$Y \times \{1\}$ respectively. Also, since $d\alpha$ is a chain on Y, $Pd\alpha$ is a chain on $Y \times I$, and so (21) simply states that $f_1(\alpha)$ and $g_1(\alpha)$ are homologous in $X \times I$ modulo $Y \times I$.

If, now, the relative cycle α is taken as a representative of a relative homology class $\bar{\alpha}$, an element of $H_p(X, Y)$, $f_1(\alpha)$ and $g_1(\alpha)$ will be representatives of the relative homology classes $f_*(\bar{\alpha})$, $g_*(\bar{\alpha})$, respectively, by Definition 53. But, since it has just been shown that $f_1(\alpha) \sim g_1(\alpha)$ modulo $Y \times I$, it follows that $f_*(\bar{\alpha}) = g_*(\bar{\alpha})$. The following theorem has thus been proved:

THEOREM 33. *Let X be a space, Y a subspace, and let f, g be the mappings of X into $X \times I$ defined by $f(q) = (q, 0)$, $g(q) = (q, 1)$ for each point q of X. Let f_*, g_* be the induced homomorphisms of $H_p(X, Y)$ into $H_p(X \times I, Y \times I)$. Then $f_* = g_*$ for each dimension p.*

This can be carried over at once into the general result which has been the aim of this chapter:

THEOREM 34. *Let f and g be homotopic mappings of a pair (X, Y) into a pair (E, F) and let f_*, g_* be the induced homomorphisms of $H_p(X, Y)$ into $H_p(E, F)$. Then $f_* = g_*$ for each dimension p.*

PROOF. Since f and g are homotopic (Definition 52) there is a continuous mapping $\phi:(X \times I, Y \times I) \to (E, F)$ agreeing with f and g for $t = 0$ and $t = 1$, respectively.

Let $\bar{f}$ and $\bar{g}$ be the mappings of X into $X \times I$ given by $\bar{f}(q) = (q, 0)$, $\bar{g}(q) = (q, 1)$ for each point q in X, and let $\bar{f}_*$, $\bar{g}_*$ be the induced homomorphisms of $H_p(X, Y)$ into $H_p(X \times I, Y \times I)$. Finally, let ϕ_* be the homomorphism of $H_p(X \times I, Y \times I)$ into $H_p(E, F)$ induced by ϕ. Now it is clear that $f = \phi \circ \bar{f}$ and $g = \phi \circ \bar{g}$, and so, by Theorem 28, $f_* = \phi_* \bar{f}_*$ and $g_* = \phi_* \bar{g}_*$. But Theorem 33 says that $\bar{f}_* = \bar{g}_*$ and so $f_* = g_*$ as required.

The following theorem is a direct consequence of Theorem 34, and exhibits the way in which this theorem is often used.

THEOREM 35. *Let (E, F), (E', F') be two pairs of spaces and f: $(E, F) \to (E', F')$, $g:(E', F') \to (E, F)$ two continuous mappings such that the composition $g \circ f$, a mapping of (E, F) into itself, is homotopic (Definition 52) to the identity mapping of (E, F) onto itself while $f \circ g$ is homotopic to the identity mapping of (E', F') onto itself. Then the induced homomorphism $f_*:H_p(E, F) \to H_p(E', F')$ is an isomorphism onto for each p.*

PROOF. Since $g \circ f$ is homotopic to the identity i of (E, F) onto itself, Theorem 34 shows that $(g \circ f)_* = i_*$, both sides of this equation being homomorphisms of $H_p(E, F)$ into itself for any p. By Theorem

28 this is equivalent to $g_* \circ f_* = i_*$, and, by the remark made at the end of §1 of this chapter, i_* is the identity homomorphism of $H_p(E, F)$ onto itself. Similarly $f_* \circ g_*$ is the identity homomorphism of $H_p(E', F',)$ onto itself for each p. That is to say f_* and g_* are inverse to each other, and so both are isomorphisms onto.

COROLLARY. *If F and F' are both empty the above theorem reduces to the following: If E and E' are two topological spaces and $f:E \to E'$ and $g:E' \to E$ are continuous mappings such that $f \circ g$ and $g \circ f$ are homotopic to the appropriate identity mappings, then f_* is an isomorphism of $H_p(E)$ onto $H_p(E')$ for each p.*

The use of this theorem and its corollary will be illustrated in some of the following exercises. Incidentally it should be noted that the result of Theorem 35 marks a limit to the usefulness of homology groups for distinguishing between non-homeomorphic spaces. For two spaces E and E' can be non-homeomorphic but there may be mappings f and g satisfying the conditions of the above corollary (cf. Exercises 2 and 3 below). It is also not hard to show that, if E, E' are as in the above corollary and are arcwise-connected, then $\pi(E) \cong \pi(E')$ (a special case appeared in Chapter IV, §4, Exercise 5). Thus such spaces are indistinguishable by means of fundamental groups and homology groups.

Exercises

1. Let E' be a subspace of a topological space E and suppose there is a continuous mapping $f:E \to E$ satisfying the following conditions:

(a) $f(E) = E'$;

(b) the restriction of f to E' is the identity mapping of E' onto itself;

(c) f is homotopic to the identity mapping of E onto itself.

Prove that $H_p(E)$ and $H_p(E')$ are isomorphic for all p, the isomorphism being induced by the inclusion mapping of E' into E.

[Hint: Regard f as a mapping into E', let g be the inclusion mapping of E' into E and use the corollary to Theorem 35.]

2. Prove that if E is a solid sphere of dimension n then $H_0(E)$ is infinite cyclic and $H_r(E)$ is zero for $r \geqslant 1$.

[Hint: Let E' denote the subspace of E consisting of its centre only; let f be defined by $f(p) = E'$ for all $p \in E$; then use Exercise 1.]

3. Prove that the homology groups of an annulus and of a solid torus are isomorphic to those of the circumference of a circle.

4. Prove that if E is a Euclidean space of any dimension $H_0(E)$ is infinite cyclic and $H_r(E)$ is zero for $r \geqslant 1$.

[Hint: Every cycle on E is actually a cycle on some solid sphere contained in E.]

5. Let E, F, G be topological spaces such that $E \supset F \supset G$ and let f be a continuous mapping of (E, F) into itself such that:

(a) f is homotopic to the identity mapping of (E, F) onto itself;

(b) if the homotopy of condition (a) is given by a continuous mapping $H{:}E \times I \to E$, then $H(G \times I) \subset G$;

(c) $f(F) \subset G$.

Prove that $H_r(E, F)$ and $H_r(E, G)$ are isomorphic, for each r, the isomorphism being induced by the inclusion mapping of (E, G) into (E, F).

[Hint: Apply Theorem 35 to f and the inclusion mapping of (E, G) into (E, F).]

6. Let E be the solid sphere in Euclidean n-space given by $\sum\limits_{i=1}^{n} x_i^2 \leqslant 1$, let F be the set defined by $\frac{1}{4} \leqslant \sum\limits_{i=1}^{n} x_i^2 \leqslant 1$, and let G be the sphere with the equation $\sum\limits_{i=1}^{n} x_i^2 = 1$. Define f by setting $f(x_1, x_2, \ldots x_n)$ equal to the point $(2x_1, 2x_2, \ldots, 2x_n)$ if $(x_1, x_2, \ldots x_n) \in E - F$ and equal to the intersection with G of the join of $(0, 0, \ldots, 0)$ to $(x_1, x_2, \ldots, x_n)$ if $(x_1, x_2, \ldots, x_n) \in F$. Prove that f satisfies the conditions of Exercise 5 and hence show that $H_r(E, F)$ and $H_r(E, G)$ are isomorphic for all r.

[Hint: The deformation of the identity mapping into f should consist in moving points radially outwards until $E - F$ fills the whole sphere and F is compressed onto G.]

7. Let E be the subset of the n-dimensional sphere $\sum\limits_{i=1}^{n+1} x_i^2 = 1$ in Euclidean $(n + 1)$-space defined by the inequality $x_{n+1} \geqslant 0$, let F be the subset of E defined by $0 \leqslant x_{n+1} \leqslant \frac{1}{2}$ and let G be the subset of F defined by $x_{n+1} = 0$. Prove that $H_r(E, F) \cong H_r(E, G)$ for all r.

[Hint: As in Exercise 6; there the homotopy required consisted in moving points radially, while here they should be moved along great circles radiating from $(0, 0, \ldots, 0, 1)$.]

CHAPTER VII

BARYCENTRIC SUBDIVISION AND EXCISION

1. Motivation for barycentric subdivision

One of the principal results to be obtained in this chapter is that in homology theory one need only consider singular simplexes on a space which are, in some sense, arbitrarily small. That is to say, given a cycle or relative cycle, one can always replace it by a homologous cycle or relative cycle each of whose singular simplexes is a mapping of a simplex into an arbitrarily small neighbourhood in the space. It should be remarked that the phrase "arbitrarily small" needs to be given a precise meaning in any given context. For example, if E is a subset of a Euclidean space smallness may be defined in E by considering only neighbourhoods in E whose diameters are less than some preassigned number. Or, if E is some more general space, smallness may be defined by some given open covering of E, a neighbourhood being considered as small if it is contained in some set of the covering.

To motivate geometrically the result stated above, let E be some subspace of Euclidean space, and let γ denote a closed surface in E. γ will be thought of in the meantime as a geometric representation of a 2-cycle on E, and so can be thought of as made up of triangles fitted together edge to edge. To make the situation pictorially simpler, assume that the triangles making up γ are all flat with straight edges. Each of these triangles may be subdivided into six smaller ones by drawing in the medians. The cycle γ is transformed in this way into a new cycle γ' whose simplexes are geometrically represented by the smaller triangles just constructed. It must be carefully noted at this point that γ and γ' are different cycles, for if one translated the situation into the rigorous language of homology theory γ and γ' would be linear combinations of different sets of singular simplexes. Nevertheless, γ and γ' are represented geometrically by the same piece of surface in E, and so it seems natural to ask whether they are homologous. Indeed, homology theory would be rather unsatisfying to one's geometrical intuition if this were not so, for one naturally feels that two pieces of surface which look the same should fulfil the same functions as regards forming boundaries. If γ and γ' can be shown to be homologous, the same will evidently hold for γ and the cycle obtained from γ' by drawing all the medians in the triangles of γ', and so on; but if this operation of subdivision is carried out sufficiently often, the triangles of which the resulting cycle are composed can be made arbitrarily small. This will give some geometrical support for the result stated at the beginning of this section.

In order to find whether γ and γ' are homologous, one must attempt to find a portion of 3-dimensional space made up of tetrahedra (and so representing geometrically a 3-chain) such that its boundary is made up of γ and γ'. More explicitly, what one wants is a union of tetrahedra whose triangular faces include all the triangles making up γ and all the smaller triangles making up γ', while all the other triangular faces coincide in pairs.

As a first step towards solving this question, displace γ' by moving the centroid of each triangle of γ out of the plane of that triangle. For example if in Fig. 26(a) ABC, ABD are two of the triangles making up γ, X, Y their centroids. In Fig. 26(b) X and Y are shown displaced out of the planes ABC and ABD, respectively. The small triangles APX, BPX, etc., which are among the triangles of which γ' is composed, are at the same time displaced as indicated. As this is done for all the triangles of γ, it is clear that a set of tetrahedra is formed with the property that γ and the displaced γ' together form the boundary of their union. This looks promising, but is not yet ready for translation into homology theory, as the triangles APX, BPX, etc. making up the displaced γ' do not appear as faces of tetrahedra.

To remedy this, take a point O, say the centroid of the tetrahedron $XABC$, and join it to X, A, B, C, P, Q, R. Thus (cf. Fig. 27(a)) the tetrahedron $XABC$ is split up into tetrahedra such that the triangles ABC, XAP, XBP, etc. all appear as faces. The only flaw is that the triangle OBC appears both as itself and as the union of OQC and OQB, with similar remarks concerning OAB, OAC. To avoid this, displace P, Q, R, from the lines AB, BC, AC, respectively (cf. Fig. 27(b)). Note that this last operation is similar in form to the displacement of X from the plane of ABC; each operation is the displacement of the mass-centre of a simplex, in the one case a 1-simplex, in the other a 2-simplex. It is to be understood that a similar construction is carried out in association with each triangle composing γ.

The polyhedron of Fig. 27 is now a union of tetrahedra whose boundary consists of the triangles XAP, XBP, etc., which belong to γ', triangle ABC, which belongs to γ, and triangles PAB, QBC, RCA, which cancel out with similar triangles obtained in a similar way from the neighbouring triangles of γ. Thus γ and the displaced

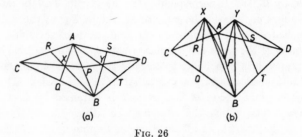

(a)   (b)

FIG. 26

γ' together form the boundary of a union of tetrahedra β, which is to be thought of as the geometrical representation of a 3-chain. Finally suppose that the polyhedron in Fig. 27 is flattened into the plane ABC, X, P, Q, R resuming their original positions, while O is made to coincide with X; a similar operation is to be performed on the

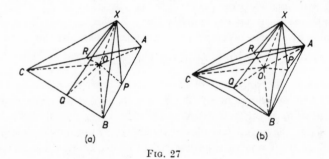

(a)   (b)

FIG. 27

polyhedron corresponding, as in Fig. 27, to each triangle of γ. The tetrahedra forming β become flattened out in this process, but they may still be thought of as geometrical representations of singular simplexes on E defined by degenerate linear maps. The geometrical reasoning just carried out thus makes it quite plausible that γ and γ' should be homologous.

In order to translate the above geometrical reasoning into terms of homology theory two operators have to be constructed, one corresponding to the transition from γ to γ', the other to the construction of a chain β such that $d\beta = \gamma - \gamma'$. These operators are to be defined on singular simplexes on any space, and so it is natural, as a first step, to attempt to define them on the standard simplexes $\Delta_0, \Delta_1, \Delta_2, \ldots$

The first operation will be called barycentric subdivision and will be denoted by B. It is to correspond to the drawing in of all the medians of a triangle, or, what is the same thing, the joining of the centroid, or barycentre, to all the vertices and mid-points of the sides. The mid-points of the sides are the mass-centres, or barycentres, of the sides, and so it is reasonable to describe the marking in of the mid-points of the sides as barycentric subdivision of the sides. Thus the barycentric subdivision of the triangle is obtained by first barycentrically subdividing the boundary and then joining the barycentre of the triangle to all the vertices so obtained. This joining operation may be interpreted as follows. If $(y_0 y_1)$ is any singular 1-simplex defined by a linear mapping of Δ_1 into a Euclidean space, then its join to the point z is to be the singular 2-simplex $(z y_0 y_1)$ (cf. Definition 38 for the definition of this notation). If $\alpha = \sum a_i \sigma_i$ is a singular 1-chain on a Euclidean space, each simplex being defined by a linear mapping, then the join of z to α will be written as $z\alpha$ and will be defined as $\sum a_i \overline{\sigma_i}$, where $\overline{\sigma_i}$ is the join of z and σ_i. With this notation it seems natural to define $B(x_0 x_1 x_2)$, for a singular 2-simplex defined by a linear mapping into a Euclidean space, by the formula

$$B(x_0 x_1 x_2) = b(Bd(x_0 x_1 x_2)) \tag{22}$$

where b is the barycentre of the triangle formed by x_0, x_1, x_2. The use of B on the right of (22) presupposes that this operator is extended by linearity to act on chains. This suggested formula (22), applied to the singular simplex on Δ_2 defined by the identity mapping of Δ_2 on itself, and then generalized to higher dimensions, gives the basis for an inductive algebraic definition of B as an operator on chain-groups.

The second operator, to be denoted by H, is to correspond to the construction of a degenerate polyhedron on a given triangle as base, as illustrated in Figs. 26, 27. Noting first the analogy already remarked on between displacing X from the plane of triangle ABC in Fig. 26 and displacing P, Q, R from the sides of this triangle, it is natural to regard the triangles PAB, QBC, RCA as representing the operation of H on the boundary of the triangle ABC. Then, according to the geometrical construction sketched above, remembering that

X and O are both, when the polyhedron of Fig. 27 is flattened out, the barycentre of triangle ABC, the operation of H on triangle ABC is obtained by joining the barycentre of this triangle to the following

(a) triangle ABC itself,

(b) the triangles forming the barycentric subdivision of ABC,

(c) the triangles obtained by operating with H on the boundary of ABC.

This can be most naturally translated into algebraic terms by saying that, if $(x_0x_1x_2)$ is a singular 2-simplex defined by a linear mapping into a Euclidean space, and if b is the barycentre of the triangle with vertices x_0, x_1, x_2, then $H(x_0x_1x_2)$ is a linear combination of:

(a) $b(x_0x_1x_2) = (bx_0x_1x_2)$,

(b) $b(B(x_0x_1x_2))$,

(c) $b(Hd(x_0x_1x_2))$.

The use of H in (c) presupposes that this operator is extended by linearity to act on chains. The coefficients of the linear combination of the terms (a), (b), (c) above must be chosen so that the boundary of $H(x_0x_1x_2)$ will work out properly. According to the geometrical picture, (Fig. 27), it should turn out that $dH(x_0x_1x_2)$ is a linear combination of:

(a) $(x_0x_1x_2)$,

(b) $B(x_0x_1x_2)$,

(c) simplexes represented by the triangles PAB, QBC, RCA, that is, $H(d(x_0x_1x_2))$.

On the basis of this condition it is not hard to see that a suitable definition for $H(x_0x_1x_2)$ is given by the formula

$$H(x_0x_1x_2) = b(x_0x_1x_2) - b(B(x_0x_1x_2)) - b(Hd(x_0x_1x_2)). \qquad (23)$$

This formula, generalized to higher dimensions, will be taken as the pattern for an inductive definition of the operator H.

2. The operator B

The ideas sketched in §1 will now be given a rigorous formal treatment, the first step being to define the operator B and to work out some of its properties. A symbol such as $(y_0y_1 \ldots y_p)$ will always mean a singular simplex defined by a linear mapping on some portion of a Euclidean space (Definition 38). In particular, the symbol $(x_0x_1 \ldots x_p)$ will always be used to denote the singular p-simplex on Δ_p defined by the identity mapping of Δ_p on itself, Δ_p being the standard Euclidean p-simplex, with vertices $x_0, \ldots, x_p$.

DEFINITION 56. Let y_i, $i = 0, 1, 2, \ldots, p$, be points of Euclidean n-space, and let the coordinates of y_i be $y_i^1, y_i^2, \ldots, y_i^n$. Then the *barycentre of the p-simplex* $[y_0y_1 \ldots y_p]$ is the point whose coordinates

$z^1, z^2, \ldots, z^n$ are given by $z^j = (\sum_{i=0}^{p} y_i^j)/(p + 1)$, $j = 1, 2, \ldots, n$.

This definition reduces to the mid-point of a line segment or the centroid of a triangle in the cases $p = 1$, $p = 2$, respectively.

DEFINITION 57. Let z, $y_0, y_1, \ldots, y_p$ be $p + 2$ points of some Euclidean space. Then the singular $(p + 1)$-simplex $(zy_0y_1y_2 \ldots y_p)$ is said to be the *join of z to the singular p-simplex* $(y_0y_1 \ldots y_p)$. If $\alpha = \sum a_i \sigma_i$ is a p-chain on some portion of a Euclidean space with each σ_i defined by a linear mapping, then *the join of z to* α is defined to be the $(p + 1)$-chain $\sum a_i \overline{\sigma_i}$, where $\overline{\sigma_i}$ is the join of z to σ_i, and this join is written as $z\alpha$.

The operation of joining a fixed point z to each p-chain has the following important property:

THEOREM 36. *For any z and α as in the last definition* $d(z\alpha) = \alpha - z(d\alpha)$.

PROOF. Since the operation of joining z to α is carried out by joining it to each singular simplex and then attaching the appropriate coefficients, it will be sufficient to prove this theorem in the case where α is a singular p-simplex $(y_0y_1 \ldots y_p)$. Thus it must be shown that $d(zy_0y_1 \ldots y_p) = (y_0y_1 \ldots y_p) - z(d(y_0y_1 \ldots y_p))$. Now, by Definition 40,

$$d(zy_0y_1 \ldots y_p) = (y_0y_1 \ldots y_p) + \sum_{i=0}^{p}(-1)^{i+1}(zy_0y_1 \ldots \hat{y}_i \ldots y_p)$$

$$= (y_0y_1 \ldots y_p) - z(d(y_0y_1 \ldots y_p)),$$

as required.

The operator of barycentric subdivision will now be defined inductively.

DEFINITION 58. Let $B\alpha = \alpha$ for any 0-chain on any space, and suppose that the meaning of $B\alpha$ has already been defined for any $(p - 1)$-chain α on any space. Then (1) $(x_0x_1 \ldots x_p)$ being the singular p-simplex on Δ_p defined by the identity mapping, and b_p being the barycentre of $\Delta_p = [x_0x_1 \ldots x_p]$, $B(x_0x_1 \ldots x_p)$ is defined as the join of b_p to $Bd(x_0x_1 \ldots x_p)$; (2) if σ is a singular p-simplex on any space E, that is a continuous mapping of Δ_p into E, and if σ_1 is the induced homomorphism of $C_p(\Delta_p)$ into $C_p(E)$ (cf. Definition 41),

$B\sigma$ is defined as $\sigma_1(B(x_0x_1 \ldots x_p))$; (3) if $\alpha = \sum a_i \sigma_i$ is any p-chain on a space E, $B\alpha$ is defined as $\sum a_i B\sigma_i$.

It will be noticed at once that this definition, or at least the first part of it, is modelled on the formula (22) which arose from the geometrical considerations of §1. The statement (2) of the definition can be described geometrically as follows, in the case $p = 2$. If a triangle T is embedded in a space E, and T is assumed to be the image under a mapping f of a plane triangle T_0, then T is to be sub-divided by drawing in the medians of T_0 and taking their images under f. It is not hard to see a similar geometrical interpretation in the case $p = 3$. The point of part (3) of the definition is to make B into a homomorphism, and so into something which is algebraically significant.

The following two theorems establish important properties of the operator B.

THEOREM 37. *Let E and E' be two spaces and let f be a continuous mapping of E into E'. Also let f_1 be the homomorphism induced on the chain groups of E by f (Definition 41). Then $B \circ f_1 = f_1 \circ B$.*

PROOF. It is to be proved that, if α is any element of $C_p(E)$, for any p, then $B(f_1(\alpha)) = f_1(B\alpha)$. And since B and f_1 are both homomorphisms and $C_p(E)$ is the free group generated by singular p-simplexes of E, it will be sufficient to prove that $B(f_1(\sigma)) = f_1(B\sigma)$ for any singular p-simplex σ on E. The geometrical plausibility of this result may be seen by thinking of σ as represented by a triangle embedded in E, and regarding the operator B as the marking in of the images under the embedding map of the medians, as described in the note following the definition of B.

To prove the theorem, let σ be a singular p-simplex on E, that is a continuous mapping of Δ_p into E, and let σ_1 be the homomorphism of $C_p(\Delta_p)$ into $C_p(E)$ induced by σ. Then

$$f_1(B\sigma) = f_1(\sigma_1(B(x_0x_1 \ldots x_p))), \qquad \text{(Definition 58)},$$
$$= (f_1 \circ \sigma_1)(B(x_0x_1 \ldots x_p))$$
$$= (f \circ \sigma)_1(B(x_0x_1 \ldots x_p)), \qquad \text{(Theorem 24)},$$
$$= B(f \circ \sigma), \qquad \text{(Definition 58)},$$
$$= Bf_1(\sigma), \qquad \text{(Definition 41)},$$

and this is the required result.

THEOREM 38. $B \circ d = d \circ B$.

PROOF. As in the last theorem it will be sufficient to prove that, if σ is a singular p-simplex on E, then $B(d\sigma) = d(B\sigma)$. This corresponds to the geometrical statement that, if one draws in the median of a triangle, the boundary of the figure so obtained consists of the sides of the original triangle with their mid-points marked in.

The proof of the theorem will be carried out by induction. The result is trivial for operations on 0-chains, and it will be assumed as induction hypothesis that $B(d\alpha) = d(B\alpha)$ for any $(p-1)$-chain α on E. Then, if σ is a singular p-simplex on E:

$$dB\sigma = d\sigma_1(B(x_0x_1 \ldots x_p))$$
$$= \sigma_1(dB(x_0x_1 \ldots x_p)) \qquad (24)$$

by Definition 58 and Theorem 25.

Now, by definition, $B(x_0x_1 \ldots x_p) = b_p(Bd(x_0x_1 \ldots x_p))$, where b_p is the barycentre of $[x_0x_1 \ldots x_p]$, and so:

$$dB(x_0x_1 \ldots x_p) = Bd(x_0x_1 \ldots x_p) - b_p(dBd(x_0x_1 \ldots x_p)),$$
$$\text{(Theorem 36)},$$
$$= Bd(x_0x_1 \ldots x_p) - b_p(Bd^2(x_0x_1 \ldots x_p)),$$
$$\text{(Induction Hypothesis)},$$
$$= Bd(x_0x_1 \ldots x_p), \quad \text{(since } d^2 = 0\text{)}.$$

Substituting $Bd(x_0x_1 \ldots x_p)$ for $dB(x_0x_1 \ldots x_p)$ in (24), it follows that:

$$dB\sigma = \sigma_1(Bd(x_0x_1 \ldots x_p))$$
$$= B\sigma_1(d(x_0x_1 \ldots x_p)),$$
$$\text{(Theorem 37 applied to } \sigma_1\text{)},$$
$$= Bd\sigma, \qquad \text{(Definition 42)},$$

and this completes the proof.

3. The operator H

The operator H will now be defined. The procedure is similar to that adopted in the definition of B. Namely, the definition of $H(x_0x_1 \ldots x_p)$ will be based on the suggested formula (23), and then H, like B, will be extended to any singular simplexes and finally to chains.

DEFINITION 59. Let $H\alpha = 0$ for any 0-chain α on any space, and suppose that the meaning of $H\alpha$ has already been defined for any $(p-1)$-chain α on any space. Then (1) if $(x_0x_1 \ldots x_p)$ has its usual meaning and if b_p is the barycentre of Δ_p, define $H(x_0x_1 \ldots x_p)$ as the join of b_p to the chain

$$(x_0x_1 \ldots x_p) - B(x_0x_1 \ldots x_p) - Hd(x_0x_1 \ldots x_p);$$

(2) if σ is a singular p-simplex on a space E, that is, a continuous mapping of Δ_p into E, and if σ_1 is the induced homomorphism of the chain groups, define $H\sigma = \sigma_1(H(x_0x_1 \ldots x_p))$;

(3) if α is a p-chain on E and $\alpha = \sum a_i \sigma_i$, define $H\alpha = \sum a_i H \sigma_i$.

The following theorem is very similar to Theorem 37, both in statement and in proof.

THEOREM 39. *If E, E' are two given spaces and f is a continuous mapping of E into E', and if f_1 is the induced homomorphism of the chain groups, then $f_1 \circ H = H \circ f_1$.*

PROOF. As in Theorem 37, it is sufficient to prove that $f_1(H\sigma) = Hf_1(\sigma)$ for any singular p-simplex σ on E.

$$\begin{aligned}
f_1(H\sigma) &= f_1(\sigma_1(H(x_0x_1 \ldots x_p))), &\text{(Definition 59)}, \\
&= (f_1 \circ \sigma_1)(H(x_0x_1 \ldots x_p)) \\
&= (f \circ \sigma)_1(H(x_0x_1 \ldots x_p)), &\text{(Theorem 24)}, \\
&= H(f \circ \sigma), &\text{(Definition 59)}, \\
&= Hf_1(\sigma), &\text{(Definition 41)},
\end{aligned}$$

as was to be shown.

The main result of the present section is the following theorem, which shows that, on the basis of the above definition of H, the boundary of $H\sigma$ for a singular simplex σ is in fact made up of the various parts indicated in the closing paragraphs of §1.

THEOREM 40. *Let α be a p-chain on a space E, for any p. Then*

$$dH\alpha = \alpha - B\alpha - Hd\alpha.$$

PROOF. The proof will be by induction. The result is trivial for a 0-chain α, and, as induction hypothesis the theorem will be assumed to hold when α is a $(p - 1)$-chain on any space. On the basis of this hypothesis, it will be sufficient, as in the proof of Theorems 37–39, to prove this theorem in the case where α is replaced by a singular p-simplex σ. Then:

$$\begin{aligned}
dH\sigma &= d\sigma_1(H(x_0x_1 \ldots x_p)), \\
&= \sigma_1(dH(x_0x_1 \ldots x_p)), &\text{(25)}
\end{aligned}$$

by Definition 59 and Theorem 25.

But $H(x_0x_1 \ldots x_p)$ is defined as

$$b_p[(x_0x_1 \ldots x_p) - B(x_0x_1 \ldots x_p) - Hd(x_0x_1 \ldots x_p)]$$

and so, by Theorem 36,

$$dH(x_0x_1 \ldots x_p) = (x_0x_1 \ldots x_p) - B(x_0x_1 \ldots x_p) - Hd(x_0x_1 \ldots x_p)$$
$$- b_p[d(x_0x_1 \ldots x_p) - dB(x_0x_1 \ldots x_p) - dHd(x_0x_1 \ldots x_p)] \quad (26)$$

By the induction hypothesis,

$$dHd(x_0x_1 \ldots x_p) = d(x_0x_1 \ldots x_p) - Bd(x_0x_1 \ldots x_p)$$
$$- Hd^2(x_0x_1 \ldots x_p)$$
$$= d(x_0x_1 \ldots x_p) - dB(x_0x_1 \ldots x_p),$$

$$\text{(since } d^2 = 0 \text{, and, by Theorem 38, } d_\circ B = B_\circ d).$$

It follows at once from this that the expression in the square brackets on the right of (26) is zero, and so

$$dH(x_0x_1 \ldots x_p) = (x_0x_1 \ldots x_p) - B(x_0x_1 \ldots x_p) - Hd(x_0x_1 \ldots x_p).$$

Substituting this in the right hand side of (25) it follows that:

$$dH\sigma = \sigma_1[(x_0x_1 \ldots x_p) - B(x_0x_1 \ldots x_p) - Hd(x_0x_1 \ldots x_p)]$$
$$= \sigma - B\sigma - Hd\sigma,$$

since σ_1 commutes with B and H, by Theorems 37 and 39, and $\sigma_1(d(x_0x_1 \ldots x_p)) = d\sigma$ by definition, while $\sigma_1(x_0x_1 \ldots x_p) = \sigma$, $(x_0x_1 \ldots x_p)$ being the identity mapping of Δ_p on itself. This completes the proof.

4. Reduction to small simplexes

The theorems of §§2 and 3 are now to be applied to the proof of the result stated at the beginning of §1, namely, that a cycle can always be replaced by a homologous cycle each of whose singular simplexes is a mapping of a standard Euclidean simplex into an arbitrarily small set. To do this it must first be verified that repeated barycentric subdivision applied to a chain yields a chain each of whose singular simplexes is a mapping into an arbitrarily small set, and that, if α is a cycle, so is $B\alpha$, and $B\alpha$ is homologous to α.

Now it is clear that, if a triangle is subdivided by drawing in its medians, each of the subdivisions is smaller than the original triangle. The object of the next two theorems is to generalize this statement to higher dimensions. In general, the size of a set in

Euclidean space is measured by its diameter, that is, the maximum distance apart of two points of the set. The following theorem gives a simple rule for finding the diameter of a simplex in Euclidean space.

THEOREM 41. *The diameter of a Euclidean simplex is the length of its longest edge.*

PROOF. Let S be a Euclidean simplex in a Euclidean space of any dimension. Suppose that A and B are two points of S, but that they are not both vertices. Assume that B is not a vertex. Construct the sphere $\sum$ of centre A and passing through the vertex of S furthest from A. All the other vertices lie in $\sum$ and so, since a sphere is convex, the whole of S lies in $\sum$ (Chapter V, §2, Exercise 6). It follows that AB is less than the distance of A from one of the vertices of S, say B'. Similarly, if A is also not a vertex there will be a vertex A' such that the distance AB' is less than the distance $A'B'$. Thus two points of S at maximum distance apart must be vertices, and so must certainly be two of the vertices which, among the pairs of vertices, are at the greatest distance apart. This completes the proof.

For convenience of statement in the next theorem, the diameter of a Euclidean simplex with vertices $y_0, y_1, \ldots, y_p$ will also be called the diameter of the singular simplex $(y_0y_1 \ldots y_p)$ defined by a linear mapping as in Definition 38.

THEOREM 42. *Let $(y_0y_1 \ldots y_p)$ be a singular simplex defined by a linear mapping of Δ_p into some Euclidean space, and let the diameter of $(y_0y_1 \ldots y_p)$ be l. Then each singular simplex appearing in the chain $B(y_0y_1 \ldots y_p)$ is of diameter at most $pl/(p + 1)$.*

PROOF. This theorem will be proved by induction on p. It is obviously true for $p = 1$, for in this case barycentric subdivision simply amounts to the bisection of a line segment. Assume then that the result is true when p is replaced by $p - 1$. The barycentric subdivision of $(y_0y_1 \ldots y_p)$ is formed by joining the barycentre b of $[y_0y_1 \ldots y_p]$ to $Bd(y_0 \ldots y_p)$, (Definition 58). Now if l is the diameter of $(y_0y_1 \ldots y_p)$, the diameter of each $(y_0 \ldots \hat{y}_i \ldots y_p)$ $(i = 0, \ldots, p)$ will not exceed l, and so by the induction hypothesis the diameter of each simplex introduced in the barycentric subdivision of $d(y_0y_1 \ldots y_p)$ will not exceed $(p - 1)l/p$, and this is less than $pl/(p + 1)$. That is to say, if $(z_0z_1 \ldots z_{p-1})$ is a singular simplex appearing in $Bd(y_0y_1 \ldots y_p)$, the length of the longest edge of the Euclidean simplex $[z_0 \ldots z_{p-1}]$ does not exceed $pl/(p + 1)$ (Theorem 41). Now if $(t_0t_1 \ldots t_p)$ is a singular simplex appearing in

$B(y_0y_1 \ldots y_p)$, the edges of $[t_0t_1 \ldots t_p]$ either belong to a simplex $[z_0z_1 \ldots z_{p-1}]$ of the type just mentioned, and so are less than $pl/(p + 1)$ in length or are obtained by joining the barycentre b of $[y_0y_1 \ldots y_p]$ to the vertices and to the barycentres of the faces. Since b divides the join of each vertex to the barycentre of the opposite face in the ratio $p : 1$, and since each of these joins is less than l, the diameter of $(y_0y_1 \ldots y_p)$, it follows that all these remaining edges are of length not greater than $pl/(p + 1)$. A final application of Theorem 41 shows that, since the edges of each simplex $[t_0t_1 \ldots t_p]$ such that $(t_0t_1 \ldots t_p)$ appears in $B(y_0y_1 \ldots y_p)$ are all not greater than $pl/(p + 1)$ in length, the diameters of these simplexes do not exceed $pl/(p + 1)$.

COROLLARY. *If ε is a given number, and r is taken large enough, $B^r(y_0y_1 \ldots y_p)$ will be a linear combination of singular simplexes of diameters less than ε.*

PROOF. Here B^r denotes the repeated application of B r times in succession. From the above theorem it follows that the diameters of the singular simplexes making up the chain $B^r(y_0y_1 \ldots y_p)$ do not exceed $p^rl/(p + 1)^r$, and the required result follows at once since $p/(p + 1) < 1$.

The above corollary shows that repeated barycentric subdivision applied to a singular simplex defined by a linear mapping in some Euclidean space yields arbitrarily small singular simplexes. The next step in the argument is to extend this to any singular simplexes on any spaces.

THEOREM 43. *Let σ be a singular simplex on a space E, and let an open covering of E be given (Definition 16). Then if r is large enough, $B^r\sigma$ will be a linear combination of singular p-simplexes each of which is a mapping of Δ_p into one of the sets of the covering of E.*

PROOF. To prove this, note first that, if f is any continuous mapping of a compact set S in some Euclidean space into a space E on which an open covering is given, then there is a number ε such that f carries the ε-neighbourhood of every point of S into some set of the covering on E. This statement can easily be established by a repeated bisection argument (cf. also Chapter III, §2, Exercise 8). Consider now in particular Δ_p as S, σ as the mapping f, and choose r, by the corollary to Theorem 42, so that $B^r(x_0x_1 \ldots x_p)$ is a linear combination of singular simplexes on Δ_p each of diameter less than ε, where, as usual $(x_0x_1 \ldots x_p)$ is defined on Δ_p by the identity mapping. Then each singular simplex of $B^r(x_0x_1 \ldots x_p)$ is a mapping of Δ_p onto a subset of Δ_p of diameter less than ε, a subset which is therefore contained in an ε-neighbourhood of any one of its points, and which is therefore carried by the mapping σ into some set of the covering on E. But, by Definition 58, $B\sigma = \sigma_1 B(x_0 x_1 \ldots x_p)$, and so, by repeated application of Theorem 37, $B^r\sigma = \sigma_1 B^r(x_0 x_1 \ldots x_p)$. Hence it follows that each singular simplex of $B^r\sigma$ is a mapping of Δ_p into some set of the given covering of E.

COROLLARY. *Let α be a p-chain on a space E, and let an open covering of E be given. Then if r is large enough $B^r\alpha$ will be a linear combination of singular simplexes each of which is a mapping of Δ_p into some set of the given covering of E.*

PROOF. α can be written as $\sum a_i \sigma_i$, with only a finite number of singular simplexes σ_i appearing. By the above theorem, r_i can be chosen so that $B^{r_i}\sigma_i$ is a linear combination of singular simplexes each of which is a mapping of Δ_p into some set of the covering. If r is taken as the greatest of the r_i the result stated in the corollary is obtained.

A special case which is of interest arises if E is a subspace of some Euclidean space, and the given covering is the collection of all $\delta/2$-neighbourhoods of the points of E. The result just proved states in this case that, if α is a chain on E then r can be so chosen that $B^r\alpha$ is a linear combination of singular simplexes each of which is a map of Δ_p into a set of diameter less than δ.

The first half of the discussion of this section is thus completed, namely the treatment of the "reduction in size" of singular simplexes brought about by barycentric subdivision. The remainder of the discussion consists in showing that $B\alpha$ is homologous to α when α is a cycle. This will actually be done for the more general situation of relative homology.

THEOREM 44. *Let E be a space and F a subspace. Let α be a relative cycle of E modulo F. Then $B\alpha$ is also a relative cycle of E modulo F and α and $B\alpha$ are relatively homologous modulo F.*

PROOF. First let σ be a singular p-simplex on F. σ is thus a mapping of Δ_p into F, and so, since $B\sigma = \sigma_1(B(x_0 x_1 \ldots x_p))$, by Definition 58, $B\sigma$ is a chain on F. Extending this by forming linear combinations, it follows that B carries chains on F into chains on F. Now if α is a relative cycle on E modulo F, $d\alpha$ is a chain on F. $dB\alpha = Bd\alpha$, by Theorem 38, and by what has just been shown this is a chain on F. That is to say, $B\alpha$ is a relative cycle modulo F.

Now by Theorem 40, $dH\alpha = \alpha - B\alpha - Hd\alpha$. Arguing as in the case of B, it is not hard to see that H carries chains on F into chains on F, and so, in particular, $Hd\alpha$ is a chain on F. Thus Theorem 40 says that $\alpha - B\alpha$ added to a chain on F is a boundary, and this means that α and $B\alpha$ are homologous modulo F.

This theorem implies at once that α is homologous modulo F to $B^r\alpha$ for any r, and this statement may be combined with Theorem 43 to give the main result of this section, which may be stated as follows:

THEOREM 45. *Let E be a space, F a subspace and let a covering of E by open sets be given. Then an element of $H_p(E, F)$, for any p, can always be represented by a relative cycle made up of singular simplexes each of which is a mapping of Δ_p into one of the sets of the given covering.*

5. The excision theorem

The object of this section is to work out a further application of the method of barycentric subdivision. The result to be obtained will be one of the most useful tools in the calculation of the homology groups of given spaces. Consider a space E, a subspace F, and a further set U contained in F, the situation being represented diagrammatically in Fig. 28. Let α be a relative cycle of E modulo F. As indicated in Fig. 28(a), it is possible, speaking geometrically, that simplexes of α may meet U and also reach outside F. Fig. 28(b) suggests, however, that if α is transformed by a sequence of bary-centric subdivisions into a chain α' whose simplexes are small enough, then those simplexes which meet U will lie entirely in F. Of course the statement just made would not be true if U and F had frontier points in common and one of the simplexes making up α were to pass through such a point. It is thus to be expected that one will want the additional condition that U should be contained in the interior of F. Suppose then that this condition holds and that α has been replaced by α' as above. In relative homology modulo F a relative cycle is always homologous to the relative cycle obtained by ignoring any simplexes of the given one which are entirely contained in F. Thus α' is homologous modulo F to the relative cycle obtained from α' by leaving out all the simplexes which meet U. Since α and α' are homologous modulo F, by Theorem 44, it follows that the given relative cycle is homologous modulo F to a relative cycle of $E-U$ modulo $F-U$.

Thus the reasoning based on Fig. 28 suggests that, under suitable topological conditions, every element of $H_p(E, F)$ can be represented by a relative cycle of $E - U$ modulo $F - U$, in other words, that the homomorphism $H_p(E - U, F - U) \to H_p(E, F)$ induced by the inclusion mapping is onto.

A similar argument suggests that the kernel of this homomorphism is zero. For if α, a relative cycle of $E - U$ modulo $F - U$, is homologous to zero modulo F, it is reasonable to hope again that, by cutting down the size of the simplexes by repeated barycentric subdivision, one may cut out all the simplexes meeting U.

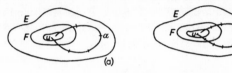

FIG. 28

The theorem below which is based on the above geometrical reasoning is called the Excision Theorem, the idea being that, under certain circumstances, a subset U of F may be excised, that is cut out, without affecting the relative homology of E modulo F.

THEOREM 46. *Let E be a space, F a subspace, and let U be a set whose closure is contained in the interior of F. Then the homomorphism $i:H_p(E - U, F - U) \to H_p(E, F)$ induced by the inclusion map is an isomorphism onto, for each p.*

PROOF. Apply Theorem 45 to the space E with the covering consisting of the two open sets $E - \bar{U}$ and the interior of F. This is a covering because of the condition imposed on U. Then any element of $H_p(E, F)$ can be represented by a relative cycle α which is a linear combination of singular simplexes each of which is a mapping of Δ_p into either $E - \bar{U}$ or the interior of F. Now if σ is a singular simplex appearing in the expression for α, and if the image set $\sigma(\Delta_p)$ has any point in common with U, then $\sigma(\Delta_p)$ is not contained in $E - \bar{U}$, and so must be contained in F. Thus σ is a singular simplex on F, and so it may be dropped from the expression for α without affecting the relative homology class of α modulo F. It follows that any element of $H_p(E, F)$ can be represented by a relative cycle which is a chain on $E - U$, that is, a relative cycle on $E - U$ modulo $F - U$. This shows that the homomorphism $i:H_p(E - U, F - U) \to H_p(E, F)$ is onto.

To show that i is an isomorphism, let α represent an element of its kernel. That is to say, let α be a relative cycle of $E - U$ modulo $F - U$ such that α is homologous to zero in E modulo F. This means that there is a chain β on E and a chain γ on F such that $\alpha = d\beta + \gamma$. Operate on this relation with B^r, noting that, by Theorem 38, this operator commutes with d. Thus $B^r\alpha = dB^r\beta + B^r\gamma$. By the corollary to Theorem 43, r can be chosen so that $B^r\beta$ is a linear combination $\sum b_i \sigma_i$ of singular simplexes each of which maps Δ_p into either $E - \bar{U}$ or the interior of F. Let β_1 be the set of terms in $\sum b_i \sigma_i$ for which $\sigma_i(\Delta_p)$ meets U and let β_2 denote the remaining terms. For each singular simplex σ_i appearing in the expression β_1, $\sigma_i(\Delta_p)$ is not contained in $E - \bar{U}$ (since it meets U) and so β_1 is a chain on F. On the other hand β_2 is a chain on $E - U$. The equation $B^r\alpha = dB^r\beta + B^r\gamma$ may be written as:

$$B^r\alpha - d\beta_2 = d\beta_1 + B^r\gamma. \tag{27}$$

$B^r\alpha$ and $d\beta_2$ are both chains on $E - U$, and so the right hand side of (27) must also be a chain on $E - U$. On the other hand β_1 and $B^r\gamma$ are chains on F, and so the right hand side of (27) is a chain on F. Combining these two statements it follows that the right hand side of (27) is a chain on $F - U$. Thus (27) says that $B^r\alpha$ added to $-(d\beta_1 + B^r\gamma)$, a chain on $F - U$, is the boundary of a chain, β_2, on $E - U$. That is to say, $B^r\alpha$ is homologous to zero in $E - U$ modulo $F - U$. But, by Theorem 44, $B^r\alpha$ and α are homologous in $E - U$ modulo $F - U$, and since α is a representative of any element of the kernel of the homomorphism $i:H_p(E - U, F - U) \to H_p(E, F)$, it follows at once that this kernel is zero, and so the theorem is completely proved.

Exercises

1. Let S^n be the sphere in Euclidean $(n + 1)$-space with the equation $\sum_{i=1}^{n+1} x_i{}^2 = 1$, let E_1 be the sub-set of S defined by $x_{n+1} \geqslant 0$, E_2 the sub-set defined by $x_{n+1} \leqslant \frac{1}{2}$ and write $F = E_1 \cap E_2$. Prove that $H_r(S^n, E_2) \cong H_r(E_1, F)$ for all r.

2. Combine Exercise 1 above with Exercise 7, §5, Chapter VI, to show that, if S^n, E_1, E_2 are as above, and S^{n-1} is the sub-set of S^n defined by $x_{n+1} = 0$, then $H_r(S^n, E_2) \cong H_r(E_1, S^{n-1})$ for all r.

NOTE. The combination of excision and homotopy used to obtain this result is an example of a technique which will be of fundamental importance in the computation of homology groups.

3. Let E be the surface of a torus and let F be the union of the two circles marked α and β in Fig. 21, Chapter V, §1. Let E' be a circular disc and F' its circumference. Prove that $H_r(E, F) \cong H_r(E', F')$ for all r.

[Hint: As an intermediate step show that $H_r(E, F) \cong H_r(E, F_1)$ where F_1 is the union of two circular bands on the surface E having the circles α and β as their central lines; use Exercise 5, §5, Chapter VI for this. Then excise the union of two circular bands contained in the interior of F_1.]

CHAPTER VIII

THE HOMOLOGY SEQUENCE

1. The exact sequence

Associated with a given pair of spaces E, F, where F is a subspace of E, there are three sets of homology groups, those of F, those of E and the relative groups of E modulo F. Three homomorphisms will now be introduced which will exhibit relations between these sets of groups, and will eventually lead to a method of calculating homology groups.

The first of these homomorphisms is already familiar. It is, namely, the homomorphism i of $H_p(F)$ into $H_p(E)$, for each p, induced by the inclusion mapping of F into E (remarks following Definition 53). Thus if $\bar{\alpha}$ is an element of $H_p(F)$, that is to say a p-dimensional homology class in F, then $i\bar{\alpha}$ is the homology class in E represented by any cycle in the class $\bar{\alpha}$. i is called the injection of $H_p(F)$ into $H_p(E)$.

The second homomorphism will be a mapping of $H_p(E)$ into $H_p(E, F)$, for each p. If α is a cycle of E, it is a chain with zero boundary, and since the zero chain may be regarded as belonging to F, α may equally well be regarded as a relative cycle of E modulo F. Moreover, if α and α' are homologous cycles of E then $\alpha - \alpha' = d\beta$ for some chain β, and, comparing this with the definition of relative homology (Definition 50) it is clear that α and α', regarded as relative cycles, are homologous modulo F. Thus if $\bar{\alpha}$ is a p-dimensional homology class of E, that is to say, an element of $H_p(E)$, all the cycles belonging to $\bar{\alpha}$ will, when regarded as relative cycles modulo F, belong to the same relative homology class. This relative homology class, an element of $H_p(E, F)$ will be denoted by $j\bar{\alpha}$. Since addition of homology or relative homology classes is defined by addition of representative cycles or relative cycles, it follows at once that j is a homomorphism. It will be called the *projection* of $H_p(E)$ into $H_p(E, F)$.

The third homomorphism arises from the following fact. If α is a relative p-cycle of E modulo F then it is, by definition, a chain whose boundary $d\alpha$ is a chain on F. But since $d^2 = 0$, $d\alpha$ is a $(p-1)$-cycle on F. Thus to each relative p-cycle on E modulo F there has been assigned a $(p-1)$-cycle of F. This assignment will now be carried over into a mapping of $H_p(E, F)$ into $H_{p-1}(F)$. Let $\bar{\alpha}$ be an element of $H_p(E, F)$ and let α and α' be two representative relative cycles. Then α and α' are homologous modulo F, and so there is a p-chain β on F and a $(p + 1)$-chain γ on E such that $\alpha - \alpha' + \beta = d\gamma$. Hence $d\alpha - d\alpha' = -d\beta$. Thus the two $(p - 1)$-cycles $d\alpha$ and $d\alpha'$ on F are homologous in F, since their difference is the boundary of a chain on F, namely $-\beta$. (Note carefully that $d\alpha$ and $d\alpha'$, although they are boundaries, are not necessarily homologous to zero on F, for they are boundaries of α and α', which are chains on E but not necessarily on F). Thus again, whatever representative α is taken for the relative homology class $\bar{\alpha}$, $d\alpha$ always belongs to the same $(p - 1)$-dimensional homology class of F. This class will be denoted by $\partial\bar{\alpha}$. As in the case of j, the fact that addition in the homology groups is defined by adding representative cycles or relative cycles, implies at once that ∂ is a homomorphism. ∂ will be called the *boundary homomorphism*.

For the discussion of the relations between these homomorphisms it is convenient to arrange the relevant groups in a sequence, as follows:

$$\to H_p(F) \xrightarrow{i} H_p(E) \xrightarrow{j} H_p(E, F) \xrightarrow{\partial} H_{p-1}(F)$$

$$\xrightarrow{i} H_{p-1}(E) \xrightarrow{j} H_{p-1}(E, F) \xrightarrow{\partial} \qquad (28)$$

where the arrows are marked according to the homomorphisms they represent. This sequence terminates on the right of course with the 0-dimensional groups, and it will appear later that, in most elementary cases, it extends only to a finite number of terms to the left.

DEFINITION 60. The sequence (28) of groups and homomorphisms is called *the homology sequence of the pair* (E, F).

The properties of the homology sequence (28) are suggested by the following considerations. Let α be a p-cycle of E, and suppose that α is homologous to a cycle α' of F. This means in the first place that the homology class of α in E is the image under i of the homology class of α' in F; but the definition of relative homology shows also that α, regarded as a relative cycle modulo F is homologous to zero modulo F. That is to say, j maps the homology class of α in E onto zero. This suggests that the image of i is connected in some way with the kernel of j. Next, a cycle of E, regarded as a relative cycle modulo F, represents a relative homology class which is mapped on zero by ∂, and is at the same time the image of a homology class of E under j; this suggests comparing the image of j with the kernel of ∂. Finally, suppose α is a cycle of F which is homologous to zero in E, that is, $\alpha = d\beta$. β is a relative cycle of E modulo F and so, by the definition of ∂, the homology class of α in F is the image under ∂ of the relative homology class of β. But in addition the class of α in F is carried onto zero by i, which suggests comparison of the image of ∂ with the kernel of i.

The results sketched above will now be stated formally in the following theorem, whose proof simply consists of a tidied up version of the above discussion.

THEOREM 47. *In the sequence* (28), (1) *the image of i coincides with the kernel of j,* (2) *the image of j coincides with the kernel of ∂, and* (3) *the image of ∂ coincides with the kernel of i, for all values of p.*

A special remark is required concerning the homomorphism j of $H_0(E)$ into $H_0(E, F)$. This mapping is not followed by a further homomorphism ∂, but it is trivial that j is onto for this case, since each singular 0-simplex on E is both a 0-cycle and a relative cycle modulo F.

PROOF. (1) Let $\bar{\alpha}$ be an element of the image of i for the dimension p. By the definition of i it follows that the class $\bar{\alpha}$ can be represented by a p-cycle on F. Regarded as a relative cycle modulo F this p-cycle is homologous to zero modulo F. And so, by the definition of j, $\bar{\alpha}$ is in the kernel of j; this shows that the image of i is contained in the kernel of j.

Next let $\bar{\alpha}$ in $H_p(E)$ be in the kernel of j. Then if α is a cycle representing $\bar{\alpha}$, the definition of j means that α is relatively homologous to zero modulo F. That is to say, $\alpha = d\beta + \gamma$ where β is a $(p + 1)$-chain on E and γ is a p-chain on F. Taking boundaries, $d\alpha = d\gamma$, and since $d\alpha = 0$ it follows that γ is a cycle of F, and is homologous to α. Thus $\bar{\alpha}$ can be represented by γ, a cycle on F, and so $\bar{\alpha}$ is in the image of i. This shows that the kernel of j is contained in the image of i, and so, combining the two inclusion relations it follows that the image of i and the kernel of j coincide.

(2) Let $\bar{\alpha}$ be an element of $H_p(E, F)$ in the image of j. That is to say, $\bar{\alpha}$ has a representative which is not only a relative cycle modulo F, but is actually a cycle on E. Then since $d\alpha = 0$ the definition of ∂ shows that $\partial\bar{\alpha} = 0$. Hence the image of j is contained in the kernel of ∂.

If $\bar{\alpha}$ is an element of $H_p(E, F)$ in the kernel of ∂, then $\bar{\alpha}$ has a representative α whose boundary is homologous to zero in F (definition of ∂). Thus $d\alpha = d\beta$, for some chain β on F. Hence $d(\alpha - \beta) = 0$ and so $\alpha - \beta$ is a cycle on E. But $\alpha - \beta$ is homologous to α modulo F by the definition of relative homology, and so $\bar{\alpha}$ has a representative, namely $\alpha - \beta$, which is a cycle; that is to say, $\bar{\alpha}$ is in the image of j and so the kernel of ∂ is contained in the image of j. The two inclusion relations just obtained show that the image of j and the kernel of ∂ coincide.

(3) Let $\bar{\alpha}$ be an element of $H_{p-1}(F)$ in the image of ∂. Then by the definition of ∂, $\bar{\alpha}$ can be represented by a cycle α which is the boundary of a relative cycle β of E modulo F. But to say that $\alpha = d\beta$ is the same as to say that α is homologous to zero in E; and this means that $\bar{\alpha}$ is in the kernel of i. Thus the image of ∂ is contained in the kernel of i.

Finally let $\bar{\alpha}$ be an element of $H_{p-1}(F)$ in the kernel of i. Then if α is a $(p-1)$-cycle on F representing $\bar{\alpha}$, α is homologous to zero in E; that is, $\alpha = d\beta$ for some p-chain β on E. But β is then a relative cycle of E modulo F, and the definition of ∂ shows that the class of β is carried by ∂ into $\bar{\alpha}$. Thus the kernel of i is contained in the image of ∂, and the two inclusion relations which have been proved show that the image of ∂ coincides with the kernel of i. All three parts of the theorem are thus completely proved.

DEFINITION 61. A sequence of groups and homomorphisms (like (28)) with the property that the image of each homomorphism is the kernel of the next is called an *exact sequence*.

This definition enables Theorem 47 to be stated briefly: *The homology sequence of a pair of spaces is exact.*

2. Homology groups in some special cases

The theory of the last section will now be illustrated by application to a number of simple cases. It will appear that the use of the exact sequence (28) along with a certain amount of ingenuity suffices to calculate the homology groups of some of the most elementary spaces. It will also become clear, however, that some more systematic method is necessary to deal with spaces which present even the mildest complications. Chapter IX will then be devoted to the task of working out such a method, applicable to a very wide class of spaces.

Examples. (1) Let E be a closed line segment and let F be the subspace consisting of the two end-points A and B. It is already known (cf. Chapter VI, §5, Exercise 2) that $H_p(E)$ is zero for $p \neq 0$ while $H_0(E)$ is infinite cyclic, a generator α being represented by the singular 0-simplex which maps Δ_0 on the point A. Also $H_p(F)$ is zero for $p \neq 0$ and $H_0(F)$ is the free abelian group of two generators a and b, where these are represented by the singular 0-simplexes mapping Δ_0 on A and B respectively (Chapter V, §9, Exercises 6 and 7).

Consider the following portion of the homology sequence of E and F:

$$\to H_p(F) \xrightarrow{i} H_p(E) \xrightarrow{j} H_p(E,F) \xrightarrow{\partial} H_{p-1}(F) \to \qquad (29)$$

for $p > 1$. As noted above, $H_{p-1}(F)$ is zero; thus ∂ maps the whole of $H_p(E, F)$ onto zero, and so $H_p(E, F)$ is itself the kernel of ∂. By Theorem 47, that is by the exactness of (29), it follows that $H_p(E, F)$ is the image of j. That is to say, j is a mapping onto. On the other hand it has been remarked that, for $p \neq 0$, $H_p(E)$ is zero. Now if j maps a zero group onto another group, that second group must also be zero. Hence $H_p(E, F)$ is zero for $p > 1$.

Consider now the following portion of the exact sequence of E and F:

$$\to H_1(F) \xrightarrow{i} H_1(E) \xrightarrow{j} H_1(E, F) \xrightarrow{\partial} H_0(F) \xrightarrow{i'} H_0(E) \xrightarrow{j'} H_0(E, F).$$

Here primes have been attached to i and j on their second appearances to avoid confusion. $H_0(E, F)$ is known to be zero (Chapter V, §9, Exercise 9) and so $H_0(E)$ is the kernel of j'. It follows from exactness that i' is a mapping onto. Also $H_1(E)$ is zero, as was remarked above, and so the image of j, that is, the kernel of ∂ is zero. ∂ is thus an isomorphism into. That is to say, $H_1(E, F)$ is mapped isomorphically on some subgroup G of $H_0(F)$. Then, since the image of ∂ is the kernel of i', and i' has been shown to be onto, it follows that $H_0(E)$ is isomorphic to $H_0(F)/G$. Now G is a sub-group of a free abelian group with two generators, and so is either zero, an infinite cyclic group or a free group with two generators. G cannot be zero, or $H_0(E)$ would be isomorphic to $H_0(F)$, and it cannot have two independent generators, or the quotient group $H_0(E)$ would be finite. Thus G, and so $H_1(E, F)$ which is isomorphic to it, is an infinite cyclic group.

The exact sequence of E and F has thus been applied to determine the groups $H_p(E, F)$ for all p from the previous knowledge of the homology groups of E and F. The result on $H_1(E, F)$ may be made a bit more explicit. For, a, b, α being as defined at the beginning of this example, it is easy to see that $i'a = i'b = \alpha$, and so, if $ma + nb$ is any element of $H_0(F)$, $i'(ma + nb) = (m + n)\alpha$; hence $ma + nb$ is in G if and only if $m = -n$, and so G is generated by $a - b$. It follows then that $H_1(E, F)$, which is isomorphic to G under ∂, is generated by an element β such that $\partial\beta = a - b$. Thus β can be represented by any relative cycle whose boundary is the difference of the singular simplexes mapping Δ_0 into the end points A and B of E. A suitable relative cycle is that formed by the singular 1-simplex which maps Δ_1 linearly onto the segment E.

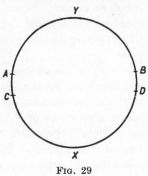

FIG. 29

(2) Let E be the circumference of a circle, made up of two overlapping closed segments (cf. Fig. 29) AXB and CYD, and let F be the segment AXB. Also let E' be the segment CYD and F' the union of the two segments AC and BD.

In the first place, the excision theorem (Theorem 46) shows that $H_p(E, F)$ is isomorphic to $H_p(E', F')$ for all p. Next, there is a homotopy of the identity mapping of the pair (E', F') on itself into a mapping of (E', F') into itself which carries the arc AC into the point C and the arc BD into the point D (cf. Chapter VI, §5, Exercise 7). It follows, (Chapter VI, §5, Exercise 5) that the homology groups of E' modulo F' are isomorphic to those of a line segment modulo its end points, which are known by Example (1) above. Thus $H_p(E', F')$ is zero for all $p \neq 1$, while for $p = 1$ it is infinite cyclic, and the same holds for $H_p(E, F)$.

Consider now the exact sequence:

$$\longrightarrow H_p(F) \xrightarrow{\ i\ } H_p(E) \xrightarrow{\ j\ } H_p(E, F) \xrightarrow{\ \partial\ } H_{p-1}(F) \longrightarrow$$

for $p > 1$. $H_p(F) = 0$ and so the image of i is zero; hence by exactness j is an isomorphism. But $H_p(E, F) = 0$ and so $H_p(E) = 0$ for $p > 1$.

In the exact sequence just considered take $p = 1$:

$$\longrightarrow H_1(F) \xrightarrow{\ i\ } H_1(E) \xrightarrow{\ j\ } H_1(E, F) \xrightarrow{\ \partial\ } H_0(F) \xrightarrow{\ i'\ } H_0(E)$$

$H_1(F) = 0$ and so i has zero image; hence j is an isomorphism (onto or into). The homomorphism i' is an isomorphism onto (Chapter VI, §1, Exercise). It follows that ∂ has zero image; that is to say the kernel of ∂ is the whole group $H_1(E, F)$ and so j is a mapping onto. Hence $H_1(E)$ is isomorphic to $H_1(E, F)$, and so by what has been shown already, is infinite cyclic.

Finally $H_0(E)$ is infinite cyclic by Chapter V, §9, Exercise 8.

Thus, summing up, $H_p(E)$ is zero for all p except $p = 0$ or 1 when the group is infinite cyclic.

To identify a 1-cycle on the circumference E representing a generator of $H_1(E)$, note first that the isomorphism of $H_1(E)$ and $H_1(E, F)$ is induced by the projection homomorphism j; and so a cycle γ on E will represent a generator of $H_1(E)$ if and only if its relative homology class modulo F generates $H_1(E, F)$. Let two singular simplexes σ_1, σ_2 on E be defined as follows. σ_1 is to be a homeomorphism of the standard 1-simplex Δ_1 on the arc CYD, say the mapping which carries each point p of Δ_1 into the point dividing CYD in the same ratio as p divides Δ_1. σ_2 is to be a similar map on the arc DXC. It is clear that $\sigma_1 + \sigma_2$ is a 1-cycle on E. Also the relative homology class of $\sigma_1 + \sigma_2$ in E modulo F can equally well be represented by σ_1, which is itself a relative cycle. Thus under the excision isomorphism between $H_1(E, F)$ and $H_1(E', F')$ the relative homology class of $\sigma_1 + \sigma_2$ in E modulo F corresponds to that of σ_1 in E' modulo F'. But by Example (1) above, σ_1 represents a generator of the 1-dimensional homology group of the arc CYD modulo its end points, and so also represents a generator of $H_1(E', F')$ (by Chapter VI, §5, Exercise 5). It follows at once that $\sigma_1 + \sigma_2$ represents a generator of $H_1(E, F)$, and so, by the remark at the beginning of this paragraph, $\sigma_1 + \sigma_2$ is a cycle whose homology class generates $H_1(E)$.

(3) As a final example, let E be a circular disc and F its circumference, and consider the exact sequence:

$$\longrightarrow H_p(F) \xrightarrow{\ i\ } H_p(E) \xrightarrow{\ j\ } H_p(E, F)$$
$$\xrightarrow{\ \partial\ } H_{p-1}(F) \xrightarrow{\ i'\ } H_{p-1}(E) \longrightarrow$$

If $p > 2$, $H_p(E) = 0$ (Chapter VI, §5, Exercise 2), and $H_{p-1}(F) = 0$ (Example (2) above), and so the exactness of the above sequence implies that $H_p(E, F) = 0$.

Suppose now that $p = 2$. $H_1(E) = 0$ and so i' maps $H_1(F)$ onto zero. That is to say, the kernel of i' is the whole group $H_1(F)$. Hence ∂ is a mapping onto. On the other hand $H_2(E) = 0$, and so j has zero image; that is, ∂ has zero kernel, and so ∂ is an isomorphism. It has already been shown to be a mapping onto, and so $H_2(E, F)$ is isomorphic to $H_1(F)$, and so, by Example (2) is infinite cyclic.

To identify a generator of $H_2(E, \check{F})$, note that the isomorphism of this group to $H_1(F)$ is induced by the boundary homomorphism ∂. Thus a generator of $H_2(E, F)$ is represented by any 2-chain on E whose boundary is a 1-cycle on F representing a generator of $H_1(F)$. To find such a representative explicitly, mark points C, X, D, Y on the circumference of E, as in Example (2). Construct a mapping of the standard 2-simplex Δ_2 onto E which maps the sides $x_0 x_1$ and $x_1 x_2$ on the arcs CYD and DXC respectively (the x_i being the vertices of Δ_2). This mapping is a singular simplex σ on E whose boundary is $\sigma_1 + \sigma_2 - \tau$, where σ_1 and σ_2 are as in Example (2) and τ is the singular 1-simplex which maps the side $x_0 x_2$ onto the point C. But τ is the boundary of the singular 2-simplex mapping Δ_2 on C, and so the boundary of σ is homologous in F to $\sigma_1 + \sigma_2$, known by Example (2) to represent a generator of $H_1(F)$. It follows from the remark at the beginning of this paragraph that σ represents a generator of $H_2(E, F)$.

To complete this example, take $p = 1$ in the homology sequence of the pair (E, F) as quoted above. If α is a relative 1-cycle of E modulo F then $d\alpha$ is homologous to zero on F (cf. Chapter V, §9, Exercise 8). Hence ∂ maps $H_1(E, F)$ onto zero. In other words $H_1(E, F)$ is the kernel of ∂ and so is the image of j. But $H_1(E) = 0$, and so $H_1(E, F) = 0$ too. Finally, $H_0(E, F)$ is zero (Chapter V, §9, Exercise 9).

Summing up the results of this example, $H_p(E, F)$ is zero for all p except $p = 2$, when the group is infinite cyclic.

Exercises

1. Let E be a topological space and F a subspace consisting of just one point. Prove that $H_r(E) \cong H_r(E, F)$ for $r \geqslant 1$.

2. Let E be a topological space consisting of two circumferences of circles having one point in common. Prove that $H_0(E)$ is infinite

cyclic, $H_1(E)$ is free abelian with two generators and $H_r(E)$ is zero for $r \geqslant 2$.

[Hint: Let F denote the subspace of E consisting of the common point p, and let F' be the union of two closed arcs, one on each circle, each having p as mid-point. Show that $H_r(E, F) \cong H_r(E, F')$ and use excision and homotopy as in Example (2) above.]

3. Generalize the result of Exercise 2 to a space E consisting of the union of any number of circles having one point in common, showing that $H_1(E)$ is free abelian with as many generators as there are circles making up E.

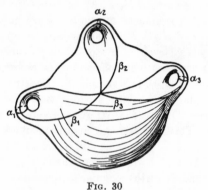

FIG. 30

4. Let E be the surface of a torus. Prove that $H_r(E)$ is zero for $r \geqslant 3$, $H_2(E)$ and $H_0(E)$ are infinite cyclic, and $H_1(E)$ is free abelian with two generators.

[Hint: Start by using Exercise 3, §5, Chapter VII; F is the union of two circles as in Exercise 2 above and so $H_r(F)$ is known for all r. The crucial point in the application of the homology sequence of the pair (E, F) is to show that $H_2(E, F)$ has a generator which can be represented by a cycle on E, thus showing that the projection homomorphism $H_2(E) \to H_2(E, F)$ is onto; to do this use Exercise 4, §9, Chapter V.]

5. Let E be the surface of a sphere with p handles attached (illustrated for $p = 3$ in Fig. 30) and let F be the subspace consisting of a circle around each handle (the α_i of Fig. 30) and a curve running along each handle (the β_i), all beginning and ending at the same point of E. Prove that $H_1(F)$ is free abelian with $2p$ generators. Then show that $H_r(E)$ is zero for $r \geqslant 3$, $H_2(E)$ and $H_0(E)$ are infinite cyclic and $H_1(E)$ is free abelian with $2p$ generators (isomorphic to $H_1(F)$ under injection).

[Hint: Note that if E is cut along F it can be flattened out into a circular disc and show that $H_r(E, F)$ is isomorphic to the rth homology group of a disc modulo its circumference. Then use the homology sequence of the pair (E, F). The essential point is to show that the kernel of the injection $H_1(F) \to H_1(E)$ is zero. To do this note that E can be mapped continuously on the surface of a torus E' by squeezing each handle to a point except one, and that a relation between the injection images of the generators of $H_1(F)$ would lead to a relation between the generators of $H_1(E')$.]

6. The real projective plane E is the set of all triples of real numbers (x, y, z), excluding the triple $(0, 0, 0)$, where the two triples (x, y, z) and (x', y', z') are regarded as the same if and only if there is a real number $c \neq 0$ such that $x' = cx$, $y' = cy$, $z' = cz$. The triples may be normalized by the condition $x^2 + y^2 + z^2 = 1$, and then it becomes clear that E is obtained from the unit sphere S in Euclidean 3-space by regarding each pair of diametrically opposite points of S as a single point of E. That is to say there is a mapping f of S onto E carrying each diametrically opposite pair of points of S onto a point of E; in fact f maps (x, y, z) and $(-x, -y, -z)$ on S into the point (x, y, z) of E. E is made into a topological space by requiring that, on a sufficiently small neighbourhood of each point of S, f should act as a homeomorphism. It should be noted also that the mapping f carries the great circles of S into the lines of E (that is, into the sets defined by linear equations in x, y, z.)

Let σ be the singular simplex on S which maps Δ_1 onto a semicircle C of a great circle such that the arc length of $\sigma(p)$ from one end of C is proportional to the distance of p from one end of Δ_1. Prove that $f_1(\sigma)$ is a cycle α of E (f_1 being the homomorphism on chain groups induced by the mapping f described above) and that 2α is homologous to zero. Also if $F = f(C)$ prove that F is homeomorphic to the circumference of a circle and that α represents a generator of $H_1(F)$. Finally note that if E is cut along F one obtains a circular disc E' with diametrically opposite points on the circumference F' identified, and prove that $H_r(E, F) \cong H_r(E', F')$. Hence show that $H_r(E)$ is zero for $r \geqslant 2$, $H_0(E)$ is infinite cyclic and $H_1(E)$ is cyclic of order two.

7. Let E be a surface obtained by cutting k circular holes in the surface of a sphere, and on the circumference of each hole identifying diametrically opposite points. Proceeding as in Exercise 5, and noting that Exercise 6 gives the case $k = 1$, prove that $H_0(E)$ is infinite cyclic, $H_1(E)$ has k generators $\alpha_1, \alpha_2, \ldots, \alpha_k$ of which $k - 1$ are not subject to any relation while $2\alpha_k = 0$, and $H_r(E)$ is zero for $r \geqslant 2$.

NOTE: If E is a topological space such that every point has a neighbourhood homeomorphic to an r-dimensional solid sphere, E is called an r-dimensional manifold. In particular it can be shown that every compact 2-dimensional manifold is homeomorphic to a sphere or to a surface of one of the types described in Exercises 5 and 7. One can distinguish the surfaces of Exercise 5 from those of Exercise 7 by the fact that $H_1(E)$ is a free abelian group for the former but involves a relation for the latter. And the number of generators of $H_1(E)$ tells which member of the set of surfaces of Exercise 5 or 7, as the case may be, is under consideration. The sphere (as will be shown in the next section) is characterized among the 2-dimensional compact manifolds by the condition $H_1(E) = 0$. Thus compact 2-dimensional manifolds are completely classified by the knowledge of their homology groups. It should be emphasized that no such complete classification exists for higher dimensional manifolds, and still less for more complicated spaces.

8. Let E be an arcwise connected space. Δ_1 is the part of the line $s + t = 1$ in the (s, t)-plane for which $s \geqslant 0, t \geqslant 0$. Let $f : I \to E$ be a closed path on E based on a point x and define the singular 1-simplex $\sigma : \Delta_1 \to E$ by setting $\sigma(s, t) = f(s)$ for $(s, t) \in \Delta_1$. Prove that σ is a cycle on E, and write it as $h(f)$ to show its dependence on the path f.

Prove that if f and g are paths based on x and are homotopic with respect to the base-point x then $h(f)$ and $h(g)$ are homologous cycles. Hence show that h induces a mapping $\bar{h} : \pi(E) \to H_1(E)$ defined by setting $\bar{h}(\alpha)$ for $\alpha \in \pi(E)$ equal to the homology class of $h(f)$, where f is a path representing the homotopy class α and $\pi(E)$ is the fundamental group of E. Prove that $\bar{h}$ is a homomorphism of $\pi(E)$ onto $H_1(E)$.

[Hint: If f and g are homotopic show that there is a continuous mapping $\lambda : \Delta_2 \to E$ (that is a singular 2-simplex) such that λ agrees with f and g along two sides of Δ_2 and carries the third side into x. Hence show that $d\lambda = h(f) - h(g) + \tau$, where τ is the singular simplex mapping Δ_1 onto x; finally show that τ is a boundary.

To show that h is a homomorphism, let f and g be two paths based on x. Construct a mapping $\lambda : \Delta_2 \to E$ agreeing with f, g and fg (Definition 28) on the sides (with suitable identifications of these sides with I). Then check that $d\lambda = h(f) + h(g) - h(fg)$.

Finally to show that h is onto, show first that any 1-cycle α on E is homologous to a 1-cycle α' each of whose singular simplexes is a mapping of Δ_1 into E carrying the endpoints into x (this is done essentially by pulling back the endpoints of the singular simplexes along paths ending at x). The singular simplexes of α' are then themselves cycles and are in the image of h.]

9. Combine Exercise 8 with Exercises 2 and 3 of §4, Chapter IV, and Example (2), §2, Chapter VIII, and Exercise 4 above to show that the fundamental group of the circumference of a circle is infinite cyclic and that of a torus is free abelian with two generators.

10. Complete the result of Exercise 8 by showing that the kernel of the homomorphism h is the commutator subgroup of $\pi(E)$, that is to say the subgroup generated by elements of the form $\alpha\beta\alpha^{-1}\beta^{-1}$.

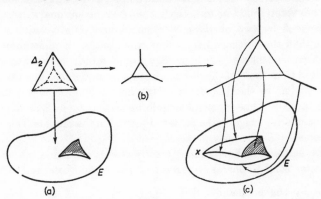

FIG. 31

[Hint: Since $H_1(E)$ is an abelian group it is obvious that the commutator subgroup of $\pi(E)$ is contained in the kernel of $\bar{h}$. Conversely, let f be a closed path based on x representing an element of the kernel of $\bar{h}$. Then $h(f)$ is a cycle on E homologous to zero, and so there is a 2-chain $\sum_{i=1}^{m} c_i\sigma_i$ such that $h(f) = d \sum_{i=1}^{m} c_i\sigma_i$. The first thing to do is to show that the σ_i can be replaced by singular simplexes which map the vertices of Δ_2 into x. The procedure is illustrated by Fig. 31. (a) shows a singular simplex σ on E. A new singular simplex σ' is to be defined by mapping Δ_2 onto the figure (b) (which is also shown by dotted lines in (a); the mapping consists simply in pushing in the sides of Δ_2) then increasing the scale so that the triangle in (b) becomes the same size as Δ_2, and finally mapping the triangle in (c) into E by the mapping σ and the three tails into paths ending at x. It has to be checked that, when each σ_i is replaced by a singular simplex σ_i' in this way, the resulting chain $\sum_{i=1}^{m} c_i\sigma_i'$ has $h(f')$ as its boundary, where $f' \sim f$. Now for each i, $d\sigma_i'$ is of the form $\tau_{i1} + \tau_{i2} + \tau_{i3}$, where each τ_{ij} is certainly in the image of h (check this in detail!) and so $d\sigma_i'$ can be written as $h(f_{i1}f_{i2}f_{i3})$. Prove that $f_{i1}f_{i2}f_{i3}$ is homotopic to a constant mapping, and so that

f' $(f_{11}^{c_1} f_{12}^{c_1} f_{13}^{c_1} f_{21}^{c_2} \ldots f_{m3}^{c_m})$ is homotopic to f', w.r.t. the base point x. But since the chains $h(f')$ and $h(f_{11}^{c_1} f_{12}^{c_1} f_{13}^{c_1} \ldots f_{m3}^{c_m})$ are equal, it follows that f' and the f_{ij} must repeat each other in such a way that each appears as often with the exponent $+1$ as with -1. It then follows easily that $f'(f_{11}^{c_1} f_{12}^{c_1} f_{13}^{c_1} f_{21}^{c_2} \ldots f_{m3}^{c_m}) \sim f$ is in the commutator subgroup of $\pi(E)$.]

3. Homology groups of cells and spheres

The most important feature of the examples in §2 is that they form the starting point of an induction for determining the homology groups associated with spheres and solid spheres of all dimensions. The next step would be to note that the two-dimensional sphere can be covered by two overlapping circular discs, one covering a bit more than the northern hemisphere, the other a bit more than the southern hemisphere. The homology groups of the sphere can then be deduced from those of the disc modulo its circumference in a manner very similar to the derivation of the homology groups of a circle from those of a line segment modulo its end points in Example (2). This similarity suggests the pattern followed in the proof of Theorem 48 below.

The notation and terminology to be used is as follows. A closed r-cell (or solid r-sphere) is the set of points in Euclidean r-space given by the inequality $\sum\limits_{i=1}^{r} x_i^2 \leqslant 1$, $(x_1, x_2, \ldots, x_r)$ being the co-ordinates of a variable point of the space. The term r-cell will also be applied to sets homeomorphic to the one just defined. A closed r-cell will be denoted by E^r, suffixes being attached if more than one cell is to be considered at a time.

An open r-cell is the interior of a closed r-cell.

An r-sphere or r-dimensional sphere is the frontier of a closed $(r + 1)$-cell. That is, an r-sphere is the set $\sum\limits_{i=1}^{r+1} x_i^2 = 1$ in Euclidean $(r + 1)$-space, or a set homeomorphic to this. An r-sphere is denoted by S^r.

It should be noted in particular that E^0 is a single point while S^0 is a pair of distinct points.

THEOREM 48. (a) $H_p(S^r) = 0$ for $p \neq 0$ or r; $H_r(S^r)$ and $H_0(S^r)$ are infinite cyclic except for $r = 0$, and $H_0(S^0)$ is a free abelian group with two generators.

(b) $H_p(E^r, S^{r-1}) = 0$ for $p \neq r$ $(r \geqslant 1)$; $H_r(E^r, S^{r-1})$ is infinite cyclic.

PROOF. Note first that (a) is trivial for $r = 0$ (cf. Chapter V, §9,

Exercises 6 and 7) and has been proved for $r = 1$ in Example (2) of §2. Also (b) has been proved for $r = 1, 2$ in Examples (1) and (3) respectively. The proofs of (a) and (b) in general will be carried out in a number of steps which imitate closely the procedure followed in the three examples already given.

The first step is to consider, corresponding to the procedure of Examples (1) and (3) of §2, the exact sequence:

$$\longrightarrow H_p(S^{r-1}) \xrightarrow{i} H_p(E^r) \xrightarrow{j} H_p(E^r, S^{r-1})$$
$$\xrightarrow{\partial} H_{p-1}(S^{r-1}) \xrightarrow{i'} H_{p-1}(E^r)$$

where $r \geqslant 2$ and $p \geqslant 2$. $H_p(E^r)$ is zero (Chapter VI, §5, Exercise 2) and so the image of j is zero; then by exactness the kernel of ∂ is zero, and so ∂ is an isomorphism. On the other hand $H_{p-1}(E^r) = 0$ for $p, r \geqslant 2$ (Chapter VI, §5, Exercise 2), and so i' maps $H_{p-1}(S^{r-1})$ onto zero. That is to say the kernel of i', which is also the image of ∂, is the whole group $H_{p-1}(S^{r-1})$. Hence ∂ is a mapping onto. It has thus been shown that

$$H_p(E^r, S^{r-1}) \cong H_{p-1}(S^{r-1}), \; (r \geqslant 2, p \geqslant 2). \tag{29}$$

To deal with the case $p = 1$ consider the sequence:

$$\longrightarrow H_1(S^{r-1}) \xrightarrow{i} H_1(E^r) \xrightarrow{j} H_1(E^r, S^{r-1})$$
$$\xrightarrow{\partial} H_0(S^{r-1}) \xrightarrow{i'} H_0(E^r) \xrightarrow{j'} H_0(E^r, S^{r-1}),$$

for $r \geqslant 2$. $H_0(S^{r-1})$ and $H_0(E^r)$ are both infinite cyclic groups and the mapping i' is an isomorphism onto (Chapter VI, §1, Exercise). Thus the kernel of i' is zero, and so ∂ maps $H_1(E^r, S^{r-1})$ onto zero. That is to say, ∂ has the whole group $H_1(E^r, S^{r-1})$ as its kernel, and so j is a mapping onto. But since $H_1(E^r) = 0$ (Chapter VI, §5, Exercise 2) the image of j must be zero. Hence

$$H_1(E^r, S^{r-1}) = 0, \quad r \geqslant 2 \tag{30}$$

The next step is to imitate the procedure of Example (2) of §2, the idea being to cover the r-sphere with two overlapping r-cells, corresponding to the two arcs AXB and CYD in Fig. 29. S^r being the set of points in Euclidean $(r + 1)$-space such that $\sum_{i=1}^{r+1} x_i^2 = 1$ for any $r \geqslant 1$, define E_1^r to be the set of points of S^r such that $x_{r+1} \geqslant -\varepsilon$, and E_2^r to be the set of points on S^r such that $x_{r+1} \leqslant \varepsilon$, where ε is any positive number less than 1. It is not hard to see that E_1^r and E_2^r are both closed r-cells; the easiest way to prove this is to carry out stereographic projections into some hyperplane $x_{r+1} = $ constant. Let $E_1^r \cap E_2^r$ be denoted by F.

It follows from the Excision Theorem (Theorem 46) that

$$H_p(S^r, E_2^r) \cong H_p(E_1^r, F) \tag{31}$$

for all p, (and $r \geqslant 1$), the set excised being the set of points on S^r such that $x_{r+1} < -\varepsilon$.

The next operation consists essentially of stretching the set $x_{r+1} \geqslant \varepsilon$ on S^r so that it covers E_1^r while F is compressed into the set $x_{r+1} = -\varepsilon$. This is done by constructing a mapping f of the pair (E_1^r, F) into itself which is homotopic to the identity mapping and is such that $f(F)$ is the set $x_{r+1} = -\varepsilon$ on S^r. The explicit construction of such a mapping has already been seen in Exercise 7, §5, of Chapter VI. Then, by Exercise 5 of Chapter VI, §5,

$$H_p(E_1^r, F) \cong H_p(E_1^r, S_1^{r-1}) \tag{32}$$

for all p, where S_1^{r-1} is the set $x_{r+1} = -\varepsilon$ on S^r. But as has already been noted E_1^r is homeomorphic to E^r, and at the same time S_1^{r-1} is its boundary and so homeomorphic to S^{r-1}. Thus (32) becomes:

$$H_p(E_1^r, F) \cong H_p(E^r, S^{r-1}) \quad \text{for all } p.$$

Combine this with (31), obtaining the result:

$$H_p(S^r, E_2^r) \cong H_p(E^r, S^{r-1}) \tag{33}$$

for all p. Note that this is also subject to the condition $r \geqslant 1$.

The group $H_p(S^r, E_2^r)$ will now be examined with the aid of the following exact sequence:

$$\longrightarrow H_p(E_2^r) \overset{i}{\longrightarrow} H_p(S^r) \overset{j}{\longrightarrow} H_p(S^r, E_2^r)$$
$$\overset{\partial}{\longrightarrow} H_{p-1}(E_2^r) \overset{i'}{\longrightarrow} H_{p-1}(S^r) \longrightarrow$$

with r assumed greater than or equal to 1.

E_2^r is a closed r-cell, and so by Chapter VI, §5, Exercise 2, $H_p(E_2^r)$ and $H_{p-1}(E_2^r)$ are both zero for $p \geqslant 2$. Hence the kernel of ∂ is the whole group $H_p(S^r, E_2^r)$ and so j is a mapping onto. And i has zero image, and so j is an isomorphism. Thus j is an isomorphism onto for $p \geqslant 2$. On the other hand, if $p = 1$, i' is an isomorphism onto (cf. Chapter VI, §1, Exercise) and so in particular i' has zero kernel. It follows that the image of ∂ is zero. Also $H_1(E_2^r)$ is zero, and so the argument just used still shows that, for $p = 1$, j is an isomorphism onto. Thus:

$$H_p(S^r, E_2^r) \cong H_p(S^r) \tag{34}$$

for all $p \geqslant 1$, and $r \geqslant 1$, the isomorphism being induced by the projection mapping j. Along with (33) this implies that

$$H_p(S^r) \cong H_p(E^r, S^{r-1}) \tag{35}$$

for all $p \geqslant 1$, $r \geqslant 1$.

The final step in the proof of this theorem is to obtain the results stated under (a) and (b) by combining the isomorphisms (29) and (35) for various values of p and r. (35) with p and r replaced by $p - 1$ and $r - 1$ respectively can be combined with (29) to give

$$H_p(E^r, S^{r-1}) \cong H_{p-1}(E^{r-1}, S^{r-2}) \tag{36}$$

for all $p \geqslant 2$, $r \geqslant 2$. The isomorphism (36) can now be applied repeatedly with p, r replaced in turn by $p - 1$, $r - 1$, then $p - 2$, $r - 2$, and so on. If $p > r$ this step by step process leads to the result:

$$H_p(E^r, S^{r-1}) \cong H_{p-r+1}(E^1, S^0)$$

and this last group is zero since $p - r + 1 \geqslant 2$ (by Example (1), §2). Thus $H_p(E^r, S^{r-1})$ is zero for $p > r$. On the other hand if $p < r$ the repeated application of (36) leads to the result:

$$H_p(E^r, S^{r-1}) \cong H_1(E^{r-p+1}, S^{r-p})$$

and this is zero by (30); and so $H_p(E^r, S^{r-1})$ is zero for $p < r$. Finally if $p = r$, the repeated application of (36) leads to:

$$H_r(E^r, S^{r-1}) \cong H_1(E^1, S^0)$$

which is infinite cyclic by Example (1) of §2. It has thus been shown that $H_p(E^r, S^{r-1})$ is zero for $p \neq r$ and $H_r(E^r, S^{r-1})$ is infinite cyclic, under the restriction $p \geqslant 2$, $r \geqslant 2$ (the result having been deduced from (36) which is restricted in this way). As has been pointed out, this result also holds for $r = 1$, p being unrestricted, by Example 1 of §2. And if $r \geqslant 2$ and $p = 0$ or 1, $H_p(E^r, S^{r-1})$ is zero, (by Chapter V, §9, Exercise 9 if $p = 0$, and by (30) if $p = 1$). Thus part (b) of the present theorem is completely proved.

Part (b) combined with (35) shows that, under the restriction $p \geqslant 1$, $r \geqslant 1$ (which arises from the restriction imposed on (35)) $H_p(S^r)$ is zero for $p \neq r$, while $H_r(S^r)$ is infinite cyclic. For $r \geqslant 1$, S^r is arcwise connected and so $H_0(S^r)$ is infinite cyclic (Chapter V, §9, Exercise 8). For $r = 0$, S^r is a pair of points, and so $H_p(S^0)$ is zero for $p \geqslant 1$, while $H_0(S^0)$ is a group with two independent generators

(Chapter V, §9, Exercises 6 and 7). This completes the proof of Part (a) and so the theorem is established.

NOTE (1). Some further information on the homology groups associated with spheres and cells may be obtained by examining the proof of the above theorem more closely. The isomorphism (29) is induced by the boundary homomorphism ∂, and so if a cycle α on S^{r-1} is known to represent a generator of the cyclic group $H_{r-1}(S^{r-1})$ for $r > 1$, it will follow that a generator of $H_r(E^r, S^{r-1})$ is represented by any chain β on E^r such that $\alpha = d\beta$. Conversely, if β is known to represent a generator of $H_r(E^r, S^{r-1})$ then $d\beta$ represents a generator of $H_{r-1}(S^{r-1})$.

NOTE (2). A connection has thus been established between generators of $H_{r-1}(S^{r-1})$ and $H_r(E^r, S^{r-1})$, or rather their representatives. A similar, but rather more complicated analysis of the isomorphism between $H_r(S^r)$ and $H_r(E^r, S^{r-1})$ will now be worked out. In the first place $H_r(S^r)$ is mapped on $H_r(S^r, E_2^r)$ by the projection homomorphism j. Suppose that an r-cycle γ can be found on S^r such that $\gamma = \gamma_1 + \gamma_2$ where all the singular simplexes making up the chain γ_1 are on the set of points of S^r for which $x_{r+1} \geqslant -\varepsilon$, while all those making up γ_2 are on the set $x_{r+1} \leqslant -\varepsilon$; then $d\gamma_1 = -d\gamma_2$ is an $(r-1)$-cycle on S_1^{r-1}, the set on S^r for which $x_{r+1} = -\varepsilon$. Then if $\bar{\gamma}$ is the homology class of γ on S^r, an element of $H_r(S^r)$, γ_1 can be taken as a representative of the element $j\bar{\gamma}$ of $H_r(S^r, E_2^r)$, and also as a representative of the image of $j\bar{\gamma}$ in $H_r(E_1^r, F)$ under the isomorphism (31) induced by excision. Now if f is the mapping already used above, of E_1^r onto E_1^r homotopic to the identity and such that $f(F) = S_1^{r-1}$, $f_1(\gamma_1)$ represents the image of $j\bar{\gamma}$ under the isomorphism (33), but also $f_1(\gamma_1)$ is relatively homologous to γ_1 in E_1^r modulo S_1^{r-1} by Theorem 34. Thus γ_1 represents the image of $\bar{\gamma}$ under the combined isomorphism (35).

It follows at once from this analysis that γ represents a generator of $H_r(S^r)$ if and only if γ_1 represents a generator of $H_r(E_1^r, S_1^{r-1})$, the latter group being, of course, isomorphic to $H_r(E^r, S^{r-1})$.

The remarks on the generators of the groups $H_r(S^r)$ and $H_r(E^r, S^{r-1})$ made in the last two paragraphs will be of essential importance in the proof of Theorem 50 in the next Chapter.

Exercises

1. Prove that there is no extension of the identity mapping of S^{r-1} onto itself to a mapping of E^r onto S^{r-1}.

[Hint: If there were, the identity mapping of S^{r-1} onto itself would be homotopic to a constant mapping, and Theorem 34 would give $H_{r-1}(S^{r-1}) = 0$, which is a contradiction.]

2 Let f be a continuous mapping of E^r into itself. Prove that f has at least one fixed point; that is, prove that there is at least one point $x \in E^r$ such that $f(x) = x$.

[Hint: Suppose there is no fixed point for f; join $f(x)$ to x for each x by a straight line segment and extend this line till it meets S^{r-1} in a point $g(x)$. Prove that g is continuous and is an extension of the identity mapping of S^{r-1} onto itself and use Exercise 1.]

CHAPTER IX

SIMPLICIAL COMPLEXES

1. Definition of complexes

This chapter will be devoted to the study of a certain class of spaces for which a systematic algebraic procedure can be worked out for calculating the homology groups. The class of spaces is described in the following definition:

DEFINITION 62. A *simplicial complex* is a subset of a Euclidean space consisting of the point-set union of a finite number of Euclidean simplexes (not necessarily all of the same dimension) with the property that the intersection of any two of these simplexes is either empty or is a face of each of them. Here the word "face" is to be understood in the general sense, not necessarily meaning a face of maximum dimension.

Examples. (1) A Euclidean simplex is obviously itself a simplicial complex.

(2) Let K denote the union of the faces of a tetrahedron. K is thus the union of four triangles any two of which intersect along a side (that is a face) of each of them. And so K is a simplicial complex. More generally the union of the $(r - 1)$-dimensional faces of a Euclidean r-simplex is a simplicial complex.

(3) Let K denote the union of the six faces of a cube, and on each face draw one of the diagonals. K is thus the union of twelve triangles. It is clear that if any two of these triangles are picked they will either be disjoint or will have a vertex or a side in common. Both vertices and sides of a triangle are faces in the general sense, and so the conditions of the above definition are satisfied, and K is a simplicial complex.

(4) In the above three examples the complex is in each case a union of simplexes all of the same dimension. The accompanying figure shows complexes which are not restricted in this way (Fig. 32).

In discussing simplicial complexes the following definitions are useful:

DEFINITION 63. If the greatest dimension of the simplexes making up a simplicial complex is n the complex is said to be *of dimension n*.

DEFINITION 64. Let K be a simplicial complex. Then *a q-simplex of K*, or *a q-dimensional simplex of K* will mean any one of the simplexes making up K which is of dimension q or any q-dimensional face of one of the higher dimensional simplexes making up K. Collectively *the simplexes of K* will mean the complete list of all the simplexes whose union is K along with all their faces of all dimensions.

DEFINITION 65. Let K be a simplicial complex. The union of all the p-simplexes of K for $p \leqslant q$ will be called *the q-skeleton of K*, and

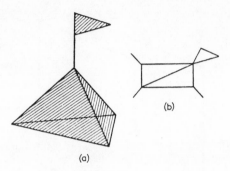

(b)

(a)

FIG. 32

will be denoted by K_q. Obviously $K_q \subset K_{q+1}$ for each q. Also it should be noted that, if K is a complex of dimension n, K_n will coincide with K.

For example, if K is the complex of Example (3) above, the 1-skeleton consists of the edges of the cube along with the diagonals which have been drawn to the faces.

The special importance of simplicial complexes from the point of view of topology arises from the fact that many of the more important topological spaces, that is those which arise frequently both in topology itself and in applications of topology to other branches of mathematics, can be proved to be homeomorphic to simplicial complexes.

DEFINITION 66. A topological space will be said to be *triangulable* if it is homeomorphic to a simplicial complex.

It was remarked in anticipation at the beginning of this chapter that for simplicial complexes the finding of the homology groups could be reduced to a systematic algebraic procedure. And so, because of the topological invariance of the homology groups, the same will be true of the wider class of all triangulable spaces.

12

Examples. (5) The surface of a sphere is a triangulable space, because it is homeomorphic to the union of the faces of a tetrahedron, which is a simplicial complex. A convenient way to set up the homeomorphism is to take the centroid of the tetrahedron as the centre of the sphere and to project the one surface onto the other from this point. It will be noticed that the images of the individual faces of the tetrahedron are curvilinear triangles on the sphere. That is to say, the setting up of this homeomorphism has the effect of

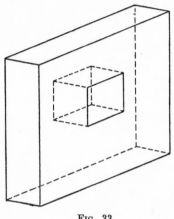

Fig. 33

subdividing the surface of the sphere into a number of curvilinear triangles. A similar remark can be made in other elementary cases, and gives an intuitive justification to the term "triangulable".

It should be noted that when a space is triangulable the homeomorphism set up between it and some simplicial complex is by no means uniquely determined. For example the surface of a sphere is also homeomorphic to the complex obtained by adding a diagonal to each face of a cube.

(6) The surface of a torus is a triangulable space. For the torus is clearly homeomorphic to the square collar illustrated in Fig. 33, and the surface of this collar can be divided into triangles to make it a simplicial complex.

(7) It should be noted on the other hand that there are plenty of spaces, even quite elementary ones, which are not triangulable. For example, a non-compact space cannot be triangulable in the present sense, since simplicial complexes, being finite unions of

simplexes which are compact, are certainly compact. This particular difficulty can be avoided by extending the notion of simplicial complex to admit infinite unions of simplexes, an extension which will not, however, be considered here. But even among compact spaces it is not hard to find examples which are not triangulable. For example let E be the set in the (x, y)-plane consisting of the union of the circumferences of circles of radii $1, \frac{1}{2}, \frac{1}{3} \ldots$ all touching the y-axis at $(0,0)$. This is a closed and bounded set in the plane, and so, in the induced topology, E is a compact space. E is not, however, triangulable. For, as was seen in Exercise 3, §2, Chapter VIII, $H_1(E)$ has an infinite number of independent generators, whereas it will be shown in Theorem 54 that the homology groups of a triangulable space are always finitely generated.

2. The direct sum theorem for complexes

The object of this section is to prove a theorem which will give all the groups $H_q(K_r, K_{r-1})$ where K is a simplicial complex. Consider first an r-dimensional Euclidean simplex S, and let $\dot{S}$ denote its frontier, that is to say the union of the $(r - 1)$-dimensional faces of S. Let G be the centroid or barycentre of S. Every point p of S other than G itself can be specified by naming the point $P(p)$ in which the segment Gp from G to p produced meets $\dot{S}$ along with the ratio $s(p)$ in which p divides the join of Gp to $GP(p)$. The set V of points p of S for which $s(p) > \frac{1}{2}$ is clearly an open set of S in the topology induced by the surrounding Euclidean space. The first thing to be done is to construct a deformation of S into itself which will compress V into the frontier $\dot{S}$ of S, and will stretch $S - V$ until it fills the whole of S.

This construction involves the definition of a mapping of S onto itself which is homotopic to the identity. To do this, define the mapping F of $S \times I$ onto S as follows, using the notation introduced in the last paragraph:

(1) $F(G, t) = G$ for all $t \in I$;

(2) if $p \neq G$ and $p \notin V$, $F(p, t)$ is the point p' on the line Gp such that $s(p') = (1 + t)s(p)$;

(3) if $p \in V$, $F(p, t)$ is the point on the line Gp such that $s(p') = t + (1 - t)s(p)$.

It is not hard to see that F is continuous, and that the mapping f defined by setting $f(p) = F(p, 0)$ is the identity mapping of S

onto itself. Hence if g is defined by setting $g(p) = F(p, 1)$, g will be a mapping of S onto itself which is homotopic to the identity.

More can be said about the mapping g, however. In the first place, in the above definition of F, it is clear that $s(p')$ is not less than $s(p)$; this is obvious in part (2) of the definition of F, and equally so in part (3) if $s(p')$ is written as $s(p) + t(1 - s(p))$. Thus F carries $V \times I$ into V. It follows that g is a mapping of the pair (S, V) into itself which is homotopic to the identity mapping of the pair (S, V) on itself. (cf. Definition 52.)

In addition, if $p \in \overset{.}{S}$, $s(p)$ will be equal to 1, and, using part (3) of the definition of F, $F(p, t) = p$ for all $t \in I$. It follows that the homotopy between f and g satisfies the conditions of Chapter VI, §5, Exercise 5, and so the following can be stated:

LEMMA a. $H_q(S, V) \cong H_q(S, \overset{.}{S})$ for all q, this isomorphism being induced by the inclusion map of $(S, \overset{.}{S})$ into (S, V).

Now let W be the set of points p in S such that $s(p) > \frac{3}{4}$. W is also an open set in the induced topology on S, and the inclusion relations $\overset{.}{S} \subset W \subset V$ hold, and also the closure of W in S is contained in V. The Excision Theorem (Theorem 46) can therefore be applied to obtain the result $H_q(S - W, V - W) \cong H_q(S, V)$ for all q. Combining this with lemma a the following is proved:

LEMMA b. $H_q(S - W, V - W) \cong H_q(S, \overset{.}{S})$ for all q.

Consider now a simplicial complex K. In each r-simplex S_i of K construct sets V_i and W_i bearing the same relation to S_i as V and W bore above to the simplex S. Define the set U as $K_{r-1} \cup (\bigcup_{i=1}^{n} V_i)$, where it is assumed that there are n r-simplexes in K. $K_r - U$ consists of the union of the sets $S_i - V_i$, and so is a closed set in the topology induced on K_r by the surrounding Euclidean space. Hence U is an open set in K_r.

Similarly, if Z is defined as $K_{r-1} \cup (\bigcup_{i=1}^{n} W_i)$, Z will be an open set in K_r.

Finally a mapping F_i may be constructed for each of the pairs (S_i, V_i) similar to the F constructed above for the pair (S, V). Using the F_i, define the mapping G of $K_r \times I$ onto K_r as follows:

(1) $G(p, t) = F_i(p, t)$ if $p \in S_i$, one of the r-simplexes of K;

(2) $G(p, t) = p$ if $p \in K_{r-1}$.

It must be checked that this definition does not contradict itself for a point p lying in both S_i and S_j, and hence lying in a face of each and so in K_{r-1}. But if p has this property, then both $F_i(p, t)$ and $F_j(p, t)$ are equal to p; thus the two possible definitions of $G(p, t)$, namely $F_i(p, t)$ and $F_j(p, t)$ coincide, and in addition they agree with the value of $G(p, t)$ according to the second part of the definition of G. Thus there is no contradiction. G is clearly a continuous mapping of the pair $(K_r \times I, U \times I)$ into (K_r, U) satisfying also the condition $G(p, t) = p$ for $p \in K_{r-1}$. Hence the argument leading to Lemma a above yields the following:

LEMMA c. *The inclusion mapping* $(K_r, K_{r-1}) \to (K_r, U)$ *induces the isomorphism* $H_q(K_r, K_{r-1}) \cong H_q(K_r, U)$ *for all* q.

The following theorem is the main result of this section.

THEOREM 49. *If K is a simplicial complex and $S_1, S_2, \ldots, S_n$ are the r-dimensional simplexes of K (or, what is the same thing in view of the definitions given in §1, the r-dimensional simplexes of K_r) then $H_q(K_r, K_{r-1})$ is a direct sum $\sum \dot{G}_i$ where G_i is isomorphic to $H_q(\dot{S}_i, \dot{S}_i)$ under the injection homomorphism* $H_q(S_i, \dot{S}_i) \to H_q(K_r, K_{r-1})$.

PROOF. To bring out as clearly as possible the meaning of this theorem, the proof will be carried out in terms of relative cycles representing elements of $H_q(K_r, K_{r-1})$. To show that $H_q(K_r, K_{r-1}) = \sum \dot{G}_i$, it must be shown that each element $\bar{a}$ of $H_q(K_r, K_{r-1})$ can be written as $\sum \bar{a}_i$ with $\bar{a}_i \in G_i$ and that if $\sum \bar{a}_i = 0$, with $\bar{a}_i \in G_i$ for each i, then each $\bar{a}_i$ is zero. This means that it must be shown first that every relative q-cycle α of K_r modulo K_{r-1} is homologous modulo K_{r-1} to a sum $\sum \alpha_i$ where α_i is a relative cycle of S_i modulo $\dot{S}_i$; the last phrase implies that the relative homology class of α_i in K_r modulo K_{r-1} is in the injection image of $H_q(S_i, \dot{S}_i)$, that is, in G_i. And second, it must be shown that if, for each i, α_i is a relative cycle of S_i modulo $\dot{S}_i$ and if $\sum \alpha_i$ is homologous to zero in K_r modulo K_{r-1}, then α_i is homologous to zero in S_i modulo $\dot{S}_i$, $i = 1, 2, \ldots, n$.

Suppose then that α is a relative q-cycle of K_r modulo K_{r-1}. Since $K_{r-1} \subset U$, α can be regarded as a relative cycle of K_r modulo U. By the Excision Theorem (Theorem 46) the inclusion mapping $(K_r - Z, U - Z) \to (K_r, U)$ induces an isomorphism onto of the corresponding homology groups, which implies that α is homologous modulo U to a relative cycle α' of $K_r - Z$ modulo $U - Z$. That is, there is a q-chain β on U and a $(q + 1)$-chain γ on K_r such that

$$\alpha = \alpha' + \beta + d\gamma. \tag{37}$$

But since $K_r - Z$ is the union of the disjoint sets $S_i - W_i$ $(i = 1, 2, \ldots, n)$, α' can be written as $\sum \alpha_i'$ where α_i' is a relative q-cycle of $S_i - W_i$ modulo $V_i - W_i$, and (37) becomes

$$\alpha = \sum \alpha_i' + \beta + d\gamma \tag{38}$$

Now α_i', for each i, is a relative cycle of S_i modulo V_i and so, by Lemma a is homologous in S_i modulo V_i to a relative cycle α_i of S_i modulo $\dot{S}_i$. That is, there is a q-chain β_i on V_i and a $(q + 1)$-chain γ_i on S_i such that $\alpha_i' = \alpha_i + \beta_i + d\gamma_i$. Combined with (38) this gives

$$\alpha = \sum \alpha_i + \beta + \sum \beta_i + d(\gamma + \sum \gamma_i) \tag{39}$$

$\beta + \sum \beta_i$ is a chain on U and $\gamma + \sum \gamma_i$ is a chain on K_r; thus (39) says that $\alpha - \sum \alpha_i$ is homologous to zero in K_r modulo U. It then follows at once from Lemma c that $\alpha - \sum \alpha_i$, which is a relative cycle of K_r modulo K_{r-1}, is homologous to zero in K_r modulo K_{r-1}, and this completes the first part of the proof of the present theorem, α having been shown to be homologous modulo K_{r-1} to $\sum \alpha_i$, where α_i is a relative cycle on S_i modulo $\dot{S}_i$.

To prove the second part of the theorem, let α_i be a relative cycle of S_i modulo $\dot{S}_i$, $i = 1, 2, \ldots, n$, and suppose that $\sum \alpha_i$ is homologous to zero in K_r modulo K_{r-1}. α_i can be regarded as a relative cycle of S_i modulo V_i and so, by the Excision Theorem, α_i is homologous modulo V_i to a relative cycle θ_i of $S_i - W_i$ modulo $V_i - W_i$. It is clear from the definitions of U and Z that $\sum \theta_i$ is a relative cycle of $K_r - Z$ modulo $U - Z$ and that $\sum \alpha_i$ and $\sum \theta_i$ are homologous in K_r modulo U. Since $\sum \alpha_i$ has been assumed homologous to zero in K_r modulo K_{r-1} it is also homologous to zero in K_r modulo U, and so $\sum \theta_i$ is homologous to zero in K_r modulo U. Hence, by the excision Theorem, $\sum \theta_i$, which has been remarked to be a relative cycle of $K_r - Z$ modulo $U - Z$, is homologous to zero in $K_r - Z$ modulo $U - Z$. But since $K_r - Z$ is the union of the disjoint sets $V_i - W_i$, it follows from this that θ_i is homologous to zero in $S_i - W_i$ modulo $V_i - W_i$ for each i. But this implies at once that θ_i is homologous to zero in S_i modulo V_i; and since θ_i and α_i are homologous in S_i modulo V_i, α_i is therefore homologous to zero in S_i modulo V_i. Finally, by Lemma a, α_i, being homologous to zero in S_i modulo V_i, is also homologous to zero in S_i modulo $\dot{S}_i$. This holds for each i, and so the second part of the theorem is proved.

COROLLARY 1. It is a simple consequence of the above theorem, combined with Theorem 48 and the fact that a Euclidean r-simplex is a closed r-cell and its frontier an $(r-1)$-sphere (Chapter V, §2, Exercise 3), that $H_q(K_r, K_{r-1})$ is zero for $q \neq r$ $(r \geq 1)$ while $H_r(K_r, K_{r-1})$ is a finitely generated free abelian group, the generators being the images of those of the groups $H_r(S_i, \dot{S}_i)$, $i = 1, 2, \ldots, n$, under injection.

COROLLARY 2. If K is a simplicial complex of dimension n, $H_q(K) = 0$ for all $q > n$.

PROOF. Since the dimension of K is n, K_n is here equal to K. Let $q > n$ and consider the following exact sequence for any r such that $1 \leq r \leq n$:

$$\longrightarrow H_q(K_{r-1}) \xrightarrow{\ i\ } H_q(K_r) \xrightarrow{\ j\ } H_q(K_r, K_{r-1}) \longrightarrow .$$

The third term appearing is zero by Corollary 1, since $q > n$ and hence $q \neq r$. And so the homomorphism i is onto. This holds for each r from 1 to n and so the injection homomorphism $H_q(K_0) \to H_q(K)$ is onto. $H_q(K_0)$ is certainly zero, and so the corollary is proved.

3. A generator for $H_r(S, \dot{S})$

The object of this section is to find explicitly a generator for a group of the form $H_r(S, \dot{S})$, where S is an r-dimensional Euclidean simplex and $\dot{S}$ is the union of its faces. Such a group has already been shown to be infinite cyclic by Theorem 48, since S is an r-cell, and in the remarks following that theorem an indication was given of a method of identifying a generator. This identification will now be carried out in detail by means of the following theorem:

THEOREM 50. Let S be an r-dimensional Euclidean simplex and Δ_r as usual the standard Euclidean r-simplex. Then the singular simplex defined by any linear mapping of Δ_r onto S is a relative cycle of S modulo $\dot{S}$ and represents a generator of $H_r(S, \dot{S})$.

PROOF. If $r = 1$, S is simply a line segment, and $\dot{S}$ consists of its end points. In this case the theorem has already been proved in the form of Example (1), §2, Chapter VIII. The general result will now be proved by induction, assuming it to be true for a simplex of dimension $r - 1$.

Pick a linear mapping of Δ_r onto S, and then name the vertices of S in such a way that this mapping is represented by the symbol

$(y_0 y_1 \ldots y_r)$ (Definition 38). Let S_0 denote the face of S whose vertices are $y_1, y_2, \ldots, y_r$, $\dot{S}_0$ denoting the frontier of S_0. By the induction hypothesis, $(y_1 y_2 \ldots y_r)$ represents a generator of the group $H_{r-1}(S_0, \dot{S}_0)$.

The boundary of $(y_0 y_1 \ldots y_r)$ is $\sum_{i=0}^{r}(-1)^i(y_0 y_1 \ldots \hat{y}_i \ldots y_r)$ and this can be written as $(y_1 y_2 \ldots y_r) + \gamma$ where $(y_1 y_2 \ldots y_r)$ is a chain on S_0, while γ is a chain on the closure of $\dot{S} - S_0$. It is not hard to see that there is a homeomorphism of $\dot{S}$ onto the $(r-1)$-sphere S^{r-1} with the equation $\sum_{i=1}^{r}x_i^2 = 1$ in Euclidean r-space, carrying S_0 onto the set $x_r \geqslant -\varepsilon$, for some positive ε less than 1, and carrying the remaining faces of S onto the set $x_r \leqslant -\varepsilon$ (cf. Chapter V, §2, Exercise 4). It follows at once from the second note following Theorem 48, that $d(y_0 y_1 \ldots y_r)$ represents a generator of $H_{r-1}(\dot{S})$ if and only if $(y_1 y_2 \ldots y_r)$ represents a generator of $H_{r-1}(S_0, \dot{S}_0)$. It has already been noted that, by the induction hypothesis, this condition holds. Hence $d(y_0 y_1 \ldots y_r)$ represents a generator of $H_{r-1}(\dot{S})$. And from this along with the first note following Theorem 48, it follows that $(y_0 y_1 \ldots y_r)$ represents a generator of $H_r(S, \dot{S})$, and so the proof by induction is completed.

At first sight it looks as if this theorem gives a choice of $(r+1)!$ generators for $H_r(S, \dot{S})$, since there are $(r+1)!$ distinct linear mappings of Δ_r onto S. But $H_r(S, \dot{S})$, being an infinite cyclic group, should have a choice of just two generators, each obtained from the other by change of sign. The $(r+1)!$ linear mappings of Δ_r onto S must therefore be divided into two classes corresponding to the two possible generators of $H_r(S, \dot{S})$. The clue as to how this division is carried out will be obtained by looking at the cases $r = 1$ and $r = 2$.

For $r = 1$ the situation is clear enough; for in this case $(r+1)! = 2$ and the two generators of $H_1(S, \dot{S})$ correspond to the two directions along the segment S. To see this in detail let y_0 and y_1 be the end points of S. Then $(y_0 y_1)$ and $(y_1 y_0)$ are linear mappings of Δ_1 onto S, mapping Δ_1 in the two opposite directions along S. If α and β are the relative homology classes in S modulo $\dot{S}$ of $(y_0 y_1)$ and $(y_1 y_0)$, then, since $d(y_0 y_1) = y_1 - y_0 = -d(y_1 y_0)$, $\partial \alpha = -\partial \beta$, where ∂

is the boundary homomorphism of $H_1(S, \dot{S})$ into $H_0(\dot{S})$. But it appeared in Example (1), §2, Chapter VIII that ∂ is, in this case, an isomorphism, and so $\alpha = -\beta$. It has thus been shown that $(y_0 y_1)$ and $(y_1 y_0)$ represent the two oppositely signed generators of $H_1(S, \dot{S})$.

If $r = 2$, S is a triangle with vertices y_0, y_1, y_2, and there are six linear mappings of Δ_2 onto S, namely the six singular simplexes $(y_i y_j y_k)$, where i, j, k is one of the six permutations of the suffixes 0, 1, 2. Consider first two of these singular simplexes, say $(y_0 y_1 y_2)$ and $(y_1 y_2 y_0)$, and let their relative homology classes in S modulo $\dot{S}$ be α and β. By the definition of the boundary operator

$$d(y_0 y_1 y_2) = (y_1 y_2) - (y_0 y_2) + (y_0 y_1) \left.\vphantom{\begin{matrix}1\\1\end{matrix}}\right\} .$$

and $$d(y_1 y_2 y_0) = (y_2 y_0) - (y_1 y_0) + (y_1 y_2) \qquad (39)$$

In order to test whether α is equal to β or to $-\beta$, it will be sufficient to test whether the difference or the sum of $d(y_0 y_1 y_2)$ and $d(y_1 y_2 y_0)$ is homologous to zero in $\dot{S}$, since, as seen in Example (3), §2, Chapter VIII, the boundary homomorphism ∂ of $H_2(S, \dot{S})$ into $H_1(\dot{S})$ is in this case an isomorphism. It will now be shown, in fact, that $d(y_0 y_1 y_2) - d(y_1 y_2 y_0)$ is homologous to zero in $\dot{S}$.

To do this, note that, by subtracting the equations (39)

$$d(y_0 y_1 y_2) - d(y_1 y_2 y_0) = (y_0 y_1) + (y_1 y_0) - [(y_0 y_2) + (y_2 y_0)]. \quad (40)$$

But $d(y_0 y_1) = y_1 - y_0 = -d(y_1 y_0)$, whence $(y_0 y_1) + (y_1 y_0)$ is a cycle on $\dot{S}$. In fact it is a cycle on the segment joining y_0 and y_1, and so is homologous to zero in that segment, and so homologous to zero in $\dot{S}$. Similarly $(y_0 y_2) + (y_2 y_0)$ is a cycle homologous to zero on $\dot{S}$.

Combining these two facts it follows from (40) that $d(y_0 y_1 y_2) - d(y_1 y_2 y_0)$ is homologous to zero in $\dot{S}$, and so, by the definition of the boundary homomorphism, $\partial\alpha = \partial\beta$. As has just been pointed out, ∂ is an isomorphism, and so $\alpha = \beta$.

In a similar manner it can be shown that $(y_2 y_0 y_1)$ is a relative cycle of S modulo $\dot{S}$ representing α, while $(y_0 y_2 y_1)$, $(y_2 y_1 y_0)$, $(y_1 y_0 y_2)$ all represent $-\alpha$.

It will be noticed at once that in this case the representatives of α and $-\alpha$ fall into classes which correspond to the even and odd permutations of the suffixes 0, 1, 2. In other words, $(y_i y_j y_k)$ represents the same generator of $H_2(S, \dot{S})$ as $(y_0 y_1 y_2)$ if i, j, k is an even permutation of 0, 1, 2 and the oppositely signed generator if the permutation is odd. This will now be shown to be true in general for any value of r; it is of course trivially true in the case $r = 1$ already treated above, for in that case there are just two permutations of the suffixes of y_0 and y_1, one odd and one even, and it was shown that $(y_0 y_1)$ and $(y_1 y_0)$ represent oppositely signed generators of $H_1(S, \dot{S})$.

THEOREM 51. *Let S be an r-dimensional Euclidean simplex with vertices* $y_0, y_1, \ldots, y_r$. *Then* $H_r(S, \dot{S})$ *has a generator* α *represented by the singular simplex* $(y_0 y_1 \ldots y_r)$. α *is also represented by* $\pm(y_{i_0} y_{i_1} \ldots y_{i_r})$, *where* $i_0, i_1, \ldots, i_r$ *is a permutation of* $0, 1, 2, \ldots, r$, *and the sign taken is* $+$ *or* $-$ *according as this permutation is even or odd.*

PROOF. The first part of the theorem, namely that a generator of $H_r(S, \dot{S})$ can be represented by $(y_0 y_1 \ldots y_r)$, has already been proved in Theorem 50. The rest of the theorem will be proved by induction; it is known to be true for $r = 1$ and $r = 2$, so this gives a starting point for the induction.

Now it is clear, that in order to prove this theorem for any permutation $i_0, i_1, \ldots, i_r$ of the suffixes $0, 1, 2, \ldots, r$ it will be sufficient to prove it for a permutation which is an interchange of just two suffixes, since any permutation can be broken down into a sequence of interchanges, the parity of the permutation depending only on the parity of the number of interchanges in this sequence. To avoid complications of notation the result will actually be proved now in the case of the interchange of the suffixes 0 and 1; the proof for any other pair of suffixes would follow exactly the same lines.

Explicitly, what has to be shown is that, if α is represented by $(y_0 y_1 \ldots y_r)$, then it is also represented by $-(y_1 y_0 y_2 \ldots y_r)$, where in the two brackets all the y_i are in the same order except the first two, which are interchanged. Imitating the procedure illustrated above in the particular case $r = 2$, consider the two boundary formulae

$$d(y_0 y_1 y_2 \ldots y_r) = (y_1 y_2 \ldots y_r) - (y_0 y_2 \ldots y_r)$$
$$+ \sum_{i=2}^{r} (-1)^i (y_0 y_1 y_2 \ldots \hat{y}_i \ldots y_r)$$
$$d(y_1 y_0 y_2 \ldots y_r) = (y_0 y_2 \ldots y_r) - (y_1 y_2 \ldots y_r)$$
$$+ \sum_{i=2}^{r} (-1)^i (y_1 y_0 y_2 \ldots \hat{y}_i \ldots y_r).$$

The first two terms in both right hand sides are the same, but oppositely signed, while in the remaining summations the corresponding terms differ only in the order of y_0 and y_1. Adding these two formulae gives

$$d(y_0y_1y_2 \ldots y_r) + d(y_1y_0y_2 \ldots y_r)$$
$$= \sum_{i=2}^{r} (-1)^i [(y_0y_1 \ldots \hat{y}_i \ldots y_r) + (y_1y_0 \ldots \hat{y}_i \ldots y_r)]. \quad (41)$$

$(y_0y_1 \ldots \hat{y}_i \ldots y_r)$ and $(y_1y_0 \ldots \hat{y}_i \ldots y_r)$ are singular simplexes on the i-th face S_i of S, and in fact are relative cycles of S_i modulo $\dot{S}_i$, which, assuming as induction hypothesis that the present theorem is true for Euclidean simplexes of dimension $r - 1$, represent oppositely signed generators of $H_{r-1}(S_i, \dot{S}_i)$. That is to say,

$$(y_0y_1 \ldots \hat{y}_i \ldots y_r) \text{ and } -(y_1y_0 \ldots \hat{y}_i \ldots y_r)$$

are homologous in S_i modulo $\dot{S}_i$, which means that there is. an $(r - 1)$-chain β_i on $\dot{S}_i$ and an r-chain γ_i on S_i such that

$$(-1)^i [(y_0y_1 \ldots \hat{y}_i \ldots y_r) + (y_1y_0 \ldots \hat{y}_i \ldots y_r)] = \beta_i + d\gamma_i.$$

An equation like this holds for each i from 2 up to r, and, combined with (41) these equations give

$$d(y_0y_1y_2 \ldots y_r) + d(y_1y_0y_2 \ldots y_r) = \sum_{i=2}^{r} \beta_i + d(\sum_{i=2}^{r} \gamma_i). \quad (42)$$

If the boundary operator d is applied to this equation, it turns out that $d(\sum_{i=2}^{r} \beta_i) = 0$; that is to say, $\sum_{i=2}^{r} \beta_i$ is a cycle. Moreover, by the definition of the β_i, it is a cycle on the union of the $(r - 2)$-dimensional faces of S. In other words it is an $(r - 1)$-cycle on an $(r - 2)$-dimensional simplicial complex, and so is homologous to zero in that complex (Theorem 49, Corollary 2). $\sum_{i=2}^{r} \beta_i$ is therefore certainly homologous to zero in $\dot{S}$. It must be noted carefully that, although every term in equation (42) except $\sum_{i=2}^{r} \beta_i$ appears explicitly as a boundary, this implies only that it is homologous to zero in S, which is trivial; it is not trivial, and requires the argument just carried out, to see that $\sum_{i=2}^{r} \beta_i$ is actually homologous to zero in $\dot{S}$.

Equation (42), along with the facts that $\sum\limits_{i=2}^{r} \beta_i$ is homologous to zero on $\dot{S}$ and that $\sum\limits_{i=2}^{r} \gamma_i$ is a chain on $\dot{S}$, shows that $d(y_0 y_1 y_2 \ldots y_r) + d(y_1 y_0 y_2 \ldots y_r)$ is homologous to zero on $\dot{S}$. Let β be the relative homology class of $(y_1 y_0 y_2 \ldots y_r)$ in S modulo $\dot{S}$, α being that of $(y_0 y_1 y_2 \ldots y_r)$, and let ∂ be the boundary homomorphism of $H_r(S, \dot{S})$ into $H_{r-1}(\dot{S})$. Then it follows that $\partial(\alpha + \beta) = 0$. But it appeared in the proof of Theorem 48 (remembering that the pairs $(S, \dot{S})$ and (E^r, S^{r-1}) are homeomorphic) that ∂ is here an isomorphism, and so it follows that $\alpha = -\beta$, in other words that $(y_1 y_0 y_2 \ldots y_r)$ represents $-\alpha$, as was to be shown.

4. The homology groups of a simplicial complex

The main results on the homology groups of simplicial complexes will be obtained in the theorems of this section. Throughout the section, K will denote a given simplicial complex of dimension n.

The first thing to do is to combine Theorems 49 and 51. It follows from these that the generators of $H_r(K_r, K_{r-1})$ are obtained by choosing for each r-dimensional simplex S_i of K an order of vertices; this fixes, for each i, a linear mapping of Δ_r onto S_i, that is to say a singular simplex σ_i on K, which is in fact a relative cycle of K_r modulo K_{r-1} whose relative homology class $\bar{\sigma}_i$ in K_r modulo K_{r-1} is the image under the injection $H_r(S_i, \dot{S}_i) \to H_r(K_r, K_{r-1})$ of a generator of $H_r(S_i, \dot{S}_i)$; $\bar{\sigma}_i$ is therefore a generator of $H_r(K_r, K_{r-1})$, and a generator is obtained in this way for each i. The same generator $\bar{\sigma}_i$ is obtained if the selected order of vertices in S_i is changed by an even permutation, while the generator $-\bar{\sigma}_i$ is obtained if an odd permutation is used.

DEFINITION 67. Each generator of $H_r(K_r, K_{r-1})$ is called an *oriented r-simplex of K*.

Clearly there are two oppositely signed oriented r-simplexes of K corresponding to each r-simplex of K in the sense of the Definition 64. It should be noted that an oriented simplex is actually a relative homology class; the justification for calling it a simplex is that it is fully specified by the naming of a simplex of K, along with an order for its vertices. The adjective "oriented" is used here because, in dimensions 1, 2, 3 the choice of an oriented simplex corresponding to a simplex of K is equivalent to the geometrical process of assigning an orientation to the simplex in question; before proceeding to the algebraic theorems this geometrical process will be described in detail.

If S is a 1-simplex of K with vertices y_0 and y_1 the two oriented simplexes associated with S are represented by the singular simplexes (y_0y_1) and (y_1y_0). In order to specify the oriented simplex one wants it is enough to mark by an arrow one of the two directions along S. Thus orientation here is simply a matter of naming direction.

If S a 2-simplex, with vertices y_0, y_1, y_2, it has already been seen that one of the oriented simplexes corresponding to S is represented by $(y_0y_1y_2)$, $(y_1y_2y_0)$, or $(y_2y_0y_1)$ while the other is represented by $(y_0y_2y_1)$, $(y_2y_1y_0)$, or $(y_1y_0y_2)$. Now it will be noticed, if a diagram is drawn, that in one of these sets of three singular simplexes the vertices are always named in clockwise order round the triangle S, and in the other set of three they are named in anti-clockwise order. Thus the geometrical process of orienting a triangle consists in marking a direction of rotation round the triangle.

Finally, let S be a tetrahedron with vertices y_0, y_1, y_2, y_3. To any order y_i, y_j, y_k, y_l of these vertices a sense of rotation can be assigned as follows. One should imagine that one is standing at the vertex y_i looking at the opposite face. If, from this point of view, y_j, y_k, y_l appear in clockwise order the sense of rotation will be called right handed, otherwise left handed. If, now, all 24 orders of the vertices are tested for right or left handedness (a diagram with the vertices named should be used for this) it will be found that the orders which have the same sense of rotation as y_0, y_1, y_2, y_3 are all even permutations of this order and those giving the opposite sense are odd permutations. But by Theorem 51 the choice of an oriented simplex corresponding to S is made by picking one of the classes of permutations of the order y_0, y_1, y_2, y_3, and so here the geometrical process of orientation consists in fixing a sense of rotation for S.

In general, in the case of an r-simplex of K, there is, of course, no intuitive geometrical idea attached to the choice of an oriented simplex corresponding to S. Nevertheless it is sometimes convenient to use geometrical language, and speak of the choice of such an oriented simplex as orienting S, or giving S an orientation. Thus to orient or give an orientation to a 1-, 2-, or 3-simplex means to pick a direction, direction of rotation or sense of rotation, respectively, as described above.

Returning now to the main argument, the object is to show that the homology groups of K can be worked out in terms of the oriented simplexes of K. The first step will be to show that an r-cycle on K is always homologous to a cycle on K_r. The idea is illustrated by the Fig. 34 where the curve α represents a 1-cycle on a 2-dimensional complex. If the part of α in any one triangle is considered, the diagram suggests that it may be pushed, as indicated by the arrows, into the sides of that triangle. If this is done for each triangle containing part of α, this cycle will end up in the 1-skeleton of K. The proper formulation of the result to be proved is as follows:

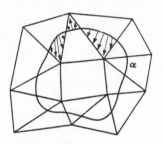

FIG. 34

THEOREM 52. *The injection homomorphism* $i:H_r(K_r) \to H_r(K)$ *is onto for all* r.

PROOF. Consider the following exact sequence for $q \geqslant r$:

$$H_{r+1}(K_{q+1}, K_q) \xrightarrow{\partial_q} H_r(K_q) \xrightarrow{i_q} H_r(K_{q+1}) \xrightarrow{j_q} H_r(K_{q+1}, K_q) \qquad (43)$$

Since $q \geqslant r$, r is certainly not equal to $q + 1$. Hence, by Theorem 49, Corollary 1, $H_r(K_{q+1}, K_q)$ is zero. Thus the kernel of j_q, and so the image of i_q, is the whole group $H_r(K_{q+1})$. It follows that in the chain of homomorphisms

$$H_r(K_r) \xrightarrow{i_r} H_r(K_{r+1}) \xrightarrow{i_{r+1}} H_r(K_{r+2}) \xrightarrow{i_{r+2}} \ldots \xrightarrow{i_{n-1}} H_r(K_n) \qquad (44)$$

each of the i_q is onto, and so their composition is also onto. If K is of dimension n, $K_n = K$, and so the composition of the i_q is i, which is therefore onto, as was to be shown.

It is worth noting now, for future use, that if q is taken strictly greater than r in the exact sequence (43), both $H_{r+1}(K_{q+1}, K_q)$ and $H_r(K_{q+1}, K_q)$ are zero. Hence the image of ∂_q, which is also the kernel of i_q is zero. It follows that, in the chain of homomorphisms (44), all the i_q for $q > r$ are isomorphisms onto. It follows from this that the kernel of i, which will be considered later, coincides with that of i_r.

The next step is to identify $H_r(K_r)$ with a subgroup of $H_r(K_r, K_{r-1})$.

THEOREM 53. *The projection homomorphism* $j : H_r(K_r) \to H_r(K_r, K_{r-1})$ *is an isomorphism* (*into, not necessarily onto*).

Expressed geometrically, this means that if an r-cycle on K_r is homologous to zero modulo K_{r-1}, then it will be homologous to zero in the ordinary sense in K_r. And this means that the ordinary homology class of an r-cycle on K_r is fully determined by its relative homology class in K_r modulo K_{r-1}. This relative homology class can be written as a linear combination, with integral coefficients, of oriented simplexes on K; and so the theorem about to be proved implies that the homology class in K_r of an r-cycle on K_r can be identified with a linear combination of oriented simplexes.

PROOF OF THEOREM 53. Consider the exact sequence

$$\longrightarrow H_r(K_{r-1}) \xrightarrow{h} H_r(K_r) \xrightarrow{j} H_r(K_r, K_{r-1}) \longrightarrow .$$

K_{r-1} is an $(r-1)$-dimensional simplicial complex, and so, by Corollary 2 of Theorem 49, $H_r(K_{r-1})$ is zero. It follows that the image of the injection homomorphism h is zero; that is to say the kernel of j is zero, and j is an isomorphism as was to be shown.

The first important result on the homology groups of simplicial complexes can be derived now:

THEOREM 54. *The homology groups of a simplicial complex* K *are finitely generated abelian groups.*

PROOF. In Theorem 53, $H_r(K_r)$ has been shown to be isomorphic to a subgroup of the group $H_r(K_r, K_{r-1})$ which is finitely generated, by Theorem 49, Corollary 1; it follows that $H_r(K_r)$ is finitely generated. But by Theorem 52 the homomorphism $i : H_r(K_r) \to H_r(K)$ is onto, and so $H_r(K)$ is a quotient group of $H_r(K_r)$ by one of its subgroups. Since a quotient group of a finitely generated group is finitely generated and $H_r(K_r)$ has been shown to be finitely generated, the group $H_r(K)$ is finitely generated, as required.

COROLLARY. *The homology groups of any triangulable space are finitely generated.*

For such a space is homeomorphic to a simplicial complex and the homology groups of homeomorphic spaces are isomorphic.

It may appear at first that the result of Theorem 54 is scarcely enough to deserve the name of theorem, for, as yet, no indication is given of a method of finding the homology groups of a simplicial complex. It can be seen, however, after a bit of reflection, that the purely qualitative statement that these groups are finitely generated is quite remarkable and surprising in itself. For, if one remembers that the homology groups are defined by starting off from the chain groups, which are generated by all singular simplexes and so are very far from being finitely generated, there seems to be no reason to expect that the homology groups of any space should be finitely generated. In fact, if a space is not triangulable, there is no reason to expect its homology groups to be finitely generated, and a simple example will suffice to show that they need not be (Chapter VIII, §2, Exercise 3).

It is worth noting, incidentally, that this is the second "finiteness" result to have been proved for the homology groups of simplicial complexes, the first being Corollary 2 to Theorem 49, where it is shown that a simplicial complex has only a finite number of non-zero homology groups.

A consequence of Theorem 54 is that, associated with a triangulable space E there are certain numerical topological invariants. For, $H_r(E)$, being a finitely generated abelian group, is a direct sum of cyclic groups. Suppose that there are p_r infinite cyclic groups, and finite cyclic groups of orders $t_{r1}, t_{r2}, \ldots, t_{rp}$. Then the integers p_r and $t_{r1}t_{r2}\ldots t_{rp}$ are topological invariants, because they are derived from the homology groups. p_r is called the *r-dimensional Betti number of E*, and the product of the t_{ri} is called *the r-dimensional torsion coefficient of E*. In particular, for a surface p_1 is the invariant introduced in Chapter V, §1, in rather an intuitive way, namely the maximum number of closed curves along which the surface can be cut without dividing it into two parts. These curves are, strictly speaking, 1-cycles, one representing each of the p_1 generators of $H_1(E)$.

5. Oriented chains and cycles

Theorems 52 and 53 of the last section contain most of the information required to show how the homology groups of an n-dimensional simplicial complex can be calculated. For Theorem 52 identifies $H_r(K)$ with the quotient group of $H_r(K_r)$ with respect to a subgroup, while, by Theorem 53, $H_r(K_r)$ is identified with a subgroup of $H_r(K_r, K_{r-1})$. Combining these two statements it follows that $H_r(K)$ is identified with the quotient group of one subgroup of $H_r(K_r, K_{r-1})$ with respect to another. It remains now to work out some sort of algebraic rule by which these two subgroups of $H_r(K_r, K_{r-1})$ can be characterized. The subgroups in question are the image of the homomorphism j of Theorem 53, and the image under j of the kernel of the homomorphism i of Theorem 52. These two groups will now be examined in turn.

Consider first the homology sequence

$$\longrightarrow H_r(K_r) \overset{j}{\longrightarrow} H_r(K_r, K_{r-1}) \overset{\partial}{\longrightarrow} H_{r-1}(K_{r-1}) \longrightarrow.$$

j is the homomorphism of Theorem 53 and ∂ the boundary homomorphism. The exactness of this sequence implies that the image of j is the same as the kernel of ∂. But, by an application of Theorem 53 with r replaced by $r-1$, $H_{r-1}(K_{r-1})$ can be identified with a subgroup of $H_{r-1}(K_{r-1}, K_{r-2})$. More precisely, the projection homomorphism $j':H_{r-1}(K_{r-1}) \to H_{r-1}(K_{r-1}, K_{r-2})$ is an isomorphism of the first group into the second. And it follows at once from this that the kernel of ∂ is the same as that of the composition $j'_o\partial$ of j' and ∂. Hence the image of j is the same as the kernel of the homomorphism $j'_o\partial$. Now this statement is an improvement on the statement that the image of j is the kernel of ∂ from the present point of view (although the statements are in fact equivalent) because $j'_o\partial$ is a homomorphism of $H_r(K_r, K_{r-1})$ into $H_{r-1}(K_{r-1}, K_{r-2})$, and so is a mapping between groups of the same kind, namely groups generated by oriented simplexes on K.

Writing δ for the homomorphism $j'_o\partial$, the above may be summed up:

COMPLEMENT TO THEOREM 53. *The image of j is the kernel of the homomorphism $\delta:H_r(K_r, K_{r-1}) \to H_{r-1}(K_{r-1}, K_{r-2})$.*

Consider now the kernel of the homomorphism i of Theorem 52. In the note following the proof of that theorem, it was pointed out that, in the chain of homomorphisms

$$H_r(K_r) \overset{i_r}{\longrightarrow} H_r(K_{r+1}) \overset{i_{r+1}}{\longrightarrow} H_r(K_{r+2}) \longrightarrow \ldots \overset{i_{n-1}}{\longrightarrow} H_r(K)$$

all the i_q except the first are isomorphisms onto. And so the kernel of i coincides with that of i_r. In the exact sequence

$$\longrightarrow H_{r+1}(K_{r+1}, K_r) \overset{\partial}{\longrightarrow} H_r(K_r) \overset{i_r}{\longrightarrow} H_r(K_{r+1}) \longrightarrow \quad (45)$$

the kernel of i_r is the same as the image of ∂. Thus the kernel of i has been shown to be the image of the boundary homomorphism $\partial:H_{r+1}(K_{r+1}, K_r) \longrightarrow H_r(K_r)$.

It is not, however, the kernel of i itself which is actually wanted, but rather the image of the kernel of i under the homomorphism j

13

of Theorem 53, and this coincides, by what has just been proved, with the image under j of the image of ∂ in the sequence (45). But the image under j of the image of ∂ is precisely the image of the composed mapping $j_{\circ}\partial$, which is a homomorphism of $H_{r+1}(K_{r+1}, K_r)$, into $H_r(K_r, K_{r-1})$, defined in the same way as the homomorphism δ introduced above, but for dimension $r + 1$ instead of r. In spite of this difference of dimension it will be convenient to call $j_{\circ}\partial$ by the same name δ as $j'_{\circ}\partial$. The following has therefore been established:

COMPLEMENT TO THEOREM 52. The image under j (the homomorphism of Theorem 53) of the kernel of i (the homomorphism of Theorem 52) coincides with the image of the homomorphism $\delta : H_{r+1}(K_{r+1}, K_r) \to H_r(K_r, K_{r-1})$.

Theorems 52 and 53 can now be connected together to give the final result. The two homomorphisms appearing in these theorems can be represented conveniently in the following diagram:

$$H_r(K_r, K_{r-1}) \xleftarrow{\ j\ } H_r(K_r) \xrightarrow{\ i\ } H_r(K).$$

Also it is to be understood that, for each value of q, a homomorphism δ is defined as the composition of the boundary homomorphism $\partial : H_q(K_q, K_{q-1}) \to H_{q-1}(K_{q-1})$ and the projection homomorphism of $H_{q-1}(K_{q-1})$ into $H_{q-1}(K_{q-1}, K_{q-2})$, no mark being attached to δ to distinguish between different dimensions.

Then, since i is onto, $H_r(K)$ is isomorphic to the quotient group $H_r(K_r)/(\text{kernel of } i)$. Since j is an isomorphism, the "numerator" and "denominator" here may be identified with their images under j. Combining the Complements to Theorems 52 and 53 with this statement, the following theorem is proved.

THEOREM 55. *The homology group $H_r(K)$ is isomorphic to the quotient group of the kernel of $\delta : H_r(K_r, K_{r-1}) \to H_{r-1}(K_{r-1}, K_{r-2})$ with respect to the image of $\delta : H_{r+1}(K_{r+1}, K_r) \to H_r(K_r, K_{r-1})$.*

Although this is the final result, it will be very much easier to apply, as well as easier to remember, when expressed in rather a different way. The clue to a convenient reformulation of Theorem 55 is obtained by noting that its statement bears a marked algebraic similarity to the statement of the original definition of the homology groups of a space. For the starting point of this definition is a set of groups, namely the chain groups on K, denoted by $C_p(K)$, $p = 0, 1, 2, \ldots$, and a homomorphism $d : C_p(K) \to C_{p-1}(K)$ defined for each p. This homomorphism has the property that the image of $d : C_{p+1}(K) \to C_p(K)$ is contained in the kernel of $d : C_p(K) \to C_{p-1}(K)$

(this statement means exactly the same as saying that $d^2 = 0$), and $L_r'(K)$ is defined as the quotient group of the kernel of $d:C_r(K) \to C_{r-1}(K)$ with respect to the image of $d:C_{r+1}(K) \to C_r(K)$. Now in the situation described by Theorem 55 there is also a sequence of groups, namely the groups $H_p(K_p, K_{p-1})$ defined for each value of $p = 0, 1, 2, \ldots, n$, and there is a homomorphism of $H_p(K_p, K_{p-1})$ into $H_{p-1}(K_{p-1}, K_{p-2})$ for each p, namely δ. And Theorem 55 implies that the image of $\delta:H_{p+1}(K_{p+1}, K_p) \to H_p(K_p, K_{p-1})$ is contained in the kernel of $\delta:H_p(K_p, K_{p-1}) \to H_{p-1}(K_{p-1}, K_{p-2})$, and says that $H_p(K)$ is the quotient of the second of these groups with respect to the first. Some new terminology will now be introduced to draw explicit attention to the algebraic similarity.

DEFINITION 68. The group $H_p(K_p, K_{p-1})$ will be called *the oriented chain group of dimension p on K*, and each of its elements will be called *an oriented p-chain on K*. $H_p(K_p, K_{p-1})$ will be denoted by $\mathscr{C}_p(K)$.

Note that, while the ordinary chain groups on K are generated by singular simplexes, the oriented chain groups are generated by oriented simplexes on K.

DEFINITION 69. The homomorphism δ introduced above will be called *the oriented boundary operator*.

DEFINITION 70. The kernel of $\delta:\mathscr{C}_p(K) \to \mathscr{C}_{p-1}(K)$ will be called *the p-dimensional oriented cycle group of K* and each of its elements will be called *an oriented p-cycle on K*. This group will be denoted by $\mathscr{Z}_p(K)$.

DEFINITION 71. The image of $\delta:\mathscr{C}_{p+1}(K) \to \mathscr{C}_p(K)$ will be called *the p-dimensional oriented boundary group of K* and each of its elements will be called *an oriented p-boundary of K*. This group will be denoted by $\mathscr{B}_p(K)$.

Theorem 55 can now be reformulated as follows:

THEOREM 56. *For a simplicial complex K, $H_r(K)$ is isomorphic to $\mathscr{Z}_r(K)/\mathscr{B}_r(K)$.*

This can be stated in words by saying that, to find the homology groups of a simplicial complex, one can use, instead of ordinary chains, cycles and boundaries, the oriented chains, cycles and boundaries. The essential algebraic simplification which this involves is, of course, that the oriented chain, cycle and boundary groups are all finitely generated.

A further useful terminology is provided by the following definition.

DEFINITION 72. Two oriented cycles α and β are said to be *homologous with respect to* δ (or just homologous if there is no danger of confusion with the other use of this term) if $\alpha - \beta$ is an oriented boundary.

6. The oriented boundary operator

The one flaw in Theorem 56 is that the identification of the groups $\mathscr{Z}_r(K)$ and $\mathscr{B}_r(K)$ depends on the use of the oriented boundary operator, which has so far been defined only in terms of the boundary

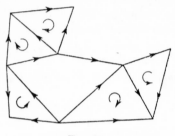

FIG. 35

homomorphism acting on a group of the form $H_r(K_r, K_{r-1})$, and mapping it into $H_{r-1}(K_{r-1})$. Thus it would appear that the action of δ could not be known without knowledge of these groups. In this case, Theorem 56 would certainly not yield the promised straightforward algebraic method of finding homology groups. It will now be shown, however, that the action of δ can be described in quite a different way, which depends only on the knowledge of the simplexes of the complex K along with the choice of an orientation on each of them.

Let K then be a given simplicial complex, and let an orientation be given to each simplex of K; these orientations can be chosen in a quite arbitrary manner. For example Fig. 35 shows a 2-dimensional simplicial complex with all its simplexes oriented; the 1-simplexes are oriented by marking a directional arrow on them and the 2-simplexes by a circular arrow to show direction of rotation. It will be remembered that, in the general case, the choice of orientation of an r-simplex can be made by specifying an order for its vertices, an order which can always by changed by an even permutation without changing the orientation.

Let S be an r-dimensional simplex of K, and let σ denote the oriented simplex on K corresponding to S along with the orientation which has been chosen for S. That is to say, suppose that the vertices of S are named in such a way that the orientation of S is defined by the order $y_0, y_1, \ldots, y_r$; then σ is the relative homology class in K_r modulo K_{r-1} represented by the singular simplex $(y_0 y_1 \ldots y_r)$. Also let $T_0, T_1, \ldots, T_r$ be the faces of S, T_i being that opposite y_i, and let $\tau_i (i = 0, 1, 2, \ldots, r)$ be the oriented simplex on K corresponding to T_i along with the orientation which has been chosen for T_i. The object of this section is to express $\delta \sigma$ in terms of the τ_i.

In the first place, the relative homology class σ can be represented by $(y_0 y_1 y_2 \ldots y_r)$, which is a relative cycle of K_r modulo K_{r-1}, and so, by the definition of the boundary homomorphism ∂, $\partial \sigma$ can be represented by the cycle $\sum_{i=0}^{r} (-1)^i (y_0 y_1 \ldots \hat{y}_i \ldots y_r)$. δ is obtained from ∂ by composing it with the projection homomorphism of $H_{r-1}(K_{r-1})$ into $H_{r-1}(K_{r-1}, K_{r-2})$, and so $\delta \sigma$ can also be represented by $\sum_{i=0}^{r} (-1)^i (y_0 y_1 \ldots \hat{y}_i \ldots y_r)$. But $(y_0 y_1 \ldots \hat{y}_i \ldots y_r)$ is a singular simplex defined by a linear mapping of Δ_{r-1} onto T_i, and so it represents $\pm \tau_i$. Thus $\delta \sigma = \sum_{i=0}^{r} \pm \tau_i$. It still remains to determine the signs in this expression.

The signs in the formula just obtained will be found with the aid of the following definition.

DEFINITION 73. Using the notations already introduced in this section, let an even permutation be performed on $y_0, y_1, \ldots, y_r$ in such a way that y_i comes into first place. This can be done, for example, by first interchanging y_0 and y_i, and then interchanging any two of $y_1, y_2, \ldots, y_0, \ldots, y_r$, where y_0 is in the ith place. The order in which $y_1, y_2, \ldots, y_0, \ldots, y_r$ appear after this rearrangement defines an orientation on T_i which will be called the *orientation induced on T_i by the given orientation on S*.

Examples. (1) In Fig. 36 the triangle is oriented in the anti-clockwise direction, corresponding to the order y_0, y_1, y_2 of vertices. According to the above definition the orientation induced on the side opposite y_0 corresponds to the order y_1, y_2. The order y_1, y_2, y_0 is an even permutation of y_0, y_1, y_2, and so the orientation induced in the side opposite y_1 is represented by the order y_2, y_0; and similarly the orientation induced in the side opposite y_2 corresponds to the order y_0, y_1. It will be noticed that the arrows marking the directions corresponding to the induced orientations on the sides all run in the anti-clockwise direction, thus agreeing with the anti-clockwise orientation of the triangle.

(2) From the definition of right- and left-handed senses of rotation in a tetrahedron it follows at once that the orientation induced in each face of a right-handedly oriented tetrahedron will appear as the

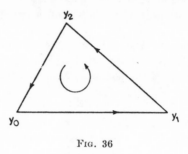

FIG. 36

clockwise direction of rotation when viewed from the opposite vertex.

Now it has already been found that $\delta\sigma$, which is a relative homology class in K_{r-1} modulo K_{r-2}, is represented by the cycle

$$\sum_{i=0}^{r}(-1)^i(y_0y_1\ldots\hat{y}_i\ldots y_r).$$

On the other hand the order $y_i, y_0, y_1, \ldots, \hat{y}_i, \ldots, y_r$ of vertices of S is obtained from the natural order by i interchanges, and so by an even or odd permutation according as i is even or odd. It follows that the order $y_0, y_1, \ldots, \hat{y}_i, \ldots, y_r$ represents the induced orientation of T_i or the orientation opposite to the induced one according as i is even or odd. That is to say, the singular simplex $(y_0y_1\ldots\hat{y}_i\ldots y_r)$ represents an oriented simplex on K which corresponds to T_i with the induced orientation if i is even and with the opposite orientation if i is odd. And this means that, for each i, $(-1)^i(y_0y_1\ldots\hat{y}_i\ldots y_r)$ represents the oriented simplex corresponding to T_i with the induced orientation. It follows that $\delta\sigma$, being represented by $\sum_{i=0}^{r}(-1)^i(y_0y_1\ldots\hat{y}_i\ldots y_r)$, is the sum of the oriented simplexes on K corresponding to the $(r-1)$-dimensional faces of S with their induced orientations.

Finally the oriented simplex on K corresponding to T_i in its induced orientation will be $+\tau_i$ or $-\tau_i$ according as this induced orientation does-or does not agree with the orientation given on T_i. The rule for finding can thus be expressed as follows:

THEOREM 57. *If an r-simplex S in a simplicial complex K and all its $(r-1)$-dimensional faces $T_0, T_1, \ldots, T_r$ are oriented in an arbitrary way and if σ and $\tau_0, \tau_1, \ldots, \tau_r$ are the corresponding oriented simplexes on K, then $\delta\sigma = \sum_{i=0}^{r} \pm\tau_i$, where τ_i is given a $+$ or $-$ sign according as the orientation given on T_i agrees or does not agree with that induced on T_i by the orientation of S.*

This theorem, along with Theorem 56, gives an algebraic rule by which the homology groups of a simplicial complex, and so also those of a triangulable space, may be calculated. The procedure will be illustrated in the following Exercises.

Exercises

1. Let K be a simplicial complex and α an oriented 1-chain on K. Remembering that orientation for a 1-simplex is specified by marking a direction on the corresponding simplex in K, show that the following condition is necessary and sufficient for α to be an oriented cycle: at each vertex p of K the sum of the coefficients in α of the 1-simplexes oriented towards p is equal to the sum of the coefficients of those oriented away from p.

2. Suppose that in a simplicial complex K two 2-simplexes appear with a common edge, forming a quadrilateral $ABCD$ with the diagonal AC. Suppose that an oriented 1-cycle α includes an oriented simplex τ corresponding to the diagonal AC with non-zero coefficient. Show that α is homologous with respect to δ to an oriented 1-cycle in which τ does not appear.

[Hint: τ can be replaced by a suitable linear combination of two sides of $ABCD$.]

NOTE. The usefulness of this result appears when one is given a space E made up of quadrilaterals fitted edge to edge. It shows that, so far as finding $H_1(E)$ is concerned, one does not need to divide E into triangles by actually marking in the diagonals of these quadrilaterals. Clearly the result can be generalized to the situation where the quadrilaterals are replaced by arbitrary polygons placed edge to edge.

3. Let a connected simplicial complex K consist of n triangles

$S_1, S_2, \ldots, S_n$ placed edge to edge in such a way that every 1-dimensional simplex of K is a side of exactly two 2-dimensional simplexes of K. Prove that there is an oriented 2-cycle on K if and only if the S_i can be oriented in such a way that for each pair of adjacent triangles the orientations induced on the common side are opposite. Prove also that, if this condition holds and if the S_i are oriented as just described, then every oriented 2-cycle on K is a multiple of $\sum\limits_{i=1}^{n} \sigma_i$, where σ_i is the oriented simplex corresponding to S_i.

[Hint: Suppose that there is an oriented 2-cycle $\sum\limits_{i=1}^{n} c_i\sigma_i$ on K; reorient the S_i if necessary to make all the $c_i \geqslant 0$. If σ_i and σ_j correspond to adjacent triangles S_i and S_j in K, then the common side must cancel out when the boundary of $\sum\limits_{i=1}^{n} c_i\sigma_i$ is formed. Check that for this to happen c_i must be equal to c_j and the orientations induced on the common side must be opposite.]

4. Let K be as in Exercise 3, and let the condition stated there on the orientations of the S_i be satisfied. Prove that $H_2(K)$ is infinite cyclic.

[Hint: Exercise 3 shows that $\mathscr{Z}_2(K)$ is infinite cyclic, and $\mathscr{B}_2(K)$ is zero since K is of dimension 2.]

Note. It can be shown that every compact 2-dimensional manifold (cf. Chapter VIII, §2, note following Exercise 7) is triangulable. Also in the resulting complex K every 1-simplex will be a side of exactly two 2-simplexes. If this complex satisfies the orientation condition of Exercise 3 the manifold is called orientable, otherwise non-orientable. In the orientable case $H_2(K)$ is infinite cyclic (by Exercise 4), while in the non-orientable case $\mathscr{Z}_2(K)$ is zero (by Exercise 3) and so $H_2(K)$ is zero. Hence the orientable compact 2-dimensional manifolds are the spheres with handles (Chapter VIII, §2, Exercise 5) and the non-orientable ones are the surfaces of Chapter VIII, §2, Exercise 7.

5. Let K be a connected 2-dimensional complex such that every 1-dimensional simplex is a common side of exactly two 2-dimensional simplexes. Let $\alpha = \sum\limits_{i=1}^{r} k_i\tau_i$ be an oriented 1-boundary on K and suppose that $T_1, T_2, \ldots, T_r$ are the 1-dimensional simplexes of K to which the oriented simplexes $\tau_1, \tau_2, \ldots, \tau_r$ correspond. Show that if $S_1, S_2, \ldots, S_n$ are the 2-simplexes of K and if $\sigma_1, \sigma_2, \ldots, \sigma_n$ are the corresponding oriented simplexes (with suitable orientations) and if $K - \bigcup_{i=1}^{r} T_i$ is connected, then α is the boundary of some multiple of $\sum_{i=1}^{n} \sigma_i$.

[Hint: Write $\alpha = \delta \sum_{i=1}^{n} c_i \sigma_i$ and orient the S_i so that the c_i are all non-negative; then proceed as in Exercise 3, noting that, by the connectedness of $K - \bigcup_{i=1}^{r} T_i$, every simplex S_i can be reached by a sequence of simplexes each having a side in common with the next, starting off from some simplex having one of the T_j as a side.]

6. In the notation of Exercise 5, prove that, if K satisfies the orientability condition stated in Exercise 3, then an oriented 1-boundary $\alpha = \sum_{i=1}^{r} k_i \tau_i$ must be such that $\bigcup_{i=1}^{r} T_i$ disconnects K.

[Hint: By Exercise 5, $\alpha = c(\delta \sum_{i=1}^{n} \sigma_i)$, but $\sum_{i=1}^{n} \sigma_i$ is an oriented cycle under the orientability condition.]

7. Use the results of the above exercises to calculate $H_1(K)$ where K is the surface of a torus.

[Hint: A torus is obtained from a square by identifying opposite sides; use the remark following Exercise 2' above to show that the only 1-simplexes which need to be considered are those (in a suitable triangulation) lying along the images on the torus of the sides of the square.]

GUIDE TO FURTHER READING

THE following suggestions are designed for the student who has had in this book his first introduction to topology and now wishes to enter more deeply into the subject. Rather than attempt to give an exhaustive bibliography, it seems more useful for this purpose to give references of a fairly general character which will, in turn, lead the reader to the threshold of special topics and research problems.

A. Point-set topology

This part of topology is touched on in Chapters I–III of this book. It consists of the theory of topological spaces subjected to various conditions (for example compactness, connectedness, etc.) without the use of algebraic methods (as in homology theory). A full account of this subject will be found in :

N. BOURBAKI; *Topologie Générale* (Hermann, Paris).

J. L. KELLEY; *General Topology* (Van Nostrand, New York).

B. Algebraic topology

The object of algebraic topology is the construction of topological invariants which are algebraic structures, such as groups or rings. One example of this is the construction of the homology groups of a space. But there are several other ways of constructing families of additive abelian groups which are topological invariants, and have similar properties to those of the homology groups described in Chapters V–IX. (On looking into the literature of the subject it will be discovered that the homology groups as constructed in this book are usually called the singular homology groups, to indicate their dependence on singular simplexes). The most comprehensive modern text on this subject is:

S. EILENBERG and N. STEENROD; *Foundations of Algebraic Topology* (Princeton University Press).

A further example of a topologically invariant group is the fundamental group of a space. This is itself merely the simplest of a family of groups known as the homotopy groups of a space. the elements of the groups in general being homotopy classes of mappings of spheres into the space. For an account of this subject see:

P. J. HILTON; *An Introduction to Homotopy Theory* (Cambridge University Press).

C. Topological algebra

The title of this section C is not merely intended as a facetious contrast to that of section B. Topological algebra refers to the introduction of a topology on a set which already has an algebraic structure (a group or a ring or a vector space for example) in such a way that the relevant algebraic operations are continuous. The resulting structures are then called topological groups or rings or vector spaces as the case may be. Groups of matrices, such as the group of all orthogonal matrices of a given order can be treated very naturally in this way, for their elements can be taken as coordinates in a Euclidean space; but of course this is a very special case, for it is not always possible to specify the points of a space by coordinates. Topological vector spaces arise in a natural way in analysis as sets of functions which form vector spaces and on which a topology is defined in such a way that some special type of convergence or continuity can be conveniently studied.

The study of topological groups leads naturally to the study of spaces on which such groups act as transformation groups. Among these spaces are the fibre bundles which play a fundamental role in modern differential geometry.

Finally, the special case of Lie groups deserves mention; these are groups in which coordinate systems can be set up around each point in such a way that the group operations are expressed in terms of coordinates by means of differentiable functions. Such groups form the subject of one of the most important branches of topological algebra.

The following references should serve to introduce the various topics mentioned under heading C:

N. BOURBAKI; *Topologie Générale*, Chapter III (Hermann, Paris).

N. BOURBAKI; *Espaces Vectoriels Topologiques* (Hermann, Paris).

C. CHEVALLEY; *Theory of Lie Groups* (Princeton University Press).

L. PONTRJAGIN; *Topological Groups* (Princeton University Press).

N. STEENROD; *The Topology of Fibre Bundles* (Princeton University Press).

A. WEIL; *L'Intégration dans les Groupes Topologiques et ses Applications* (Hermann, Paris).

INDEX